341

ELEMENTS OF
OPTICAL MINERALOGY

By ALEXANDER N. WINCHELL

THE MICROSCOPIC CHARACTERS OF ARTIFICIAL INORGANIC SOLID SUBSTANCES OR ARTIFICIAL MINERALS

With a chapter on the Universal Stage by RICHARD CONRAD EMMONS. Second Edition. Cloth; 6 by 9; 403 pages; 311 figures; determinative tables.

———

ELEMENTS OF OPTICAL MINERALOGY

AN INTRODUCTION TO MICROSCOPIC PETROGRAPHY

———

Part I. Principles and Methods. Fifth Edition. Cloth; 6 by 9; 262 pages; 305 figures.

Part II. Descriptions of Minerals. With Special Reference to Their Optic and Microscopic Characters. Third Edition. Cloth; 6 by 9; 459 pages; 362 figures.

Part III. Determinative Tables. Second Edition, New Printing. Cloth; 6 by 9; 231 pages; three folding charts.

PUBLISHED BY

JOHN WILEY & SONS, INC.

ELEMENTS OF
OPTICAL MINERALOGY

AN INTRODUCTION TO
MICROSCOPIC PETROGRAPHY

BY

ALEXANDER N. WINCHELL

Emeritus Professor of Mineralogy and Petrology,
University of Wisconsin

FIFTH EDITION

PART I. PRINCIPLES AND METHODS

WITH OVER 300 ILLUSTRATIONS

NEW YORK

JOHN WILEY & SONS, INC.

LONDON: CHAPMAN & HALL, LIMITED

PREFACE TO FIFTH EDITION

In the preparation of the fifth edition of this work no great changes have been made, but it has been possible to make some corrections and additions. These include more than sixty new or revised illustrations, among which are those showing the latest models of polarizing microscopes and certain accessories.

The author has been assisted by his son, Horace Winchell, in revising the theoretical discussion of the refractive index and elements of symmetry, as suggested by George Tunell and George W. Morey. In preparing other modifications he has benefited by discussions with his colleague, Professor R. C. Emmons.

Part I of the first edition of this work was prepared chiefly by N. H. Winchell, while State Geologist of Minnesota, and Parts II and III were prepared by Alexander N. Winchell, while Professor of Geology and Mineralogy at the Montana School of Mines. The preparation and publication of the book were due largely to the work and inspiration of N. H. Winchell. The second edition was entirely rewritten and much enlarged by the present author.

Alexander N. Winchell.

January 1, 1937.

PREFACE TO THIRD EDITION

During the past decade one of the chief advances in the field of petrography has been the continued development of the application of petrographic methods to the study of sediments. This movement is still in progress and is destined to reach still higher and wider levels of usefulness, since the improved technique, recently devised, is not yet widely known and is still less widely used. Moreover, the new methods of study of sediments by immersion in liquids are applicable, not only to sediments, but also to all kinds of rocks, and, indeed, to all solid substances which are transparent or translucent in fine particles. These new methods are so easy to understand and so accurate in results that they deserve, and will attain, much wider use than they have yet achieved.

The most important optical property (possessed by all minerals) which is capable of quantitative measurement is the index of refraction. In the study of thin sections this property can only be estimated approximately from the evident relief, no accurate and simple method of measurement being known. In the study of powdered minerals immersed in liquids, however, an accurate measurement can be made very readily. Indeed, with the new double variation method of measuring the index of refraction in immersion liquids it is possible under favorable conditions to attain an accuracy of $\pm$ 0.001, which is sufficient in many cases to permit the measurement of both indices of refraction from each of several grains and thereby deduce the uniaxial or biaxial character of the mineral, the optic sign, the size of the optic angle, and the birefringence. Of course, this is enough to determine the mineral completely in most cases.

During the past decade, also, the universal stage apparatus has been improved so much, and its use has been simplified to such an extent, that the method is now practical for students. These improvements have made it possible to examine any ordinary thin section of standard size with the universal stage and to obtain full information regarding the position of the optic elements from a section of any biaxial mineral, no matter what its orientation may be; in other

words, the new methods with the new universal stage apparatus make it possible to measure the true optic angle, determine the optic sign, and measure the angles between the optic axes, the triaxial ellipsoid axes, X, Y, and Z, and the normal to the plane of the section or any other observable crystallographic direction from any section of any biaxial mineral in any thin section of standard size.

These are the facts which have led the author to introduce into this third edition, not only various minor changes and improvements scattered throughout the text, but also an additional chapter describing the universal stage apparatus and methods and the index-variation methods of measuring refractive indices in immersion liquids.

The author is indebted to Professor C. S. Corbett, formerly of the University of Kansas, for numerous constructive criticisms of the text of the second edition, and to Professor R. C. Emmons, of the University of Wisconsin, for important contributions to the new chapter.

ALEXANDER N. WINCHELL.

MADISON, WISCONSIN, May 1, 1928.

CONTENTS

ELEMENTS OF OPTICAL MINERALOGY

PART I

PRINCIPLES AND METHODS

CHAPTER I

ELEMENTARY CONCEPTIONS OF MINERALOGY

THE intelligent study of the optical properties of minerals requires at least an elementary knowledge of the minerals themselves and also an understanding of the nature of light and its properties. Therefore, before taking up the main theme of optical mineralogy, it is desirable to present a brief review of the general subject of mineralogy and a summary of some of the simplest principles of optics.

A **mineral species** is a natural inorganic substance which is either definite in chemical composition and physical characters or varies in these respects between definite natural limits. It is typically alike in all its parts and in most cases capable of taking upon itself, under favorable conditions, a regular internal structure and a regular external form. A mineral may be a chemical element, a definite chemical compound, or a mutual crystal solution of two or more elements or compounds in one another. If a mineral varies considerably in composition, the extremes, and also various intermediate types, may be regarded as **subspecies.** Most minerals are capable of assuming a regular internal arrangement and a regular external form, but a few, like opal, are devoid of this power. The regular external solid forms assumed by minerals (and by many other substances) are called crystals. A **group** of minerals consists of species which are closely related chemically and also much alike in their crystal forms and physical characters.

Crystals are bodies bounded by smooth surfaces having their constituent atoms[1] arranged in a definite and regular order. Crystals are produced when a substance passes from the state of a fluid to that of a solid, under conditions favorable to the natural adjustment of the atoms, so that they form networks or " space lattices," such that there is the same arrangement of atoms of one kind about any one atom as about any other one within the crystal. In case this natural adjustment is attained, the interatomic forces are in equilibrium. In general, liquids and gases are composed of molecules, which are groups of atoms; while most crystals (at least those of minerals) are now known to be built of atoms, in some cases in such arrangement as to suggest the presence of radicals, or parts of molecules, like CO_3, but free from molecules, unless a whole crystal may be considered an enormous molecule.

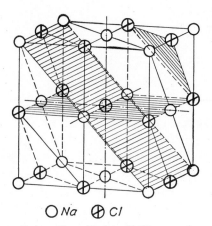

○ *Na*   ⊕ *Cl*

Fig. 1.—Space lattice of halite crystals.

One of the simplest types of space lattices is illustrated in Fig. 1; this is the arrangement in ordinary salt (sodium chloride or halite). Three kinds of planes passing through such crystals are shown by the shading. Another type of space lattice, showing a group like a radical, is shown in Fig. 2; this is the arrangement of the atoms in calcite, magnesite, siderite, and rhodochrosite.

If a mineral has the regular internal arrangement of atoms without smooth external faces, it is said to be **crystalline** or to have crystal structure. A compact aggregate of crystalline material is described as **massive.** A single unit, having the same crystal structure throughout, but devoid of crystal faces, is known as an *anhedron.* If a substance has neither the smooth external faces nor the regular internal arrangement of atoms, it is said to be **amorphous.** This is the condition of a piece of glass, of opal, etc. Some substances solidify to the amorphous state if they are cooled very rapidly, because time is necessary to permit the atoms to change

[1] An atom is the smallest portion of an element which can enter into chemical combination; each element has atoms of definite constant weight.

from the molecular groupings into regular arrangements, or lattices, in which the interatomic forces are in equilibrium.

Symmetry of crystals.—All the faces of a crystal, as well as all the constituent atoms, are arranged in accordance with certain elements of symmetry, which are fixed in their position for a given crystal, and determine, not merely its external form, but also the distribution of all its internal physical characters. The essential feature of symmetry is repetition. Thus, a right triangle *abc* (Fig. 3) may be divided symmetrically by a line *de*, if every line, point and angle on one side of *de* is repeated on the other side in the same relative position. There are three types of symmetry commonly recognized in crystals, namely, symmetry with respect to (1) a point,[1] (2) a line, (3) a plane. One, two, or three of these types of symmetry may be present in a given crystal.

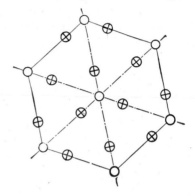

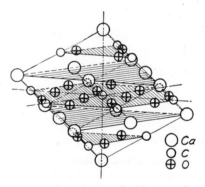

FIG. 2.—Space lattice of calcite crystals.

A crystal is symmetrical with respect to a point when for each face and edge on one side of the point (or center) there is a similar face and edge directly on the other side of the center. This is the only element of symmetry in triclinic crystals, as illustrated in Figs. 36 and 37.

A crystal is symmetrical with respect to a line (or axis) when a rotation of less than 360° about this line causes the crystal to occupy exactly the same position in space as at first. If a rotation of 180°

[1] As pointed out by Niggli (Lehr. Mineral., 2nd Ed., 1924, pp. 30–33), a point or center of symmetry, sometimes combined with one or more other elements of symmetry, is the equivalent of a more fundamental element of symmetry, known as the axis of rotary-reflection. But the symmetry of all crystals, except those of the tetartohedral class of the tetragonal system, may be completely described without the use of this rather unusual type of symmetry. The compound $Ca_2Al_2SiO_7$ is said to have the symmetry of the tetartohedral class of the tetragonal system.

produces the first repetition of position, there are two repetitions in a complete rotation, and the line is said to be an axis of twofold or binary symmetry, as illustrated by each axis in Figs. 26–30. An axis of threefold or ternary symmetry is illustrated by the vertical axis in Figs. 18–23; one of fourfold symmetry is shown by each axis in Figs. 5–9; and the vertical axis in Figs. 15–17 is an axis of sixfold symmetry.

A crystal is symmetrical with respect to a plane when for each face or edge on one side of the plane there is a similar face or edge directly opposite on the other side, so that one side is the mirror image in the given plane of the other. Each axial plane is a plane of symmetry in Figs. 5–17 and 24–30.

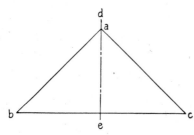

FIG. 3.—Symmetry of a simple plane figure.

All the corresponding interfacial angles on all crystals of the same species are constant, that is, they all have the same value. This is a consequence of the fact that the external faces of a crystal are determined by the internal structure, and of the further fact that all crystals of the same species have the same internal structure.

Crystal axes.—In the description of the form of a crystal, especially as regards the position of its faces, it is convenient to assume, as is done in analytical geometry, certain axes of reference, passing through the center of the ideal form. These imaginary lines are called crystallographic axes. Their directions are more or less fixed by the symmetry of the crystal, for an axis of symmetry is a crystallographic axis, in most cases. These axes (denoted a, b, and c, if unequal in length) are shown in their normal position in Fig. 4.

Parameters and symbols.—The position of any face of a crystal is conveniently expressed by stating the lengths on the axes at which the face (or its extension) cuts these axes. These lengths are known as the coordinates of the plane. A simple mathematical ratio exists between the coordinates of all planes which are possible on all crystals of the same species. For example, in Fig. 4, the plane ABC cuts the axis a at a distance which may be 19 millimeters, the axis b at 36 millimeters, and the axis c at 32 millimeters. Then 19, 36, and 32 are the coordinates of ABC. Another face may have coordinates which are entirely different, for example, 28.5, 27 and 12 millimeters. The coordinates are always written in the same order, and it is therefore unnecessary to write the axes. The second set of coordinates divided by the first set gives fractions which express the position of the second plane with respect to the first, as follows: $\frac{285}{190}$, $\frac{27}{36}$, $\frac{12}{32}$. In order to simplify these ratios, either set of coordinates may be multiplied (or divided) by any suitable number (an operation which is equivalent to moving the plane parallel with itself, maintaining constantly the same *relative* position on the axes). For example, if the second set of coordinates be multiplied by $\frac{8}{3}$ so as to make the ratio unity on c, the fractions become $\frac{76}{19}$, $\frac{72}{36}$, $\frac{32}{32}$, which equal 4, 2, 1. Again, if the second set of coordinates be multiplied by $\frac{4}{3}$, the fractions become $\frac{38}{19}$, $\frac{36}{36}$, $\frac{16}{32}$, or 2, 1, $\frac{1}{2}$. This expresses the relative position of HKL (of Fig. 4) as compared with ABC. Numbers of this kind, which express in their simplest terms the relative positions of faces, are known as the parameters of the faces. The Miller symbols may be obtained from the parameters of any face by taking the reciprocal of each number and then clearing of fractions, if necessary. Accordingly, the Miller symbols of HKL are obtained by taking the reciprocals of the parameters 2, 1, $\frac{1}{2}$, which are $\frac{1}{2}$, 1, 2, and clearing of fractions, with the following result: 1, 2, 4. The plane at the end of the b axis parallel with a and c has the parameters ∞, 1, ∞; since the reciprocal of ∞ is 0, the Miller symbols of this plane are 0, 1, 0. A plane in any octant is exactly expressed by using negative signs over the Miller symbols whenever the plane cuts an axis in the negative direction (see Fig. 4).

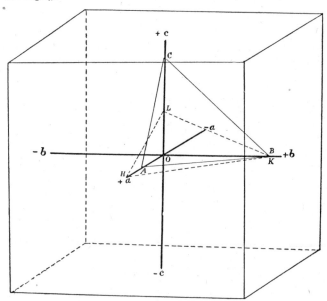

Fig. 4.—Crystal axes and intersecting planes.

A crystal **form** includes all the faces of a crystal which are required by the symmetry if one face is present. Thus, referring to Fig. 4, if the face HKL or 124 is present on an orthorhombic crystal having three planes of symmetry at right angles, the crystal form would consist of eight faces having the following symbols: 124, $\bar{1}$24, $\bar{1}\bar{2}$4, $\bar{1}\bar{2}$4, 12$\bar{4}$, $\bar{1}$2$\bar{4}$, $\bar{1}\bar{2}\bar{4}$, $\bar{1}\bar{2}\bar{4}$.

CHAPTER II

CRYSTALLOGRAPHY

ALL crystals may be classified as belonging to six different crystal systems, distinguished by the relative lengths and angular inclinations of the assumed crystallographic axes. These systems are called the isometric, tetragonal, hexagonal, orthorhombic, monoclinic, and triclinic.

Isometric System.—All crystals which are referred to the isometric system have three equal rectangular axes. The forms of this system are numerous, but many of them are of no importance in the microscopic study of minerals. Those of the highest grade of symmetry are the cube, octahedron, dodecahedron, trisoctahedron, trapezohedron, tetrahexahedron, and hexoctahedron; combinations of these forms, such as the octahedron and cube of Fig. 7, are very common. They have three principal [1] planes of symmetry parallel with the faces of the cube whose intersections determine the position of the crystallographic axes; they have also six auxiliary planes of symmetry, which bisect the angles between the principal planes, and are parallel with the faces of the dodecahedron. They have, further, three axes of fourfold symmetry coincident with the crystal axes, four axes of threefold symmetry normal to the octahedral faces, six axes of twofold symmetry normal to the dodecahedral faces, and a center of symmetry.

The cube, Fig. 5, is a form assumed by some crystals of fluorite and pyrite; other crystals of pyrite, like Fig. 9a, are called pyritohedrons. Sections of the cube are often squares. The octahedron, Fig. 6, is a common form of magnetite, pyrite, and spinel; sections may be squares, rhombs, hexagons, or triangles. The dodecahedron, Fig. 8, is a form shown by magnetite and sodalite; sections are apt to be hexagons. The trapezohedron, Fig. 9, is so common in leucite that the form is sometimes called the leucitohedron; sections may be octagons.

[1] A principal plane of symmetry is one containing two or more like axes of symmetry, and in the isometric system these must be axes of maximum symmetry.

6

The isometric crystals are of little importance in the microscopic study of minerals, because they are not common among rock-forming minerals and are usually identifiable by the simplest tests.

Each form of the isometric system completely encloses space and can occur alone; each one is therefore a geometrical solid, and has its

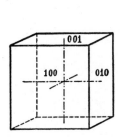

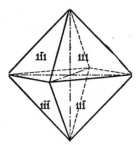

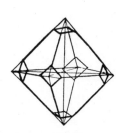

FIG. 5.—Cube.   FIG. 6.—Octahedron.   FIG. 7.—Combination of cube and octahedron.

special name, as illustrated above. In the other crystal systems, most of the crystal forms do not completely enclose space and cannot occur alone. Most of them belong to three types, namely:

1. Pyramids, which are forms each of whose faces cuts all three crystal axes.

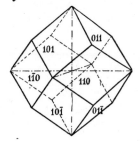

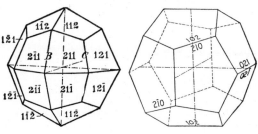

FIG. 8.—Rhombic dodecahedron.   FIG. 9.—Trapezohedron.   FIG. 9a.—Pyritohedron.

2. Prisms, which are forms each of whose faces cuts the two lateral axes and is parallel to the vertical axis.

3. Pinacoids, which are forms each of whose faces cuts only one axis and is parallel to the other two.

Tetragonal System.—All crystals which are referred to the tetragonal system have three rectangular axes, two being of equal length, and the third, which is the vertical axis, of unequal length, as in Fig. 10. The forms of this system include the base, unit prism, diametral prism, ditetragonal prism, unit pyramid, diametral pyramid, and ditetragonal pyramid. These forms have one principal plane of symmetry parallel to the base, two axial planes of symmetry normal to the base (each including two crystal axes), and two other planes of symmetry bisecting the angles between the axial planes; they have

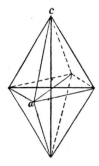

also one axis of fourfold symmetry coincident with the vertical axis, and four axes of twofold symmetry parallel with the base, two being coincident with the lateral axes and the other two bisecting their angles; they have a center of symmetry.

The base or basal pinacoid consists of only two faces (001 and 00$\bar{1}$); it is present on some crystals of vesuvianite (Fig. 12) and scapolite. The unit prism (Fig. 11) consists of four faces (110, 1$\bar{1}$0, $\bar{1}\bar{1}$0,

FIG. 10.—Axes within tetragonal pyramid.

and $\bar{1}$10); it is common on zircon (Fig. 12), rutile, and cassiterite. Sections are apt to be squares. The diametral prism[1] consists of four faces (100, 010, $\bar{1}$00, and 0$\bar{1}$0); it is found on some crystals of rutile (Fig. 13) and scapolite; sections of this form alone are often squares. The ditetragonal prism consists of eight faces (for example: 210, 120,

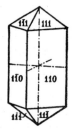

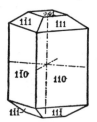

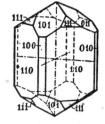

FIG. 11.—Tetragonal prism and pyramid; zircon.

FIG. 12.—Tetragonal prism, pyramid and base; vesuvianite.

FIG. 13.—Prisms with two pyramids; rutile.

$\bar{1}$20, $\bar{2}$10, $\bar{2}\bar{1}$0, $\bar{1}\bar{2}$0, 1$\bar{2}$0, and 2$\bar{1}$0), and the ditetragonal pyramid consists of sixteen faces; these are rare in rock-forming minerals. The unit pyramid consists of eight faces, illustrated by the terminal faces in Fig. 12. The diametral pyramid[2] consists of eight faces (101,

---

[1] The diametral prism is called a prism rather than a pinacoid because another selection of the position of the lateral axes—equally correct—would make it conform to the definition of a prism, and because it is geometrically a prism.

[2] The diametral pyramid is called a pyramid, though it does not conform to the definition of a pyramid, because another selection of the position of the lateral axes—equally correct—would make it conform, and because geometrically it is a double pyramid.

o11, $\overline{1}$o1, o$\overline{1}$1, 1o$\overline{1}$, o1$\overline{1}$, $\overline{1}$o$\overline{1}$, and o$\overline{1}\overline{1}$), which are present in combination with the unit pyramid as terminal faces in Fig. 13.

Hexagonal System.—All crystals which belong to the hexagonal system have three equal axes making angles of 60° in one plane, and one unequal axis normal to this plane, as shown in Fig. 14. The hexagonal system consists of two parts which differ distinctly in symmetry and are known as the hexagonal and trigonal divisions.

Hexagonal Division.—All crystals of the hexagonal division have a vertical axis of sixfold symmetry; the forms of highest grade of symmetry have also a principal plane of symmetry parallel with the base, three

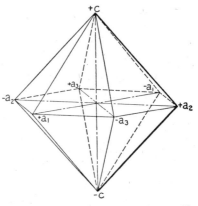

FIG. 14.—Axes within hexagonal pyramid.

axial planes of symmetry normal to the base (each including two crystal axes), and three other planes of symmetry bisecting the angles between the axial planes. They have also six axes of twofold symmetry (three being coincident with the lateral crystal axes and the other three bisecting their angles) as well as a center of symmetry.

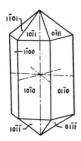

FIG. 15.—Hexagonal prism and pyramid; apatite.

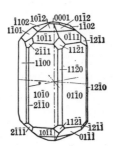

FIG. 16.—Hexagonal prisms, pyramid and base; apatite.

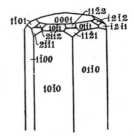

FIG. 17.—Hexagonal prism, base and pyramids; beryl.

The forms of this division include the base, unit prism, diametral prism, dihexagonal prism, unit pyramid, diametral pyramid, and dihexagonal pyramid.

The base consists of only two faces (0001 and 000$\overline{1}$); it is present on some crystals of apatite and beryl (see Fig. 17). The unit prism consists of six faces (1010, 0110, 1100, 1010, 0110, and 1100); it occurs on some crystals of apatite in combination with the unit pyramid, as shown in Fig. 15; cross-sections are hexagons. The diametral prism also consists of six faces (2110, 1120, 1210, 2110,

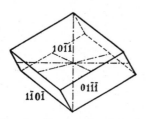

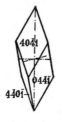

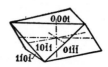

FIG. 18.—Cleavage rhombohedron of calcite. FIG. 19.—Acute rhombohedron of calcite. FIG. 20.—Rhombohedron and base; hematite.

1120, and 1210) which may be developed with or without other vertical faces; in Fig. 16 they truncate the edges of the unit prism, as in some crystals of apatite. The dihexagonal forms are rare. The unit pyramid is present in **Fig. 15** and the diametral pyramid in Fig. 16.

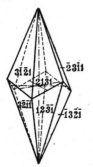

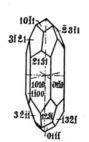

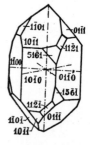

FIG. 21.—Scalenohedron of calcite. FIG. 22.—Prism, scalenohedron and rhombohedron; calcite. FIG. 23.—Prism and rhombohedrons, modified by right trigonal pyramid and right plus trapezohedron. Right-handed quartz.

Trigonal Division.—All crystals of the trigonal division have a vertical axis of threefold symmetry; the forms of highest grade of symmetry have three auxiliary planes of symmetry normal to the base and bisecting the angles between the lateral crystal axes; they have three axes of twofold symmetry (which coincide with the lateral crystal axes) and a center of symmetry. The special forms of this division include the rhombohedron and the scalenohedron. These forms, alone and in combinations, are illustrated in Figs. 18–23; they are especially common in calcite and quartz. The rhombohedron has six faces, each being a rhomb; it has six like lateral edges forming a zigzag around the crystal and six like terminal edges, three above and three below. The vertical axis connects the two trihedral angles; the lateral axes connect the middle points of opposite edges. The scalenohedron has twelve faces, each being a scalene triangle. The lateral edges form a zigzag around the crystal just like that around the rhombohedron, but the terminal edges are not all alike.

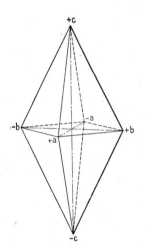

FIG. 24.—Axes within orthorhombic pyramid.

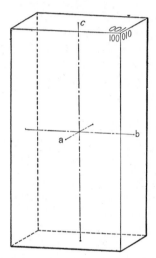

FIG. 25.—Macro-, brachy-, and basal pinacoids.

Orthorhombic System.—All crystals which belong to the ortho-rhombic system have three unequal rectangular axes, as shown in Fig. 24. Such crystals[1] have no principal plane of symmetry, but have three axial planes of symmetry, three axes of twofold symmetry (which coincide with the crystal axes) and a center of symmetry. To orient an orthorhombic crystal, that is, to place it in the conventional position, any axis is made vertical and the longer lateral axis, known as the macro axis, is made to extend right and left. The shorter lateral axis, known as the brachy axis, then extends from front to rear. A form whose faces are parallel to one of these axes (and not parallel to the other) is named accordingly. Thus, the

[1] This refers to crystals of the highest grade of symmetry in the orthorhombic system.

pinacoid parallel to the brachy axis is the brachypinacoid. A dome is a form each of whose faces is parallel to one lateral axis and cuts the other two axes; therefore, there are brachydomes and macrodomes. Other forms of this system include the base, prism, pyramid, and macropinacoid. The three pinacoids are shown in Fig. 25. The unit pyramid is shown in Fig. 24 with the axes. Four different

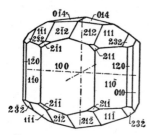

FIG. 26.—A combination of crystal forms in hypersthene.

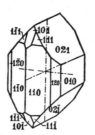

FIG. 27.—A combination of crystal forms in chrysolite.

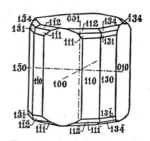

FIG. 28.—A combination of crystal forms in cordierite.

pyramids are illustrated in Fig. 26, a crystal form of hypersthene. Both kinds of domes are found in Fig. 27, as seen in chrysolite. The brachyprism (130) and unit prism (110) with the base (001), other pinacoids (100 and 010), and four pyramids, are in combination in Fig. 28, which is a drawing of a common form of cordierite. Figs. 29 and 30 illustrate combinations of base, prism and domes occurring in barite crystals.

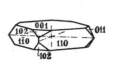

FIG. 29

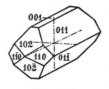

FIG. 30.

FIGS. 29, 30.—Combinations of crystal forms in barite.

Monoclinic System.—All crystals of the monoclinic system have three unequal axes, one being at right angles to the other two, which are not at right angles to each other, as shown in Fig. 31. The axis which is normal to the other two is called the ortho axis; one of the other two is the vertical axis (c), and the other is called the clino or inclined axis. To orient the crystal, the ortho axis (b) is made to extend right and left and one of the others is placed vertically; the third axis (a) is made to extend downward to the front. A form parallel with one lateral axis, and not parallel to the other, is named from that fact. Therefore, 100 is the orthopinacoid, 010 is the clinopinacoid, 101 is an orthodome, 011 is a clinodome; 130 is similarly called a clinoprism, since it is more nearly parallel with the clino axis than is the unit prism, 110. The other forms of this system include the base (001) (which is not horizontal in the conventional position), prism and pyramid. Crystals of maximum symmetry in this system have only one secondary plane of symmetry, one axis of twofold symmetry, and a center of symmetry. Fig. 32 shows a combination of

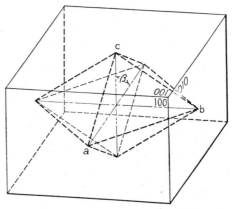

FIG. 31.—Crystal axes and pyramids within pinacoids of a monoclinic crystal.

the orthopinacoid (100), clinopinacoid (010), unit prism (110), and unit pyramid (11ī), in augite. Fig. 33 shows a combination of the base (001), clinopinacoid (010), unit prism (110), clinoprism (130), orthodome (20ī), and unit pyramid (11ī), common in orthoclase. Fig. 34 is a crystal habit of epidote, consisting of the base (001), orthopinacoid (100), orthodome (10ī), and unit pyramid (111).

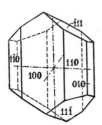

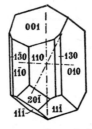

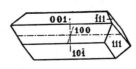

FIG. 32.—Crystal of augite.

FIG. 33.—Crystal of orthoclase.

FIG. 34.—Common habit of epidote; base, orthopinacoid, orthodome, and unit pyramid.

Triclinic System.—All crystals of the triclinic system are referred to three unequal axes whose intersections are all oblique, as shown in Fig. 35. To orient the crystal, any axis is placed vertically, the longer lateral axis is made to extend downward to the right and the other downward to the front. The angle between the front and rear axis *a* and the vertical axis *c* is denoted by β (as in the monoclinic system), that between *a* and *b* is denoted by γ, and that between *b* and *c* by α. Crystals of minerals in this system have no plane nor axis of symmetry, but have a center of symmetry. Therefore, each form consists of only two faces, one opposite the other. As in orthorhombic crystals, the longer lateral axis is known as the macro axis and the shorter as the brachy axis. Forms are named from parallelism with axes; therefore, 100 is the macropinacoid, 010 the brachypinacoid, 101 a macrodome, and 011 a brachydome. The other forms include the base, prism, and pyramid. Fig. 36 shows a common habit of albite, consisting of a combination of the base (001), the unit prisms (110 and 1̄10), the unit pyramids (11̄1 and 1̄1̄1), and the brachypinacoid (010). Fig. 37 illustrates a crystal of rhodonite having a well-devel-

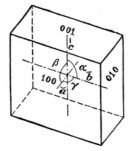 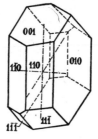 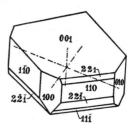

FIG. 35.—Triclinic axes and pinacoids.　　FIG. 36.—Combination of forms in albite.　　FIG. 37.—Triclinic crystal of rhodonite.

oped base (001) with the unit prisms (110 and 1̄10), the macropinacoid (100), the brachypinacoid (010) and four pyramids (11̄1, 22̄1, 221, and 2̄2̄1).

Crystal habit.—Crystals vary not only in their angular relations and symmetry, but also in their size, the relative development of their faces and the number and kind of faces or forms that are present. Variations in the angular relations of the faces and the symmetry of the forms are of fundamental importance and constitute the chief differences between the six crystal systems just described. Variations in the size of crystals, the relative development of their faces and the number and kind of faces or forms that are present are of no fundamental significance; crystals of any substance always show such variations to some extent, and in some cases these variations produce a great variety in the crystals of one substance. Such variations are said to produce different *crystal habits*. It should be emphasized that variation in crystal habit occurs without the slightest variation in angular relations of the faces and therefore without the slightest variation in the crystallographic symmetry. In spite of the fact that any substance may show two (or even many) crystal habits under varying conditions of formation, many substances so frequently exhibit more or less constancy in crystal habit that a knowledge of their crystal habits is of importance in their study.

The relative development of the faces and the number and kind of faces or forms of crystals vary so greatly when different substances are compared and are so nearly constant in different crystals of one substance in some cases that they furnish data of considerable value in the study of crystals. The relative development of the faces of crystals is one of the chief factors in determining their general shape; if the faces are all of nearly the same size the crystal is likely to be nearly equidimensional, such crystals are said to be *equant*. If a pair of opposite faces are decidedly larger than the other faces, the crystals are necessarily *flattened* and are said to be *tabular*; if this tendency is carried to an extreme they are called *lamellar* or even *foliated*. If three or more faces belonging to one zone, that is, all parallel to any one line, are decidedly larger than the other faces, the crystal is necessarily *elongated* in that direction and is described as *columnar*;[1] if this tendency is carried to an extreme the crystal is described as *acicular* or even *fibrous*. Crystals of any crystal system may be equant, tabular, lamellar, columnar or fibrous, but isometric crystals are usually equant; tetragonal and hexagonal crystals are equant or flattened normal to the vertical axis or elongated parallel thereto; other crystals may be flattened parallel with any pinacoid (or even any other pair of opposite faces) or elongated parallel with any crystal axis (or, rarely, parallel with some other crystal direction).

Crystals which show only one crystal form, or have the faces of one form decidedly larger than those of any other, are easily described as characterized by that form; for example, isometric crystals may be cubic, octahedral, dodecahedral, etc.; tetragonal crystals may be pyramidal, prismatic or pinacoidal; hexagonal crystals may be pyramidal, prismatic, pinacoidal, rhombohedral or scalenohedral; orthorhombic, monoclinic and triclinic crystals may be pyramidal, prismatic, domatic or pinacoidal.

A cubic isometric crystal (Fig. 38*b*) may be flattened to a tabular

---

[1] Some writers describe columnar and acicular crystals as prismatic; this is correct geometrically, but incorrect crystallographically unless the long faces are prisms; they may be domes or pinacoids or even pyramids.

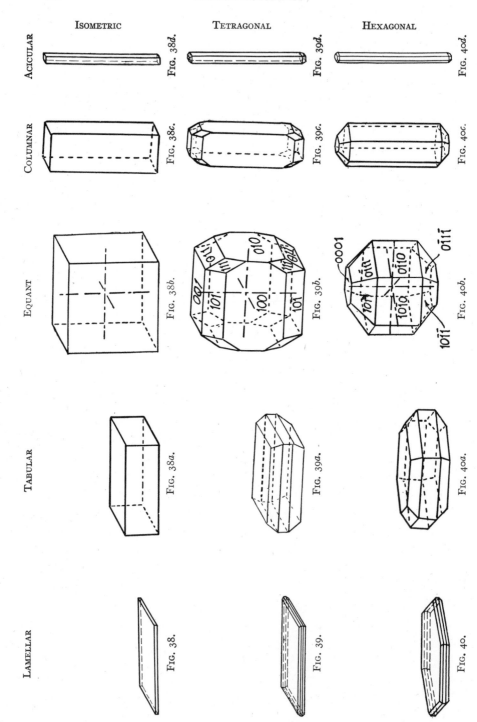

ORTHORHOMBIC   MONOCLINIC   TRICLINIC

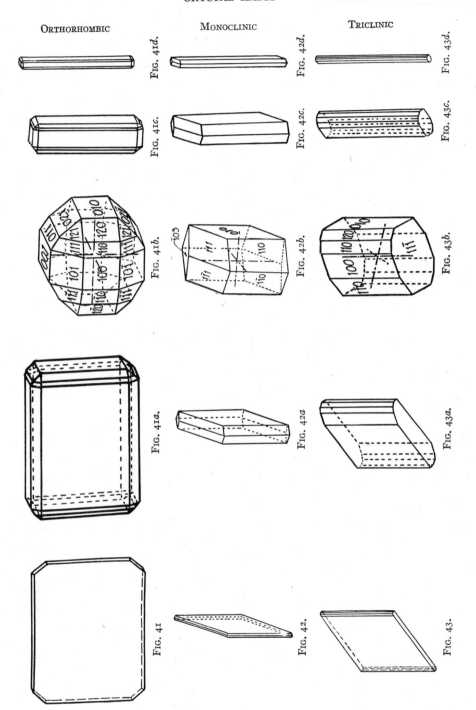

FIG. 41d.

FIG. 42d.

FIG. 43d.

FIG. 41c.

FIG. 42c.

FIG. 43c.

FIG. 41b.

FIG. 42b.

FIG. 43b.

FIG. 41a.

FIG. 42a.

FIG. 43a.

FIG. 41.

FIG. 42.

FIG. 43.

habit as in Fig. 38a; by more flattening it may become lamellar as in
Fig. 38, or even foliated; by elongation it may become columnar as in
Fig. 38c, or even acicular as in Fig. 38d. Isometric crystals are usually
equant or nearly so. An equant tetragonal crystal of calomel (Hg_2Cl_2)
is shown in Fig. 39b; this substance often forms crystals of columnar
habit as in Fig. 39c; acicular crystals (Fig. 39d) are not common; tabular crystals (Fig. 39a) are not rare in the natural substance, but lamellar
crystals (Fig. 39) are very scarce. An equant hexagonal crystal of
apatite ($Ca_5FP_3O_{12}$) is shown in Fig. 40b; the columnar habit (Fig. 40c)
is the common one in this substance, but acicular forms (Fig. 40d) are
not rare; tabular crystals (Fig. 40a) and lamellar crystals (Fig. 40) are
very rare or unknown in this substance. An equant orthorhombic
crystal of olivine [$(Mg,Fe)_2SiO_4$] is shown in Fig. 41b; natural olivine

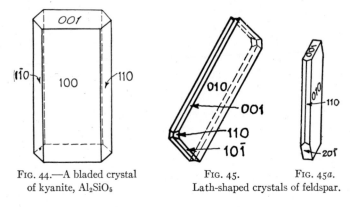

FIG. 44.—A bladed crystal   FIG. 45.   FIG. 45a.
of kyanite, Al_2SiO_5 Lath-shaped crystals of feldspar.

is often tabular parallel to 100 as in Fig. 41a, while natural iron olivine
or fayalite is likely to be lamellar in that direction as in Fig. 41; the
columnar habit (Fig. 41c) is found in magnesian olivine or forsterite;
the acicular habit (Fig. 41d) is unknown or rare in olivine. Fig. 42b
shows an equant monoclinic crystal of gypsum ($CaSO_4 \cdot 2H_2O$); such
crystals are often tabular parallel to 010 as in Fig. 42a; the lamellar
habit (Fig. 42) is less common; a columnar habit (Fig. 42c) is shown
by crystals formed in a $MgCl_2$ solution; a fibrous habit (Fig. 42d) is
also known in the natural mineral. An equant triclinic crystal of
chalcanthite [1] ($CuSO_4 \cdot 5H_2O$) is illustrated in Fig. 43b; such crystals
are often columnar as in Fig. 43c, or even fibrous as in Fig. 43d; when
formed artificially on a glass slide they are tabular to lamellar, lying
on 110, as shown in Figs. 43 and 43a.

[1] The orientation differs from that of Tutton and Barker by reversing the c axis so as
to make the b axis incline downward to the *right*, as usual in triclinic crystals.

Crystals which are much flattened or much elongated tend to be simpler, that is, have fewer faces, than corresponding equant crystals; this tendency is illustrated in Figs. 39, 39*a*, and 39*d* as compared with Fig. 39*b*, Figs. 41 and 41*d* as compared with Fig. 41*b*, and Figs. 43 and 43*d* as compared with Fig. 43*b*.

Some crystals show both elongation and flattening; such crystals are described as *bladed* if developed as in Fig. 44 or *lath-shaped* if similar to Figs. 45 or 45*a* in development.

Crystal aggregates.—Crystals frequently grow in groups or aggregates in which the various crystals show more or less tendency to parallelism. In case all the axes of one are parallel to corresponding axes in the other, the aggregate is called a **parallel growth.** Such growths may consist of many crystals, rather than merely two, and

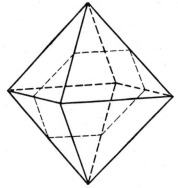
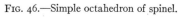

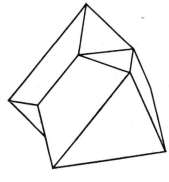

FIG. 46.—Simple octahedron of spinel.   FIG. 46*a*.—Spinel octahedron in twinning position.

then the grouping is apt to be such as to form the axes (or other chief parts) of a much larger crystal of the same kind. Such **skeleton crystals** may continue to grow and fill out to form one large crystal. Snowflakes are excellent examples of skeleton crystals. When a flake fills out, it forms one hexagonal crystal of ice.

Twins.—Crystals of a single species also frequently grow in positions in which the parallelism of the parts is incomplete; that is, some corresponding directions are exactly parallel and others are not. Two crystals of the same kind, which form an aggregate exhibiting such partial parallelism, are called a twin, or are said to be in twinning position. The relative position of two crystals in twinning position may be most readily understood by *assuming* that one has been revolved through 180° about some direction or axis, which thus remains common to both. Thus, in Fig. 46, a crystal, say, of spinel, forms a

simple octahedron.   If this octahedron be supposed to be cut in two
parts along the dotted plane parallel to an octahedral face and the
lower half be supposed to be revolved through 180° about an axis
normal to this plane, the twinned form of Fig. 46a is produced.   It
should be emphasized that twins are not produced by such a revolution, but by regular growth (except the secondary twins produced by
shearing, etc.);   this is merely a convenient way to describe the
relative positions.

The axis about which one part is supposed to be revolved is called
the **twinning axis,** and the plane normal to this is the **twinning plane.**
The plane by which twinned crystals are united is called the **composition plane.**   This is often the same as the twinning plane, but it
is not necessarily so;   when it is not the same as the twinning plane,
the composition plane is apt to be parallel with the twinning axis,
as in Carlsbad twins of feldspar (see Fig. 55).   The twinning axis is
nearly always a crystal axis or normal to a possible crystal face.   If
twins are simply adherent by the composition face, they are **contact
twins;**   if they interpenetrate more or less, they commonly have an
irregular composition surface and are called **penetration twins,** as
illustrated in Fig. 56.   In many cases twins are composed of more
than two parts, the mutual relations of any two adjacent parts being
the same.   In this case the twinning is described as **multiple** or
polysynthetic, if the composition faces are parallel, and **cyclic** or
symmetrical, if the composition faces are not parallel and therefore
tend to turn in a circle.   Repeated twinning of the cyclic type often
gives rise to an apparent symmetry, called **pseudosymmetry,** greater
than that actually possessed by the crystal.   Thus, orthorhombic
cordierite may seem to be hexagonal on account of cyclic twinning.

Twinning may be produced artificially, in some cases, by shearing
or other stresses;   such twinning is called **secondary.**   It is illustrated
by some twinning in calcite and by some multiple twinning in feldspar and pyroxene.

Common twinning laws.—The most important type of twinning,
in crystals of the isometric system, is that illustrated in Fig. 46a;
this, like all other types of twinning, is most conveniently described
by stating the crystallographic position of the twinning axis or the
twinning plane, and such a statement is known as a twinning law.
Twins whose twinning axis is normal to an octahedral face, as in
Fig. 46a, are especially common in spinel and are therefore known as
spinel twins; they may be either contact twins, or penetration forms,

as illustrated by Fig. 47 for hauynite, by Fig. 47*a* for tetrahedrite, and by Fig. 47*b* for fluorite.   Fig. 47 requires two revolutions of 180° about different octahedral axes or one revolution of 180° about a dodecahedral axis.

In the tetragonal system, the most important type of twinning is that which corresponds to the spinel law, but in this case the twinning axis is normal to the face of a pyramid.   Such twins are especially

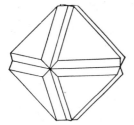

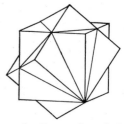

FIG. 47.—Penetration spinel twin in hauynite.   FIG. 47*a*.—Penetration spinel twin in tetrahedrite.   FIG. 47*b*.—Penetration spinel twin in fluorite.

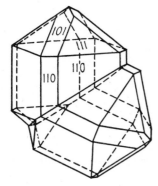
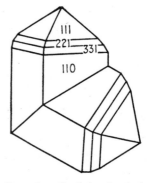

FIG. 48.—Geniculated twin in cassiterite.   FIG. 48*a*.—Geniculated twin in zircon.

common in rutile and cassiterite; when simple they are described as **geniculated,** or knee-shaped, as in Figs. 48 and 48*a*.

In the hexagonal system, twins are rare and unimportant in crystals of the hexagonal division, but are common in those of the trigonal division.   The calcite crystals and anhedra in rocks often show twinning lamellæ (twinned on $01\bar{1}2$), which may be of secondary origin, as shown by the fact that a single cleavage piece of calcite may be changed, in part, into a twin, by pressure with a dull knife on an obtuse edge of a piece of columnar form, the other obtuse edge resting on a firm support.   This is illustrated in Fig. 49; the portion moved (that is, *abcd* to *a'b'cd*) takes a position as if twinned on $01\bar{1}2$ (or *edc*); it is not broken off, but is in a new position of stability.

In the orthorhombic system the commonest type of twinning has

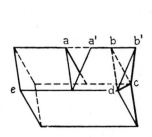

Fig. 49.—Artificial twin produced in calcite.

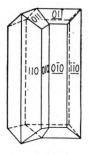

Fig. 50.—Aragonite twinned on $1\bar{1}0$.

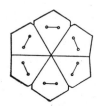

Fig. 50*a*.—Cross-section of pseudohexagonal cyclic twin of aragonite.

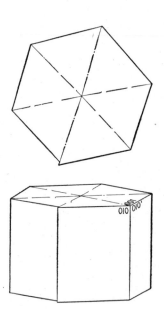

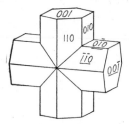

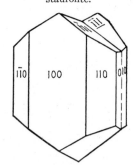

Fig. 52.—Cruciform twin of staurolite.

Fig. 51.—Pseudohexagonal cyclic twin of cordierite.

Fig. 53.—Augite twinned on vertical axis.

the twinning axis normal to the face of a prism whose prismatic angle is about 60°. This is well illustrated in aragonite and in cordierite, as shown in Figs. 50 and 50*a* of aragonite, and 51 of cordierite. In staurolite, twinning on the face of a dome whose angle is nearly equal to 45° produces a group resembling a Greek cross; this is illustrated in Fig. 52.

Twinning is more important in the monoclinic system. The commonest type has the vertical axis as the twinning axis, as illustrated by Fig. 53 for augite and by Fig. 54 for gypsum. The same law gives the groups called **Carlsbad** twins in orthoclase, which are either contact forms or penetration twins, as shown in Figs. 55 and 56. This type of twinning may be explained equally well by referring it to the

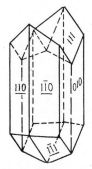

FIG. 54.—Gypsum twinned on vertical axis.

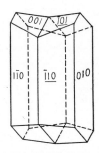

FIG. 55.—Contact Carlsbad twin of albite.

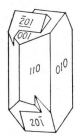

FIG. 56.—Partial penetration Carlsbad twin of orthoclase.

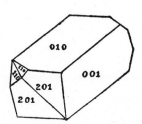

FIG. 57.—Baveno twin of orthoclase.

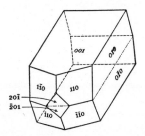

FIG. 58.—Manebach twin of orthoclase.

orthopinacoid, 100, as the twinning plane. In **Baveno** twins of orthoclase the twinning plane is the clinodome, 021, and since the angle between this face and the base is 44° 56', nearly square forms result, as illustrated in Fig. 57; they are commonly elongated parallel to the *a* axis. A rare type of twinning in orthoclase is known as the **Manebach,** in which the basal plane is the twinning plane and also the composition face, as shown in Fig. 58. Multiple twinning, in the form of fine lamellæ-producing striations on vertical faces and a parting parallel to 001, is common in monoclinic pyroxene; the twinning plane is the base; the aspect of such an aggregate is shown in Fig. 59.

In microscopic work, the most important twins are those shown by the feldspars, and, of these, the twins of the triclinic forms are the most useful. The twinning peculiar to triclinic feldspar is of several types, the more abundant being the albite and pericline. The former type has 010 as the twinning plane, the latter has the *b* axis as the twinning axis. Both types are nearly always polysynthetic, producing narrow lamellæ which are parallel to 010 in albite twinning and parallel to the axis *b* in pericline twinning. Therefore, albite twinning produces fine striations on a basal cleavage surface and pericline twinning produces similar striations on the brachypinacoidal cleavage or face. A simple albite twin is shown in Fig. 60; this type of twinning

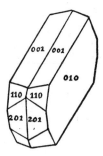

FIG. 59.—Multiple twinning on 001   FIG. 60.—Simple albite twin in
            in augite.   plagioclase.

is nearly always present, and many times repeated, in all kinds of plagioclase, and thus produces striations on the base parallel to 010, as illustrated in Fig. 61. A simple pericline twin is represented in Fig. 62; in such twins the composition plane passes through the crystal in such a direction that its intersections with the prismatic faces make an equilateral oblique-angled parallelogram or rhombus. The position of this "*rhombic section*" changes materially with small changes in the axial angle γ. It is always parallel to the axis *b*, and varies from parallel to the base in one type of andesine to an angle of plus 21° with the trace of the base in 010 in albite and to minus 18° with the same trace in 010 in anorthite, as shown in Fig. 63. Except rarely in albite, pericline twinning is polysynthetic and invisible without the microscope and polarized light; it produces striations on brachypinacoidal sections, as shown in Fig. 61. The plagioclase feldspars often show simple twinning of the same types known in orthoclase, in combination with these polysynthetic types. Microcline exhibits polysynthetic albite twinning combined with multiple twinning of the same kind as the pericline, except that the composition

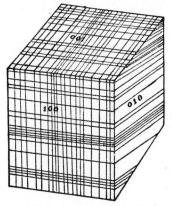

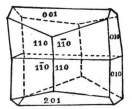

FIG. 61.—External albite and pericline striations in plagioclase.

FIG. 62.—Simple pericline twin in albite.

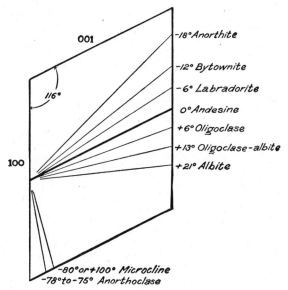

FIG. 63.—Position of composition face of pericline (and microcline) twinning in triclinic feldspars.

face is not a rhombic section, but is nearly normal to the base, as shown in Fig. 63.

Hitherto, aggregates have been described in which all the crystals are of one kind or species. Aggregates of crystals of two (or more) kinds may show similar relations in position. Thus, aggregates of isomorphous crystals (that is, crystals chemically and crystallographically similar, but not identical) may be in almost completely parallel positions, as illustrated in the **zonal growths** of pyroxene and of feldspar; twinning may extend continuously through such zones. The zones are usually bounded by planes which were once crystal faces, each zone representing a period of additional growth of the crystal. The composition of the zones varies, often in regular sequence or progression; thus, in plagioclase of igneous rocks, the zones commonly are progressively richer in albite from the center outward.

Aggregates of crystals which are wholly unlike, chemically and crystallographically, usually show no definite relations in their mutual positions, but even in this case definite relations are sometimes found. Thus, quartz has been observed growing in parallel position on rhombohedral faces of calcite, rutile may develop in three directions parallel to prominent edges on the basal plane of mica, etc. But in such aggregates one mineral is apt to be completely enclosed by another.

Inclusions.—Any substance completely enclosed by another is known as an inclusion, no matter what its nature or origin may be. Accordingly, inclusions may be gaseous, liquid, or solid. If they originate at the time of formation of the enclosing crystal, they are called primary; if they originate by alteration or introduction after the formation of the enclosing crystal, they are called secondary. A crystal which grows very rapidly may shoot out in various chief directions, like frost of one orientation on a window pane, and then the skeleton form may be filled in during a period of slow growth. In such cases, deeply reentrant angles may be filled with foreign material which is finally completely surrounded by the growth of the crystal. If the enclosed material is a liquid, it may contract, upon cooling, so that it no longer fills the whole space; the cavity will then be occupied by a liquid and its gas. Or, the enclosed liquid may consist of parts immiscible at ordinary temperatures, so that the cavity may contain two liquids and a gas, as illustrated by cavities in quartz containing water, liquid carbon dioxide, and gas. The nature of the liquid is determinable, in some cases, by measuring its index of refraction, by determining its critical point, or by chemical tests. In many cases the liquid is water or carbon dioxide, or a solution in which the crystals grew.

When the enclosed liquid contains molecules of the enclosing crystal in solution these may crystallize on the walls of the cavity during cooling, and thus give it crystal faces. The cavity is then called a negative crystal; such forms are common in quartz and halite. Such negative crystals probably may be produced also' by simple growth of the enclosing crystal. Sufficient growth of the halite to cover one side of a hollow cube is all that is necessary to change the deep reentrant cubic spaces on crystals of halite into negative cubic crystals.

When crystals of other substances are present in a liquid, they may be enclosed by another growing crystal. This may happen with or without evidence that the growing crystal moves the other. The concentration of enclosed crystals in certain zones in leucite and feldspar is probably due to their being thrust aside for a time by the growing crystal, until more rapid growth results in their being surrounded. In other cases, inclusions are arranged radially; Pirsson

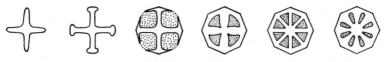

Fig. 64.—Radial inclusions in leucite resulting from development of skeletal forms. (After Pirsson.)

has shown how this condition may result from progressive growth from skeletal forms, as illustrated in Fig. 64.

When one large mineral contains numerous inclusions of notable size having no definite orientation, the texture is said to be **poikilitic**. When pyroxene (or other mineral) contains partly or wholly enclosed euhedral crystals of plagioclase, the texture is called **ophitic**; if the enclosing mineral is large enough to surround several crystals of plagioclase the texture is called **poikilophitic**.

If large crystals of two kinds are growing simultaneously in a liquid they may interpenetrate, each maintaining its continuity and crystal orientation, though irregularly dividing the space with the other. The best example of this form of mutual inclusion is furnished by intergrowths of quartz and orthoclase; in such cases the quartz commonly shows skeletal forms and the texture is then known as **graphic**.

Secondary inclusions may originate in several different ways. They may be due to: (1) separation, on cooling, of material previously held in crystal solution; this is believed to be the mode of origin of the brown to opaque inclusions which produce submetallic luster or **schiller** in hypersthene (Fig. 65) and some other pyroxenes. They may be due to: (2) **replacement** of part of a crystal by foreign material brought through the solid exterior in solution, as in the case of pyrite introduced into quartz or feldspar near veins by hot vein-forming solutions, the portion of the mineral replaced being simultaneously removed by the solutions. They may be due to: (3) alteration caused by reactions between the crystal and solutions permeating it, as illustrated by some of the alteration products seen in feldspar and in olivine. Still other modes of origin are possible, but the preceding are the best known and probably the most important.

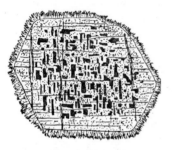

FIG. 65.—"Schiller" inclusions in hypersthene. (After Lacroix.)

Alteration is a general term applied to all changes in crystals after their formation. It is desirable, however, to draw a distinction between alteration products and substances produced by replacement, whenever, in the latter, no part of the original material is present in the replacing substances, as illustrated when pyrite replaces calcite or quartz. Alteration usually begins on the outer surfaces of crystals and penetrates them progressively, or by taking advantage of fractures or cleavages. In such cases, the products are not inclusions at any stage of the process, and this is the simplest means of distinguishing between alteration products and inclusions. It is convenient to discuss secondary inclusions which are also alteration products under the latter designation, and to describe only primary inclusions under that name, as is done in this book.

CHAPTER III

PHYSICAL CHARACTERS OF MINERALS

THE physical characters of minerals which relate to their effects on light will be described in detail in later sections of this book. The other physical characters, aside from crystallization, will be briefly summarized here, with special reference to their use in optical study with the microscope.

Cleavage is the property of some crystals to break along definite smooth planes, which are called cleavage planes, and are always possible crystal faces, since they are determined by the regular internal arrangement of the atoms. Cleavages (like crystal faces) occur parallel with planes in which the atoms are closely packed together, and normal to which the distance between adjacent layers of atoms is relatively great. Cleavage is described, according to its crystallographic direction, as cubic, octahedral, rhombohedral, basal, prismatic, etc. It is also described, according to the ease with which it is obtained and the smoothness of the surfaces produced, as perfect or eminent, distinct, indistinct or imperfect, and difficult. Cleavage is perfect when it is obtained with great ease and yields smooth, lustrous surfaces, as in mica, calcite, etc. The other terms express inferior degrees of cleavage.

In all directions, in a crystal, which are crystallographically the same, cleavage is the same in quality; conversely, if the crystallography of a given mineral is unknown, the cleavage provides a means by which identical crystal directions may be recognized. A single cleavage, crystallographically, may exist in a mineral in one, two, three, four, or even six different directions; thus, muscovite (isinglass) has basal cleavage in only one direction; pyroxene and amphibole have prismatic cleavage in two directions parallel to the prism faces; calcite has rhombohedral cleavage in three directions; fluorite has octahedral cleavage in four directions; and garnet may have *parting* (similar to cleavage, but secondarily developed by strain and not always present) in six directions parallel to dodecahedral faces. Sphalerite has cleavage in these directions.

29

Also, a mineral may have only one cleavage, or two, or even more cleavages crystallographically unlike; they are then unlike in quality. Thus, chlorite has only one perfect cleavage, which is parallel to the base; orthoclase has two cleavages parallel to two of the pinacoids (001 and 010); and anhydrite has three pinacoidal cleavages.

In thin sections of crystals, cleavage is seen as one or more sets of more or less narrow, straight and parallel cracks, which are continuous or interrupted (and perhaps offset), according to the quality of the cleavage. These cracks are unquestionably developed in part during the grinding of the section, but in part they are present inde-

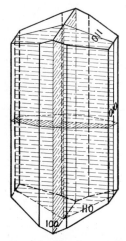

FIG. 66.—Simple crystal of hornblende.

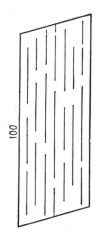

FIG. 67.—Clinopinacoid section of hornblende crystal.

pendent of the grinding. Sections of varying orientation through a single crystal may not show the same abundance of cleavages; those cut about at right angles to the cleavage planes commonly show them more abundantly than others cut nearly parallel with these planes. For example, a simple crystal of hornblende, like Fig. 66, will show its prismatic cleavages well developed in two sets of narrow, straight, parallel cracks, forming an angle of 124° in a cross-section which is normal to both cleavage planes, as in Fig. 69. In a section parallel to the clinopinacoid (010) the cleavage cracks are not so numerous nor so closely spaced, and they are apt to be discontinuous, as in Fig. 67. The traces of these cleavages are parallel, but the planes of the cleavages are not parallel, being inclined in two directions, making angles of 62° with the plane of the section. In a section parallel to the orthopinacoid, cleavage cracks are still less abundant, and, in fact, may be entirely lacking, or, at least, invisible. If present, as in Fig. 68, they are likely to be widely spaced, discontinuous, and rather indistinct; their traces are parallel, but their planes are inclined in two directions, making angles of 28° with the plane of the section.

Cleavages in section are more easily seen in minerals of higher index of refraction, because this results in more reflection and refraction along the cleavage plane. For a similar reason, cleavages may be less distinct, because apparently narrower, in sections normal to the cleavage planes than in others varying somewhat from this direction. The relation of the plane of cleavage to the plane of the section may

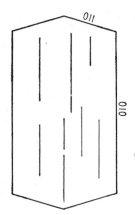

FIG. 68.—Orthopinacoid section of hornblende crystal.

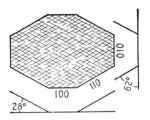

FIG. 69.—Cross-section of hornblende crystal.

be learned in an approximate way by focusing a high power objective first on the upper edge of the cleavage crack and then on the lower edge, and noting whether the image shifts to one side or the other or remains stationary. In the latter case the cleavage plane is normal to the plane of the section.

The development of cleavage cracks depends, in some cases, upon the magnitude of the stresses produced in a crystal (for example, during grinding) in comparison with its cohesion. The stresses are naturally less in tiny crystals than in large ones; so it happens that small crystals of enstatite in norite may be quite devoid of cleavage cracks in thin section, though larger crystals show them plainly.

Cleavage is very useful in the microscopic study of minerals, as will be evident from its applications in the later portions of this book.

Fracture.—Minerals which have no cleavage are said to fracture rather than to cleave. Further, the break of a cleavable crystal in any direction other than that of the cleavage is also fracture. Fracture differs from cleavage in being more or less irregular, uneven, or curved, and in no definite crystal direction. Fracture is described as **conchoidal** when the surfaces produced are smooth and curved, often concave, like those of some shells. It is described as **uneven** when the surface is rough and entirely irregular; this is the commonest type in minerals. It is described as **even** when the surface, though rough with many small irregularities, is approximately a plane.

Hardness is a term ordinarily used with a rather vague meaning; as applied to crystals it refers to the resistance offered to the production of a scratch on a smooth surface. In minerals there are all grades of hardness, from that of talc, easily scratched with the fingernail, to that of the diamond, which is the hardest substance known, either natural or artificial. Hardness (H) is always expressed in terms of the scale devised by Mohs, which is as follows:[1] 1. Talc; 2. Gypsum; 3. Calcite; 4. Fluorite; 5. Apatite; 6. Orthoclase; 7. Quartz; 8. Topaz; 9. Corundum; 10. Diamond.

A crystal which scratches and also is scratched by one of the minerals of this scale has the same hardness as that mineral. A mineral which scratches one of the scale, as fluorite, but not the next higher (being scratched by that) has an intermediate hardness, commonly expressed by the lower number with a fraction—in this case the hardness would be four and a half, or $H = 4.5$. In testing hardness it is important to distinguish between a scratch and a chalk mark; the latter is easily rubbed off; the former is not.

Hardness is of little importance in the microscopic study of crystals, but it is an important factor in the preparation of thin sections, in determining the smoothness or polish attained. Hard minerals are likely to be left slightly thicker than soft ones and may have scratches unremoved by the polishing with the finer powders. Also, the soft minerals may be torn or pitted or even bent by the coarse grinding; this is illustrated on a small scale by the waviness or crinkling so common in micas in thin sections.

[1] Recent work indicates that fluorite and apatite are nearly alike in hardness, and that topaz is only a little harder than quartz. See A. Rosiwal: *Mitth. Wiener Min. Gesell.* 1917, No. 80, p. 69; issued with *T. M. P. M.*, 1917, vol. 39; and P. J. Holmquist: *Geol. För. Förh., Stockholm*, vol. 38, p. 501.

Specific gravity.—The specific gravity of a mineral is the numerical ratio between its weight and the weight of an equal volume of water. Specific gravity is a definite characteristic which does not vary (at given temperature and pressure) so long as the composition of the mineral does not vary. The specific gravity may be determined by weighing a substance in air and then weighing it when suspended in water; the loss of weight in water is equal to the weight of an equal volume of water. The second weighing may be replaced by a measurement of the volume of the substance, as by immersion in a burette, since one cubic centimeter of water weighs one gram. In measuring specific gravity it is important to obtain pure material and remove

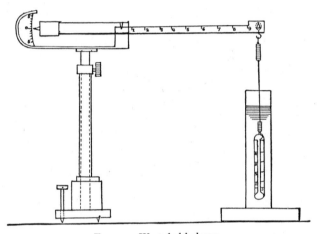

FIG. 70.—Westphal balance.

all the air from the fragments, under an exhaust-pump. Indirect methods of measuring specific gravity by comparison with that of liquids are of special importance, because they also furnish methods of separating rock powders into their constituent mineral components. Several liquids are known to be heavier than the common rock-forming minerals. By dilution with an appropriate liquid, the density of these liquids may be lowered at will to any desired extent, and thus made equal to that of any mineral whose specific gravity is to be determined. This condition of equality is easily recognized by the fact that the mineral stays indefinitely in any part of the liquid, neither rising nor sinking. The specific gravity of the liquid (and therefore of the mineral) may then be quickly determined by the use of the **Westphal balance,** shown in Fig. 70. By hanging suitable

weights on the long arm at the end, or at a decimal division, until the
sinker remains suspended in the liquid and the balance is in equilibrium, the specific gravity may be read from the number, kind, and
position of the weights.   Heavy liquids are used to separate the
powdered constituents of a rock;   when the powder is put into the
liquid, the heaviest minerals will sink to the bottom and others will
rise to the top.   Those on top may be decanted off, or otherwise
removed, and the process repeated with a lighter liquid.   The most
important " heavy solutions " for measuring specific gravity or separating powders are Thoulet's solution, and methylene iodide.   A cheaper
substitute for these is acetylene tetrabromide.

Thoulet's solution is a very poisonous solution of iodide of potassium and mercury, which may be readily prepared by heating 270
grams of mercuric iodide and 230 grams of potassium iodide in 80
cubic centimeters of distilled water in a porcelain evaporating dish
on a water-bath.   After a little evaporation, a crystal of fluorite
($G = 3.18$) will float on the liquid, or a crystalline film will form on the
surface.   Upon cooling, the density reaches about 3.19;   the liquid
should be transparent and of a yellowish green color;   it is stable,
provided a few drops of mercury are added;   otherwise, iodine slowly
separates and darkens the color.   It may be diluted with water in any
proportions and subsequently reconcentrated by evaporation.

Methylene iodide is a thin, light-yellow fluid of high refractive
index and maximum density of about 3.3, which cannot be diluted
with water or alcohol (which spoil it), but mixes in all proportions
with benzol or ether.   It is stable in air, but slowly darkens in sunlight;   mercury restores the color.   It is so mobile that very fine
powders may be separated—much finer than can be used in Thoulet's
solution.   The cleaning of the recovered powder is very simple,
being accomplished by washing with benzol.   Methylene iodide may
be used in separating minerals which are soluble in water.   It is quite
expensive.

Acetylene tetrabromide has a maximum density of 3.0;   it may be
diluted with benzol, ether, or toluol, and restored to the maximum by
evaporation.   It is not decomposed by minerals, not even by ore
minerals.   Its chief advantage is its cheapness.

Clerici's solution [1] is a mutual solution of thallium malonate,
$CH_2(COOTl)_2$ and thallium formate, $HCOOTl$, which is remarkable

---

[1] *Rend. Accad. Lincei, Roma*, XVI, 1907, p. 187 and XXXI, 1922, p. 116;   see also
H. E. Vassar;   *Am. Mineral.*, X, 1925, p.123.

for its high density of 4.25 at ordinary temperature and about 4.65 at 50° C. It may be diluted with water in any quantity and reconcentrated by evaporation. It is more mobile than Thoulet's solution, odorless and slightly amber colored. At ordinary temperature the solution is quite stable; it is able to attack sulphides when heated. It may be prepared by dissolving the dry salts in water; seven grams of each will dissolve completely in one cubic centimeter of water. It is quite expensive, but the high density and convenience of use make it indispensable for some purposes.

Fusibility.—Most minerals melt at high temperatures; the relative temperatures of melting determine their fusibility. The approximate relative fusibility is usually expressed in terms of the following scale:

SCALE OF FUSIBILITY

No.	Mineral	Approximate Fusing Point	Notes
1	Stibnite	525° C.	Fuses easily in a candle flame.
2	Chalcopyrite	800° C.	Fuses slowly in a gas flame.
3	Almandite	1050° C.	Only finest splinters rounded in a gas flame.
4	Actinolite	1200° C.	Standard-size fragments are rounded easily before the blowpipe.
5	Orthoclase	1300° C.	Standard-size fragments are rounded with difficulty before the blowpipe.
6	Bronzite	1400° C.	Only finest splinters rounded on points with difficulty before the blowpipe.
7	Quartz	Above 1400° C.	Entirely infusible before the blowpipe.

A fragment of standard size is 1.5 mm. in diameter.

A mineral which melts more easily than actinolite and less easily than almandite is said to have a fusibility of three and a half, or, in brief, $F = 3.5$.

Fusibility is rarely employed in the microscopic study of minerals, but grains of rock powders may readily be tested in this way.

Electrical conductivity is of some importance, because the development of electrostatic charges depends upon it. Most minerals are very poor conductors of the electric current, but strictly opaque minerals are commonly good conductors. Electrostatic charges may be produced, under suitable conditions, in good conductors, which may thus be separated from bad conductors. For example, if a mixture of ilmenite and monazite, or of pyrite and quartz or calcite, is placed on a good conducting surface, such as a copper plate, and dried thoroughly, and a flattened stick of sealing wax, which has been previously excited by rubbing, is brought near, grains of the former mineral (in each case) will be attracted to the sealing wax, and may be thus entirely separated. The method may be applied to rock and ore powders.

Magnetism in minerals varies very greatly. A few minerals in their natural state are attracted by a strong steel magnet; they are said to be magnetic; the only common mineral exhibiting this property is called magnetite because of it. Some other minerals show the same property in less and variable degree; these include hematite and pyrrhotite. But in a very strong electric field, like that between the poles of a powerful electromagnet, all minerals (and all substances) are influenced by the magnetic force. If they are attracted to the poles they are called paramagnetic; if they are repelled they are called diamagnetic. Most minerals which contain iron are paramagnetic; diamagnetic minerals include calcite, quartz, and zircon. This method is in use in the separation of ore minerals from gangue and is of value in separating rock powders.

CHAPTER IV

CHEMICAL CHARACTERS OF MINERALS

Elements are substances which cannot be decomposed, or separated into unlike parts, by any known process of chemical analysis; about eighty are now recognized, such as iron, gold, copper, oxygen, carbon, etc.

Atoms are the smallest parts of elements which can enter into combinations; each element is believed to have an atom of definite and characteristic mass, and probably of definite shape and constitution. With rare exceptions, an atom cannot exist alone, but forms a regular space lattice with other atoms, or combines with other atoms to form a **molecule,** which may be considered to be the smallest portion of any substance which can exist alone. The atomic weight of an element is the weight or mass of its atom as compared with that of hydrogen taken as unity, or with that of oxygen taken as 16. The **symbol** of an element is the initial letter or letters of its Latin name, by which it is represented in chemical notation. This symbol, as O for oxygen or Fe for iron (Latin, *ferrum*) stands not only for the element, but for a definite amount of the element, namely, one atom. In order to express more than one atom, the appropriate number is written as a subscript after the symbol, thus: Fe_3 means three atoms of iron and Fe_2O_3 means a compound consisting of two atoms of iron and three of oxygen. Since the weight of an atom of iron is 55.8, this represents a compound consisting of 111.6 parts, by weight, of iron and 48 parts, by weight, of oxygen. An expression such as Fe_2O_3 is known as a chemical formula.

The following table gives a list of all the definitely established elements, with their symbols and atomic weights. Of these elements, only ten or twelve are really abundant in the material of the earth known to man; the most widespread are oxygen, silicon, aluminum, iron, magnesium, calcium, sodium, potassium, hydrogen, titanium, chlorine, phosphorus, manganese, carbon, and sulphur. Most of the elements are solids under ordinary conditions; mercury and bromine are

ALPHABETICAL LIST OF THE CHEMICAL ELEMENTS

Name	Symbol	O=16 Atomic Weight	Name	Symbol	O=16 Atomic Weight
Aluminum	Al	27.0	Mercury	Hg	200.6
Antimony	Sb	121.8	Molybdenum	Mo	96.0
Argon	A	39.9	Neodymium	Nd	144.3
Arsenic	As	74.9	Neon	Ne	20.2
Barium	Ba	137.4	Nickel	Ni	58.7
Beryllium	Be	9.1	Niton	Nt	222.4
Bismuth	Bi	209.0	Nitrogen	N	14.0
Boron	B	10.8	Osmium	Os	190.8
Bromine	Br	79.9	Oxygen	O	16.0
Cadmium	Cd	112.4	Palladium	Pd	106.7
Cæsium	Cs	132.8	Phosphorus	P	31.0
Calcium	Ca	40.1	Platinum	Pt	195.2
Carbon	C	12.0	Potassium	K	39.1
Cerium	Ce	140.2	Praseodymium	Pr	140.9
Chlorine	Cl	35.5	Radium	Ra	226.0
Chromium	Cr	52.0	Rhodium	Rh	102.9
Cobalt	Co	59.0	Rubidium	Rb	85.4
Columbium	Cb	93.1	Ruthenium	Ru	101.7
Copper	Cu	63.6	Samarium	Sa	150.4
Dysprosium	Dy	162.5	Scandium	Sc	45.1
Erbium	Er	167.7	Selenium	Se	79.2
Europium	Eu	152.0	Silicon	Si	28.1
Fluorine	F	19.0	Silver	Ag	107.9
Gadolinium	Gd	157.3	Sodium	Na	23.0
Gallium	Ga	69.7	Strontium	Sr	87.6
Germanium	Ge	72.4	Sulphur	S	32.1
Gold	Au	197.2	Tantalum	Ta	181.5
Hafnium	Hf	178.6	Tellurium	Te	127.5
Helium	He	4.0	Terbium	Tb	159.2
Holmium	Ho	163.4	Thallium	Tl	204.0
Hydrogen	H	1.0	Thorium	Th	232.2
Indium	In	114.8	Thulium	Tm	169.4
Iodine	I	126.9	Tin	Sn	118.7
Iridium	Ir	193.1	Titanium	Ti	48.1
Iron	Fe	55.8	Tungsten	W	184.0
Krypton	Kr	82.9	Uranium	U	238.2
Lanthanum	La	138.9	Vanadium	V	51.0
Lead	Pb	207.2	Xenon	Xe	130.2
Lithium	Li	6.9	Ytterbium	Yb	173.6
Lutecium	Lu	175.0	Yttrium	Y	89.0
Magnesium	Mg	24.3	Zinc	Zn	65.4
Manganese	Mn	54.9	Zirconium	Zr	90.6

liquids; chlorine, fluorine, nitrogen, oxygen, hydrogen, and the rare elements, helium, neon, argon, krypton, xenon, and niton, are gases.

Elements are classified as metals and non-metals, certain ones of intermediate characters being called semi-metals. A **metal** possesses more or less completely the physical properties of opacity to light, metallic luster, malleability, and conductivity for heat and electricity; it is the positive or basic element in simple compounds. The **non-metals** have none of the physical characters named and play the negative or acid part in chemical compounds. In writing formulas, it is common to express the basic elements first.

The relations of the elements to one another and the parts they play in minerals are best understood by a study of the so-called **periodic law**, which is a classification of the elements shown in the table on the next page:

The **molecular weight** of a compound is the weight of the molecule, as compared with the standard ($H = 1$ or $O = 16$). The molecular weight of gases is accurately known from the law that like volumes of different gases under the same conditions of temperature and pressure contain the same number of molecules; the molecular weight of liquids is less definitely known, and that of solids is unknown, but for purposes of comparison it is usually assumed to be equal to the sum of the weights of the atoms when the formula is written in its simplest form. It should be remembered that molecules, in the usual sense, seem to be lacking in inorganic crystals.

The **valence** of an element is measured by the capacity of an atom of the element to combine with the atoms of some standard unit element, like hydrogen or chlorine. Thus, the valence of sodium is one, since one atom of it combines with one atom of the standard chlorine in NaCl. Similarly, the formula $CaCl_2$ shows that calcium is bivalent; $AuCl_3$, that gold is trivalent; and $SnCl_4$, that tin is tetravalent. Some elements have more than one possible valence, thus iron is bivalent in FeO and trivalent in Fe_2O_3.

Radicals.—A compound of two or more elements, according to their valence, in which the valence of each is satisfied, is said to be **saturated**; this is the condition of H_2O, as shown when it is written H—O—H. A group of elements in which one (or more) of the bonds of valence is not satisfied cannot exist alone, but can enter into combinations; such a group is known as a radical; it may be illustrated by —O—H, which is called hydroxyl, —Ca—F, a radical known in apatite, NH_4, which is called ammonium, etc.

THE PERIODIC CLASSIFICATION OF ELEMENTS

Series	Group 0	Group 1 R_2O	Group 2 RO	Group 3 R_2O_3	Group 4 RH_4 RO_2	Group 5 RH_3 R_2O_5	Group 6 RH_2 RO_3	Group 7 RH R_2O_7	Group 8 RO_4
1		H=1							
2	He=4	Li=7	Be=9	B=11	C=12	N=14	O=16	F=19	
3	Ne=20	Na=23	Mg=24	Al=27	Si=28	P=31	S=32	Cl=35	
4	A=40	K=39	Ca=40	Sc=45	Ti=48	V=51	Cr=52	Mn=55	Fe=56, Co=59, Ni=59
5		Cu=64	Zn=65	Ga=70	Ge=72	As=75	Se=79	Br=80	
6	Kr=83	Rb=85	Sr=88	Yt=89	Zr=91	Cb=93	Mo=96	......	Ru=102,Rh=103,Pd=107
7		Ag=108	Cd=112	In=115	Sn=119	Sb=122	Te=127	I=127	
8	Xe=130	Cs=133	Ba=137	La=139	Ce, etc., 140-175	Ta=181	W=184	......	Os=191, Ir=193, Pt=195
9		Au=197	Hg=201	Tl=204	Pb=207	Bi=209	......	......	
10	Nt=222	......	Ra=226	......	Th=232	......	U=238	......	

Acids and bases.—An **acid** is a compound of hydrogen or hydroxyl with a non-metallic element or a radical containing such an element. A **base** is a compound of a metallic element (or radical) and hydroxyl. A **salt** is formed when the hydrogen of an acid is replaced by a metal; if all the hydrogen is replaced, the salt is **normal;** if only a part is replaced, the salt is **acidic;** if part of the acid radical is replaced by hydroxyl, the salt is **basic.**

Isomorphism.—Chemical compounds which have analogous chemical composition and only slightly different crystal form are said to be isomorphous. Many exar. ples of isomorphism are known among minerals; thus, aragonite, $CaCO_3$, witherite, $BaCO_3$, strontianite, $SrCO_3$, and cerussite, $PbCO_3$, are analogous in chemical composition and closely alike in crystal form; they are said to form an isomorphous group, called the aragonite group of minerals. The calcite group, the garnet group, and many others illustrate the same condition. It is commonly true that such minerals can intercrystallize to form one homogeneous crystal. In some cases simple isomorphous compounds can intercrystallize or form mutual crystal solutions in all proportions; in other cases there are definite limits to the solubility, and greater amounts are not found in single crystals. For example, only a little $MgCO_3$ can enter $CaCO_3$ in crystal solution, but any proportions of $MgCO_3$ and $FeCO_3$ form such solutions. Such isomorphous series show a regular gradation in physical characters from one end to the other. In some cases compounds which are only approximately analogous are, nevertheless, crystallographically so closely alike that they can form mutual crystal solutions in all proportions; this condition is well illustrated in the feldspar group, in which albite, $NaAlSi_3O_8$, and anorthite, $CaAl_2Si_2O_8$, are miscible in any proportions as crystals; strangely enough, the compounds $NaAlSi_3O_8$ and $KAlSi_3O_8$, which are much more alike chemically, are not so closely alike crystallographically and exhibit only limited mutual solubility. In such cases the facts are approximately expressed by saying that potassium may replace a certain amount of sodium in albite, while sodium may isomorphously replace (or "proxy" for) a limited amount of potassium in orthoclase. Such isomorphous replacement of one base by a limited amount of another is very common among silicate minerals; in some cases two or more bases partially replace the chief base. Similar replacement by acid elements is well known, but not so common.

Polymorphism.—A compound which crystallizes in two or more different forms is said to be polymorphous; for example, TiO_2 crystallizes as the tetragonal mineral rutile with the vertical axis $c = 0.644$ and $G = 4.25$, the orthorhombic mineral brookite with $G = 4.15$, and the tetragonal mineral octahedrite with $c = 1.778$ and $G = 3.9$. Other examples include $MgSiO_3$ in four different crystal forms, namely, orthorhombic and monoclinic amphibole and pyroxene, SiO_2 in six and perhaps seven different crystal forms, and many others.

Chemical methods of separating minerals depend chiefly upon variations in solubility in various reagents. Thus, most silicates can be separated from carbonates by dissolving the latter in weak acids. Silicates resistant to hydrochloric acid may be separated similarly from those that are easily attacked. By careful manipulation to control the temperature and length of attack, separation of rock substances into several groups may be accomplished by taking advantage of their unequal solubilities in hydrofluoric acid; in fact, this acid attacks rock glass first of all, then feldspars and feldspathoids, then quartz, and lastly pyroxenes, amphiboles, olivine, etc. The least soluble minerals in both hydrofluoric and sulphuric acids include tourmaline, zircon, rutile, and spinel.

Microchemical methods of testing minerals are of various kinds; for example, the solubility may be tested in various reagents, the mode or product of attack may be noted, or tests may be made for certain constituents that may be characteristic. Methods of testing solubility are so simple that they need no description; also, if the mode of attack involves the evolution of a gas, its presence is easily made manifest by covering the surface with a film of liquid, usually water, and a cover glass, and then allowing a weak acid to diffuse into the liquid over the mineral. But special methods have been devised for studying certain products of attack, and elaborate systems are used in testing for definite constituents. The most important of these are staining, color reactions, and formation of crystals characteristic of certain elements.

Staining.—One of the most important uses of staining is to render visible the film of gelatinous silica produced when an acid attacks some silicate minerals. To accomplish this the acid must be removed in a gentle current of running water after it has been on the uncovered and balsam-free upper surface of a thin section long enough to produce an appreciable effect; then an aniline color (malachite green is very satisfactory) in solution is brought into contact with the surface of the thin section, the excess color is washed away and the cover glass is replaced.

Staining of carbonates is very useful, as it permits distinctions between them which are otherwise difficult. For this purpose a normal neutral solution of silver nitrate is best, according to Cayeux; the powder or thin section is treated with this reagent for two to five minutes, and carefully washed with distilled water to remove every trace of the reagent; it is then immersed in a solution of neutral potassium chromate for one minute, and again washed with water. Calcite is now colored a brownish red, which is darker the longer the attack by the nitrate. Aragonite and dolomite require longer treatment to give this color, and when obtained it is irregularly distributed. The only limitation to the use of this method is that it fails with extremely fine-grained material; it can be employed if the grains attain some hundredths of a millimeter.

Staining may also be used to render visible amorphous constituents of rocks which may be otherwise so inconspicuous as to be practically invisible. It is particularly useful to bring out shaly constituents in limestone or sandstone. The chief limitation of its use is that amorphous material is not the only substance that absorbs the color; some minerals which are poorly crystallized and of very small size also take up the stain; this is true of talc, glauconite, etc.

Color reactions.—Extremely small crystals or powders may be tested, in some cases with decisive results, by means of the colors of certain compounds of organic substances, involving minute amounts of characteristic elements. In this manner rutile may be readily distinguished from cassiterite or zircon. The organic substance (more than $\frac{1}{4}$ mg.) is first dissolved in pure sulphuric acid on an object glass, and then the mineral to be tested is placed in the solution. If the mineral is entirely insoluble in sulphuric acid, a preliminary fusion with sodium carbonate or acid potassium sulphate may be necessary, but a solubility so slight as to produce no visible effect on the size may be ample to give the desired result. It is necessary to exclude all nitric or nitrous acids—even traces—as impurities in the sulphuric acid are fatal to the process. After a short time, titanic acid gives a brick-red color with phenol, a crimson color with morphine and a violet color with papaverine. Tin gives a brown color with papaverine and a red or orange color with pyrogallol; zirconium gives no colors.[1]

Colorless minerals of the sodalite group may be colored blue by

[1] See further: P. Gaubert: *Bull Soc. Fr. Min.*, XXXIII, 1910, p. 326; L. Lévy: *C. R.*, CIII, pp. 1074, 1195; and *Ann. Phys. Chim.*, XXV, 1892, p. 433.

heating, expecially in the presence of sulphur; this is readily accomplished by heating the uncovered thin section in a closed vessel, in the bottom of which is placed a little powdered sulphur.

Characteristic crystals.—There are various ways to cause the formation of crystals which are characteristic of certain bases. The first essential is to dissolve the mineral under consideration; after that, the solution may be evaporated directly to cause formation of salts with the solvent, as in the method first worked out by Boricky, or reagents may be added after solution to cause the formation of other salts, as fully described by Behrens.

Boricky method.—To dissolve the mineral, Boricky proposed the use of hydrofluosilicic acid (or hydrofluoric acid gas, as an alternative). A minute fragment of the mineral is placed on the surface of hard balsam on a glass slide and covered by a tiny drop of the acid from a platinum wire; the drop is allowed to evaporate, and the preparation examined. The tiny crystals formed are fluosilicates of the bases present in the mineral. The reagent must be absolutely pure, leaving no residue on evaporation; it must be kept in platinum; a $3\frac{1}{2}$ per cent strength is recommended.

The fluosilicates of potassium, cæsium and rubidium are isometric; those of sodium, magnesium, and iron are hexagonal; and those of lithium, calcium, and strontium are monoclinic. Fluosilicates of aluminum are insoluble, and the others are soluble in water; it is therefore easy to separate them. This test may be applied to a mineral in a thin section by removing the cover glass and the covering Canada balsam and applying the acid directly to the grain in question.

Fluosilicate of lithium forms pseudohexagonal basal plates, easily recognized. To distinguish fluosilicate of calcium from fluosilicate of strontium, apply dilute sulphuric acid; in a short time calcium gives monoclinic artificial gypsum, while strontium gives orthorhombic celestite.

Behrens method.—To dissolve the mineral, Behrens proposed the use of pure hydrofluoric acid, which causes the formation of fluorides; these are dried and then redissolved in dilute sulphuric acid. The solution is evaporated until white fumes appear. To the sulphate liquid, add an excess of water and then evaporate until the volume of the solution is about one cubic centimeter for each milligram of mineral attacked. If the solution contains calcium, simple evaporation will cause the formation of monoclinic gypsum crystals. To test for potassium, add to the solution a small drop of platinic chloride;

after several minutes, if the liquid contains potassium, octahedrons (or dodecahedrons or cubes) of the double chloride appear; they are bright yellow, isotropic and highly refringent. To test for sodium, add a drop of sulphate of cerium, bringing the two liquids together through a capillary glass tube about 5 mm. long. If sodium is present, tiny brown crystals appear; potassium forms larger crystals which are gray in color. To test for magnesium, add a drop of salt of phosphorus solution through a capillary glass tube. If magnesium is present, the crystals are either oblique cross twins or orthorhombic forms with domes well developed. Iron and manganese give similar crystals, but they may be removed by previous addition of ammonia. To test for aluminum, add cæsium chloride after careful expulsion of any excess of the acid. If aluminum is present, large crystals of cæsium alum form quickly; they are octahedrons or cubo-octahedrons which are strictly isotropic. Iron alum crystals form more slowly.

CHAPTER V

ELEMENTARY CONCEPTIONS OF OPTICS

Since energy, in the form of heat and light, comes to the earth from the sun and stars through interplanetary spaces, it is believed that these spaces are occupied by a medium called the ether, which is able to transmit the energy by means of undulations similar to the motion of waves on a liquid surface. Since it is found that heat and light are transmitted in general in the same way, and therefore doubtless by the same medium, through the atmosphere and also through liquid and solid bodies, it is believed that the ether pervades all space, existing in all parts of all fluid, and even of all solid bodies. But the phenomena of transmission are modified by fluids and solids, and especially by the molecular structure of crystals.

Light is a form of energy which may be considered to consist of an undulatory motion. Since these undulations, once initiated at any point, propagate themselves in all directions, light is said to be transmitted by wave motion of that substance which pervades all space, namely, the ether. The nature of these undulations must be thoroughly understood. A general conception of them may be obtained by considering the motion of any particle of water when a wave motion is produced on the quiet surface of a lake by a stone dropped into it. Any particle of the water moves in a tiny circle having one diameter parallel to the wave motion and another straight up and down, while the wave as a whole moves outward horizontally in all directions from the center of disturbance. When the vertical motion of any particle is considered in detail, it will be readily understood that it moves most rapidly through its position of rest, and least rapidly as it approaches its extreme positions where the direction of motion is reversed.

Simple harmonic motion.—A more precise conception of this motion may be derived from the study of a body traveling in a circular path. Thus, in Fig. 71, let the body A be moving in the path $AGMN$ at uniform speed. If this body be observed from a point directly below, it will be seen to be moving in a circle; but if it be observed from any point in the plane of the circle and outside of it, it will seem to be moving back and forth in a straight line, namely, in that diameter of the circular path which is perpendicular to the line of sight. It will seem to move most rapidly at the center of the straight line and least rapidly at the ends. Since the body is traveling at uniform speed, it will move through any of the equal distances, AB, BC, GH, etc., in equal intervals of time, and it will require the same equal intervals for the body

to move apparently through the unequal distances Ab, bc, gh, etc. Motion back and forth along a straight line at constantly varying rate, like the apparent motion of the body A along the line AgM, is called simple harmonic motion, or periodic vibration. Our knowledge of this kind of motion cannot be too complete.

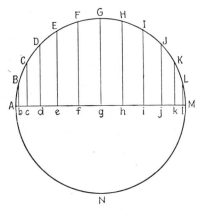

FIG. 71.—Simple harmonic motion.

The **amplitude** of vibration is the distance of gA or gM, that is, the distance from the central point to either point of reversal of motion. In the case of unpolarized light, the **intensity** is proportional to the square of the amplitude of vibration.

The **period** of vibration is the interval of time required for the body or particle to move from any point back to the same point, when traveling in the same direction; for example, the period is the time required to move from f to M, then back through f to A, then to f (moving in the original direction).

Wave motion.—The combination of a simple harmonic vibration with a uniform motion at right angles to the direction of vibration produces a harmonic curve, as shown in Fig. 72, in which simple harmonic vibration, beginning at O and vibrating to A, back to B, etc., is compounded with a uniform motion from O along ODF, the resultant motion being along $OCDEF$.

The point of maximum upward displacement is called the crest of the wave, and the point of maximum downward displacement, the trough. The distance between two successive crests or troughs, or from any point, as O, to the next corresponding point, as F, is a wave length (denoted by the Greek letter, lambda λ).

The phase of a wave at any instant is its distance, measured in wave lengths, from some given point taken as the origin of the motion.

Two waves are in the same phase when they are at corresponding points of their vibrations. When two waves have a difference of phase of one-half a wave length ($\frac{1}{2}\lambda$), their vibrations are similar, but in opposite directions; if one is at the crest the other is at the trough.

Waves of light are very short; the wave length of the yellow light of sodium is 0.000023 of an inch or 0.000589 of a millimeter. The period of vibration of light is extremely short, about 510 million million vibrations of sodium light occurring in one second. Light travels with great velocity, about 186,000 miles per second. The velocity of light of all wave lengths is the same in a vacuum; therefore, the period of vibration is exactly inversely proportional to the wave length. Ether waves of different periods of vibration (and of

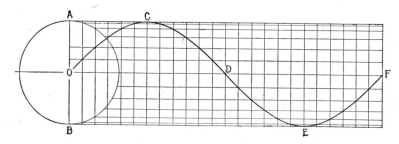

Fig. 72.—Wave motion.

different wave lengths) give rise to different colors of light. The wave length of violet light, at one end of the spectrum, is about 0.000380 mm., while that of red, near the other end, is about 0.000760 mm. The velocity of light is less in most substances than in a vacuum, and varies with the substance and also with the wave length; therefore, in any medium, whether gaseous, liquid, or solid, violet light has one velocity and red light another, which is greater.

Wave-surface.—If wave motion of light be produced at a point in a vacuum, it will be transmitted outward from the point in all directions at the same velocity. Therefore, at any instant, all points in the same phase will be equally distant from the point of origin. The locus of all these points is called the wave-surface, and in this instance it is a spherical surface. If the wave motion originated in a plane instead of a point, it would be transmitted in spherical waves from every point of the plane; and the plane tangent to all these waves on each side of the plane of origin would be the wave-surface. If the wave motion were transmitted from a point at velocities varying gradually with the direction, the wave-surface would be a warped surface of some kind.

The line along which the wave motion travels from the point of origin to any other point is called a **ray.** In a vacuum the light ray from the point of origin to any point on the wave-surface is perpendicular to the tangent plane at that point.

Isotropic substances (and the ether of a vacuum) transmit light with equal velocity in all directions. They include all gases, most liquids, and all glasses and isometric crystals when not under strain.

Anisotropic substances transmit light with unequal velocities in different directions; they include all crystals except those of the isometric system which are unstrained. Glass under strain is also anisotropic. In non-isometric crystals the velocity varies gradually with the direction in such a way that most sections of the wave-surface are elliptical. In Fig. 73 it may be seen that the light ray from the point of origin to any point on the wave-surface is not perpendicular

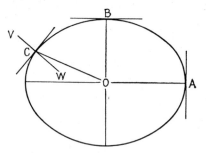

FIG. 73.—Wave-front in an anisotropic body.

dicular to the tangent plane at that point except when the ray coincides with the major or minor axis of the ellipse. The line (*VW*) perpendicular to the tangent plane is called the **wave-normal.** When the wave-surface is elliptical, as in Fig. 73, the wave-normal does not coincide with the light ray except in the directions of the principal axes of the ellipse. In some crystals the wave-surface is spherical; in others it is ellipsoidal. The tangent plane to the wave-surface at the point reached by any ray is called the **wave-front** of that ray.

CHAPTER VI

OPTICAL PROPERTIES OF ISOTROPIC MINERALS

In all unstrained isotropic minerals, light travels with equal velocity in all directions; therefore, in such minerals, the wave-front is always a sphere. The velocity of light in isotropic bodies varies, however, with the nature of the body, and also with the color of the light.

Reflection.—When light reaches the boundary between two isotropic substances it is usually divided into two parts, one of which is turned back into the first medium, while the other penetrates the second medium. That portion of the light which is turned back or reflected does not return along its original path, except in the case of a ray striking a reflecting surface perpendicularly. The path of the reflected ray can be deduced

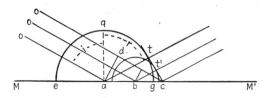

Fig. 74.—Reflection.

from the position of the new wave-front. Thus, if Oa, Ob, Oc, in Fig. 74, represent parallel rays (that is, a beam) of monochromatic light striking the boundary MM'—here, for simplicity of construction, a plane surface—between two isotropic substances, the wave-front of the light at the point a is the line ad, at right angles to the beam. During the time that the ray Oc travels from d to c it is evident that the ray Oa, turned back from a into the same medium in which Oc is moving, must go a distance equal to dc. Therefore, when Oc reaches c, Oa must be at some point on the semicircle eqg whose radius is equal to dc, and the wave-front must be a line from c to the point of tangency, t. A similar construction gives the direction bt' of the ray Ob after reflection at b; in like manner the direction of any reflected ray can be found.

Erecting a perpendicular at *a*, the angle *Oaq* is called the angle of incidence (*i*) and *qat* is called the angle of reflection (*r*). The right triangles *adc* and *atc* are equal, having one side in common and the side *at* equal to the side *dc*; therefore, the angle *dac* equals the angle *tca*, and the angle *Oaq* (=*dac*) equals the angle *qat* (=*tca*). That is, *the angle of reflection is equal to the angle of incidence.* Also, the incident and reflected rays lie in the same plane with the normal to the surface at the point of incidence if the medium is isotropic.

The amount of light reflected from a surface varies greatly, and depends upon the relative density of the two media, the angle of incidence, the smoothness of the reflecting surface, and the internal structure of the reflecting body. The manner and quantity of light reflected from a surface determine its *luster*.

That light penetrates somewhat even those bodies called opaque is shown by the fact that the light reflected is less than the incident light. Many substances commonly called opaque are transparent in very thin pieces.

Refraction.—When light strikes the boundary between two isotropic substances, that portion which penetrates the second medium is, in general, turned somewhat from its path. This is called refraction, and the property (of the substance) to which it is due is called refringence.

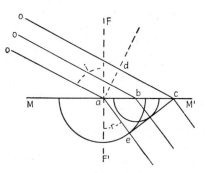

If a beam of light, *Oa*, *Ob*, *Oc*, in Fig. 75, strikes the plane surface *MM'* of a second medium, its velocity in this medium depends upon the relative densities of the two substances. Accordingly, while the ray *Oc* travels from *d* to *c*, the ray

FIG. 75.—Simple refraction.

Oa will travel a shorter distance, say, *ae*, if the second medium is denser than the first. Therefore, the wave-front through the point *c* must pass through the point of tangency *e*, and the direction of the ray *Oa* in the second medium must be shown by *ae*, since it must be perpendicular to the wave-front *ec*. Erecting a perpendicular *FF'* at *a*, the angle *F'ae* is called the angle of refraction (*r*). Let *v* be the velocity of light in the first medium and *v'* that in the second. Then, by construction, $\dfrac{v}{v'} = \dfrac{dc}{ae}$. Now, in the right triangles *adc* and *aec:*

$$dc = ac \sin dac = ac \sin OaF = ac \sin i$$

$$ae = ac \sin ace = ac \sin eaF' = ac \sin r$$

Therefore $\dfrac{v}{v'} = \dfrac{ac \sin i}{ac \sin r} = \dfrac{\sin i}{\sin r}.$

For monochromatic light and isotropic substances, the velocity in one medium divided by the velocity in another medium is evidently constant. Let this constant be denoted by N. Then,

$$\frac{v}{v'} = \frac{\sin i}{\sin r} = N;$$

that is, the sine of the angle of incidence bears a constant ratio to the sine of the angle of refraction, the ratio being the same as that between the velocities of light in the two substances. Further, the incident and refracted rays lie in a common plane with the normal to the surface.

The velocity of light is less, the denser the medium. Therefore, when the light passes from a rarer to a denser medium, the ratio $\dfrac{v}{v'} = \dfrac{\sin i}{\sin r}$ is greater than unity, the angle of refraction is less than the angle of incidence, and the refracted ray is bent toward the perpendicular. Also, when light passes from a denser to a rarer medium, the ratio $\dfrac{v}{v'} = \dfrac{\sin i}{\sin r}$ is less than unity, the angle of refraction is greater than the angle of incidence, and the refracted ray is bent away from the perpendicular.

The constant N is called the **index of refraction** of the second medium as compared with the first. The medium chosen as a standard and assigned a refractive index of unity is the ether of a vacuum. Air has an index (1.000294) so near unity that it is commonly used as a more convenient standard. After measurement of the index of a substance in any medium, as air, its index in a vacuum may be computed. It is equal to the index measured multiplied by the index (measured in a vacuum) of the medium used.

The index of refraction of any substance varies for different colors of light, and increases as the wave length decreases; therefore, the index for violet light is greater than for red, while the index for the yellow light of sodium (Na) is commonly used as an approximate mean value.

EXAMPLES OF INDICES OF REFRACTION

Substance	Index of Refraction
Air..	1.000294
Ice...	1.309
Water.......................................	1.336
Alcohol.....................................	1.36
Clove oil...................................	1.53
Light flint glass...........................	1.54±
Canada balsam...............................	1.54±
Quartz......................................	1.547
Bromoform...................................	1.59
α-Monobromnaphthalene.......................	1.66
Methylene iodide............................	1.74
Methylene iodide saturated with sulphur......	1.78
Sphalerite..................................	2.37
Diamond.....................................	2.42
Rutile......................................	2.71

Total reflection.—In general, the index of refraction is measured from a rarer (ether or air) to a denser medium, so that the index is greater than unity, the refracted ray is bent toward the perpendicular, and light of any angle of incidence can enter the second medium. Thus, if the angle of incidence is 0°, then $\sin i = 0$, and since in this case $N = \dfrac{0}{\sin r}$, $\sin r$ must also equal 0; that is, a ray of light striking a surface perpendicularly enters the new medium with no change in direction, but with a change in velocity. Also, if the angle of incidence is 90°, then $\sin i = 1$, and $N = \dfrac{1}{\sin r}$ or $\sin r = \dfrac{1}{N}$. For any substance, the sine of the angle of refraction for light whose angle of incidence is 90° is therefore the reciprocal of the index of refraction. For example, for water, $\sin r = \dfrac{1}{1.336}$, and $r = 48° \, 31'$; for Canada balsam, $\sin r = \dfrac{1}{1.54}$ and $r = 40° \, 29'$; for diamond, $\sin r = \dfrac{1}{2.42}$ and $r = 24° \, 24'$.

When light passes from a denser to a rarer medium, the refracted ray is bent away from the perpendicular and only light within a certain limiting angle of incidence can enter the second substance. In Fig. 76 let AA' be the upper surface of a plate of glass, and BB' the normal to the surface. Light from within the glass, as the ray DC, will be refracted in the air away from the perpendicular, to such a direction as *CE*. If the refractive index of the glass as compared with air is 1.54, the refractive index of air as compared with the glass

must be $\dfrac{1}{1.54}$; therefore

$$\frac{1}{1.54} = \frac{\sin DCB'}{\sin BCE}.$$

From this equation it is easy to calculate that, if the angle *DCB'* is 30°, the angle *BCE* must be 50°. Another ray, such as *FC*, at an

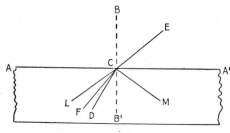

FIG. 76.—Total reflection.

angle of incidence of 40° 29′ will be refracted in air at an angle of 90° along the path *CA'*, grazing the surface of the glass. Any light from within the glass striking the bounding surface at an angle greater than 40° 29′ cannot enter the air, cannot obey the law of refraction, and must be wholly reflected. For example, the ray *LC* would be wholly reflected in the direction *CM*. This is called total reflection, and the angle of incidence at which the refracted light grazes the surface is called the **critical angle.**

It is evident that the critical angle for any substance, with respect to ether or air, is easily obtained (if its refractive index is known) from the equation $\sin r = \dfrac{1}{N}$, in which *r* is the critical angle. Also, the index of refraction may be calculated from the same equation if the critical angle is known. The experimental measurement of the critical angle is frequently used as a means of determining the refractive index.

Smith's refractometer, shown in Fig. 77, is an apparatus devised to measure index of refraction by means of its relation to the critical angle. Any liquid is applied directly to the flat surface of a hemisphere of dense glass, having a refractive index of 1.79, and so inclined to the axis of the instrument that the center of the field corresponds to an index of 1.61. At the eyepiece of the instrument a scale is seen within, across which falls a boundary between light and dark, that is, the line limiting total reflection for the substance under examination.

From the scale, the index is read at this line directly to the second place of decimals, and the intervals are such that the tenths of each can be estimated. The index of any solid may be determined just as easily and satisfactorily, provided a liquid whose index is higher than that of the solid be interposed between a polished surface of the solid and the flat surface of the hemisphere. This liquid is necessary in order to eliminate the air film which is otherwise present. Methylene iodide (with or without dissolved sulphur) is a convenient liquid for this purpose.

The dark borders and unevenly darkened surfaces of some minerals, as observed under the microscope, are due in part to total reflection. In this case some of the light striking the border or the slightly uneven

Fig. 77.—Smith's refractometer.
Made by J. H. Steward, 450 Strand, London, England.

upper surface of the mineral is totally reflected and therefore does not pass on through the microscope. Minerals which show such dark borders and " rough " surfaces are said to have relief, and the amount of **relief** exhibited is an important character in determining rock constituents microscopically.

Absorption and color.—That form of energy which is called light may be transformed into various other forms of energy, and it is easily changed into heat. In such change a wave motion of the ether is converted into a wave motion of the same medium of a wave length not included in the spectrum (whose wave lengths range from 380 to 760 millionths of a millimeter) or is converted into motion of the particles of some other medium. During transmission, all substances (except, perhaps, the ether) cause transformation, especially into heat, of more or less of the light energy; this process is called absorption of light, and it occurs in extremely variable amounts. The proportion of the light which is absorbed depends upon the substance and also upon the length of the path of the light in the given substance. Thus, very little light is absorbed by glass, but some absorption occurs, as may readily be shown by increasing the thickness of the glass. Objects which produce little or no perceptible absorption of light are said to be colorless; substances which absorb more light are said to be gray or dark gray, if all the different wave lengths constituting white light are equally absorbed; objects which absorb all the perceptible light are said to be black. Finally, if the different wave lengths of light are unequally absorbed, the object is seen to have that color which corresponds to the wave length of the light transmitted most freely.

Similarly, by reflected light an object may appear colorless, white, gray, black, or colored, depending upon the quantity and wave length of the light reflected most abundantly.

CHAPTER VII

MICROSCOPES

As an optical instrument, a microscope is merely a set of lenses arranged so as to produce an image larger than the object. A lens is a transparent, homogeneous, isotropic object, usually made of glass, having one or both sides curved so as to change the path of a beam of light in some way. A doubly convex lens (both sides convex) changes the path of a beam of parallel light so that all its rays intersect at a common point, called the focus. Ordinarily, a microscope is so arranged that light is received upon a mirror, from which it is reflected upward through the object and thence through the magnifying lenses to the eye. The light is preferably obtained from the clear sky, or from an artificial source of diffused light in which the color values are as nearly equal to daylight as possible. It is reflected from the mirror, shown at M in Fig. 78, through the condenser C to the object O_1 on the stage S. Thence it passes into the objective (just below F_1), which is screwed or clamped on the lower end of the tube; through it, and up to the ocular at the other end of the tube. The objective and ocular are the essential parts of the microscope and produce the magnification of the object O_1 to the image O_4, as seen by the eye at *EP*. When an object is in place on the stage and the mirror is turned so as to reflect light to the condenser, the magnifying lenses may be brought to focus by means of the screws at the right and left of the tube and usually by means of another screw of much slower motion called the "fine adjustment." In order to avoid the possibility of crushing the object, the microscope should always be focused by lowering the tube while observing it from the side, and then raising it to its focus while looking through the instrument.

Every petrographic microscope has at least two Nicol prisms as additional optical equipment, one being placed between the mirror and the condenser and the other above the objective. Both nicols can be removed from the path of light, if desired, and, in some microscopes, they can be rotated singly or together. Nicol prisms and their uses will be described in detail in a later chapter; they are of fundamental importance in petrographic work.

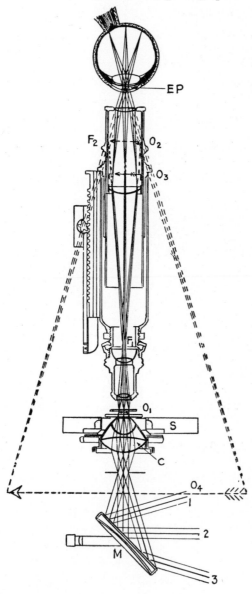

For nearly all preliminary work, the objective of low magnifying power is most suitable. It is the one of longest focus and largest lower glass lens.

The magnifying power of a microscope depends upon the lenses used and may be varied by changing either the objective or the ocular. The measurement of the magnifying power is accomplished conveniently by means of a **camera lucida,** which consists of a prism placed above the ocular and a mirror arranged to produce by reflection an image of an object (a scale, or a pencil and paper, for example) placed beside the microscope, this image being superposed over that seen by direct vision through the microscope, so that the two are seen at the same time and apparently in the same plane. One type of camera lucida used with the Bausch & Lomb microscopes is shown in Fig. 79, in place above the ocular.

Fig. 78.—The path of light in a microscope.

The magnification [1] produced by the microscope is the product of that caused by the

[1] It also varies with the tube length and depends upon the distance of distinct vision of the observer's eye.

objective and that effected by the ocular. By observing a scale of small divisions (called a micrometer) etched on glass and placed on the stage of the microscope, through the ocular which contains a similar scale in its focal plane (F_2 in Fig. 78), it is possible to measure the magnification produced by each objective, and also to determine the relative value of the smallest divisions in the ocular micrometer with each objective, so that these divisions can be used to measure other objects.

FIG. 79.—Camera lucida.

A rather complicated petrographic microscope, made by Swift, of London, is illustrated in Fig. 80. One of the unusual features is the absence of a rotating stage; angular measurements of extinction angles, etc., are made by rotating the nicols instead of the stage. This arrangement obviates the necessity of recentering objectives after each change. The substage arrangement is especially convenient, as three condensers of varying power are provided, and are easily interchangeable; the possibility of using an oil immersion condenser with a large angle objective and no rotation of the stage renders this microscope particularly valuable in the examination of small mineral grains and powders.

One of the petrographic microscopes of R. Fuess, Steglitz bei Berlin, is illustrated in Fig. 81. This model is satisfactory for student use since it is of sturdy and relatively simple construction. The condenser consisting of a four-lens system (of numerical aperture of 1.4) is easily removed or lowered. Each nicol may be rotated, but

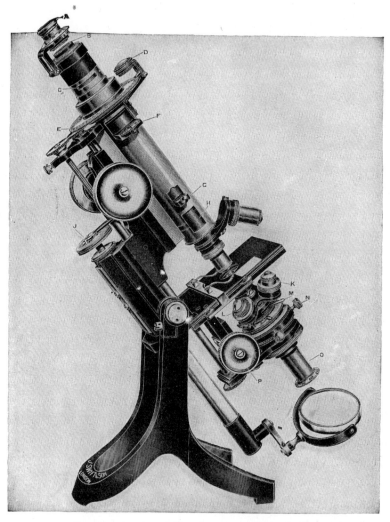

Fig. 80.—A petrographic microscope made by Swift.

their rotations are mutually independent. Recentering of objectives is accomplished by two screws on each objective. The Bertrand lens is equipped with an iris diaphragm. The polarizer is an Ahrens prism. Fuess makes several other models including an elaborate research type.

Bausch and Lomb, of Rochester, New York, have made petrographic microscopes for many years. One of their recent models is
shown in Fig. 82. In this model the condenser may be lowered or

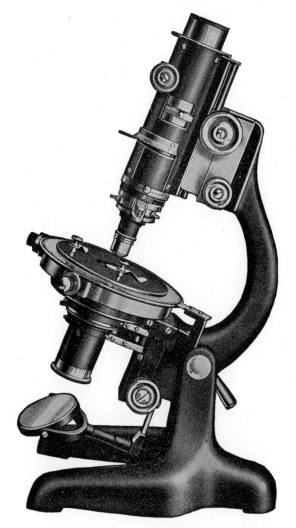

Fig. 81.—A Fuess petrographic microscope.

thrown out of the optical system very conveniently. The upper nicol
slides in and out of the tube, and may be rotated through ninety
degrees. Diaphragms are provided to cut down the field, one below
the stage and another on the Bertrand lens. The lower nicol may be

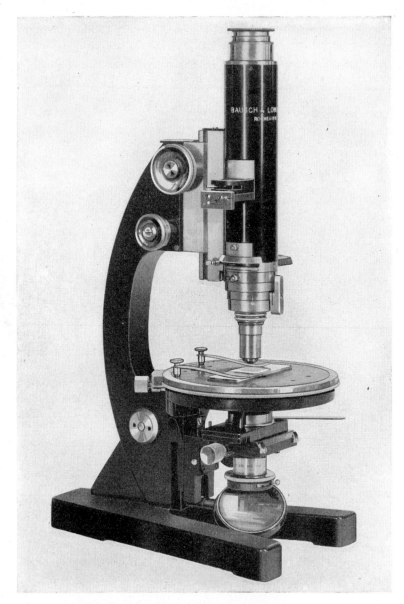

Fig. 82.—A petrographic microscope of Bausch & Lomb.

rotated through 360°. The centering screws on the objectives work parallel with the cross hairs. Bausch and Lomb make several other types of polarizing microscopes including one with rapid change of objectives by means of a revolvable nose-piece.

A petrographic microscope which is remarkable on account of the excellence of its mechanical construction is made by Winkel.[1] In this instrument special provision is made for securing clear interference figures even from very small crystals. It is also equipped with a revolving nose-piece, which permits rapid changing of the objectives and makes recentering unnecessary; it is not even necessary to refocus (except with the fine adjustment) when changing from the low to intermediate power, or *vice versa*. This microscope, shown in Fig. 83, has ample working distance to permit the use of the universal stage.

A new model of polarizing microscope made by the Spencer Lens Company of Buffalo, New York, is shown in Fig. 84. The free space above the stage is 75 mm., which is sufficient for the use of such accessories as the universal stage. The tube and oculars provide a wide field of view. The Bertrand lens is equipped with an iris diaphragm and convenient devices for focusing and centering. The stage is 150 mm. in diameter and rotates on roller bearings. The condenser consists of four or five lenses, three being easily swung out of the optical system. Three iris diaphragms are available, one on the Bertrand lens, one just below the upper condenser and one below the polarizer. Both nicols are Ahrens prisms arranged for rotation independently.

One of the most elaborate petrographic microscopes is the recent type made by Leitz,[2] illustrated in Fig. 85. In this model the nicols may be rotated together through an angle of 240°, and during rotation the analyzer and Bertrand lens may be removed or inserted at any position. The cross hairs of the ocular remain parallel with the vibration planes of the nicols at all positions of rotation. It is equipped with a special clutch and objective adapters which make recentering unnecessary. It is designed with special reference to the use of the Fedoroff universal stage, shown in Fig. 86.

Objectives for all kinds of microscopes vary in focal length from 48 to 1.5 mm. and in magnification from 2× to 100×. The long focal length objectives have low magnification and small angular aperture,[3] and the short focal length objectives have high magnifications and

---

[1] Göttingen, Germany; these "Winkel-Zeiss" microscopes are sold by C. Zeiss of Jena, Germany.

[2] Wetzlar, Germany.

[3] The angular aperture is commonly measured in terms of the "numerical aperture" which is equal to the index of the medium through which the light enters the objective (air or an immersion oil) multiplied by the sine of half the angular aperture.

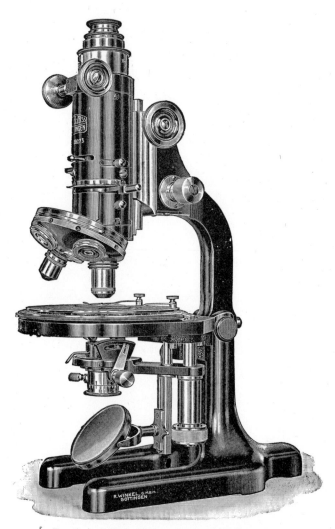

FIG. 83.—A Winkel-Zeiss petrographic microscope.

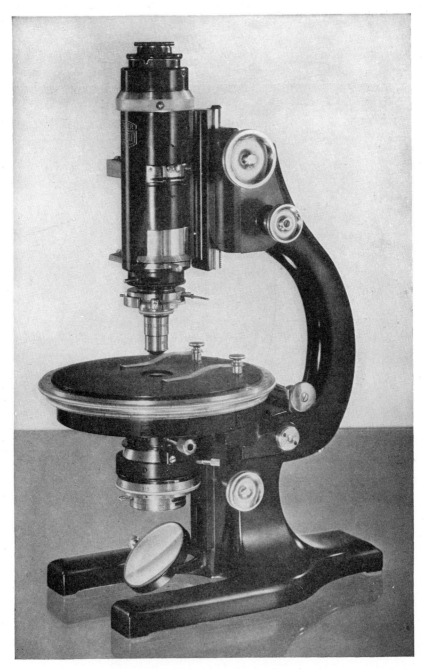

FIG. 84.—A Spencer Lens Co. petrographic microscope.

high "numerical" apertures. Objectives always have a certain curvature of their field of view, which could be eliminated only at the cost of definition or resolving power. This curvature is slight in low power objectives and considerable in high power ones. Objectives also have chromatic difference of magnification, that is, they do not have the same focal length for all parts of the spectrum.

By a suitable choice of eyepieces the inherent defects of objectives may be corrected in large measure. For example, using achromatic objectives and Huygenian eyepieces the residual chromatic difference of magnification is given in the following table.[1]

Focal length	Magnification	Residual chrom. diff. magnification
48.0 mm.	2 ×	+0.25%
32.0 mm.	4 ×	+0.25%
16.0 mm.	10 ×	None
9.0 mm.	21 ×	−0.4%
4.0 mm.	45 ×	−0.7%

The results shown in this table are due to the fact that Huygenian eyepieces are not strictly achromatic, but have focal lengths which are slightly longer for blue light than for red, which is exactly contrary to the condition in achromatic objectives. The differences are such that correction is complete for 16 mm. objectives.

Hyperplane and compensating eyepieces have focal lengths which are longer for blue than for red and the difference is greater than in Huygenian eyepieces. This is illustrated in the following table:

Achromatic objectives	Magnification	Residual chrom. diff. of magnification
		With hyperplane eyepieces
8.0 mm.	21 ×	+0.15%
4.0 mm.	45 ×	−0.15%
Apochromatic objectives		With compensating eyepieces
16.0 mm.	10 ×	+0.1%
8.0 mm.	20 ×	−0.1%
4.0 mm.	45 ×	None

As suggested in this table hyperplane eyepieces are used only with high power achromatic objectives and apochromatic objectives are used only with compensating eyepieces.

[1] From L. V. Foster: *Jour. Biol. Phot. Assoc.* II, 1934, p. 140.

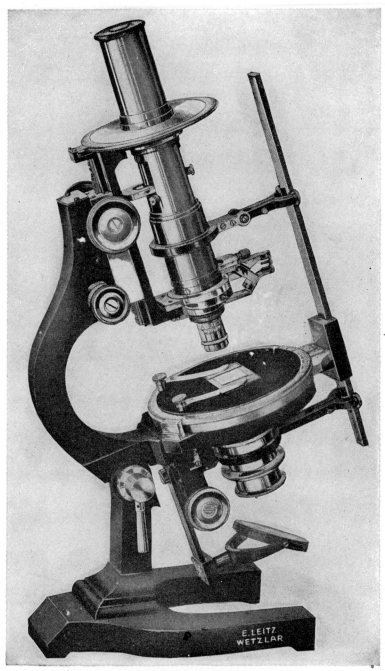

Fig. 85.—A Leitz model petrographic microscope.

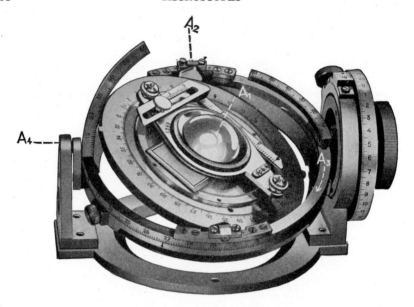

Fig. 86.—Fedoroff universal stage of Leitz.

Fig. 87.—Leitz special objective for use with the universal stage.

For use with the universal stage special objectives have been made. Thus, Leitz has made a special achromatic objective (Fig. 87) magnifying 20× permitting the use of the standard hemispheres. Bausch & Lomb have made a special achromatic objective magnifying 20×, requiring the use of a small hemisphere, as illustrated in Fig. 88. This should be used with a Huygenian eyepiece of 10× to 15×,

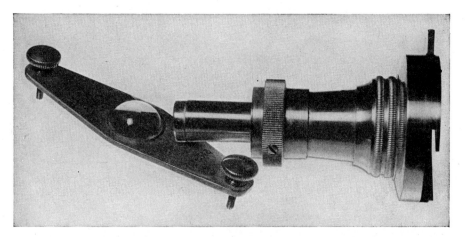

FIG. 88.—A special achromatic objective (with small hemisphere) made by Bausch & Lomb.

giving a total magnification of 200× to 300×. Bausch & Lomb have also made a special apochromatic objective magnifying 20× and requiring the use of a small hemisphere as shown in Fig. 89. This is used with a compensating eyepiece up to 25× thus giving a total magnification of 500× with good definition.

FIG. 89.—A special apochromatic universal stage objective for magnifications to ×500 made by Bausch & Lomb for use in the mineral laboratories at the University of Wisconsin.

DIRECTIONS FOR LABORATORY WORK

Study the petrographic microscope and become familiar with its parts. Find the reflecting mirror, the lower nicol, or polarizer, the condenser, the revolving stage, the objectives, the centering screws (present on many microscopes, but needless on Nachet and Swift types), the oculars with cross hairs or micrometer, the coarse focusing adjustment, the fine adjustment, the Bertrand lens, the mica plate, the sensitive tint plate, the quartz wedge.

Learn to focus the microscope with each objective. Learn how to center the objectives if you do not use a Nachet or Swift model.

Make drawings of the divisions of the stage micrometer with a camera lucida, as seen with every possible combination of oculars and objectives. The drawing paper should be placed close beside the microscope and about as high as the stage. The line of sight from the eye through the camera lucida to the drawing paper should be 250 mm. in length for standard conditions. By measuring, with a millimeter scale, the distances between the divisions in the drawings, compute the magnification of the microscope for each combination of lenses. The divisions on the stage micrometer are usually tenths and hundredths of a millimeter.

Determine, for each objective, the relative value of one of the smallest divisions of the ocular micrometer by means of a comparison with the divisions on a stage micrometer. Express the results in tabular form in terms of decimal parts of a millimeter.

Measure the thickness of a glass plate by means of the ocular micrometer. For this purpose set the glass plate on edge, supporting it on another glass plate by wax or paraffin or other means. Take measures at more than one point along the edge, to learn whether the glass plate is of uniform thickness.

Determine the tread of the fine adjustment screw by measuring the thickness of the glass plate (just examined) in terms of the revolutions of the fine adjustment screw. For this purpose, focus on a tiny dust or oil particle on the upper surface of a glass plate lying on the stage, then interpose the glass plate of measured thickness, clamp it down firmly, and determine the exact rotation of the fine adjustment screw necessary to raise the focus to the top of the interposed plate. Do not try to measure this thickness by focusing *through* either plate.

CHAPTER VIII

PREPARATION OF MATERIAL FOR MICROSCOPIC STUDY

MINERALS and rocks are most conveniently examined microscopically either in the condition of minute grains or fragments or in thin slices or sections.

Preparation of fragments.—For some purposes it is sufficient to break off minute fragments, put them on a glass slide, and cover them with a drop of water ($N = 1.33$) and a cover glass. A more desirable liquid for some optical tests is one whose index of refraction is nearer that of the fragment. Liquids easily obtained and convenient in use include glycerine, $N = 1.46$; xylol, $N = 1.49$; cedar oil, $N = 1.51$; clove oil, $N = 1.53$; monobrombenzol, $N = 1.56$; bromoform, $N = 1.59$; cassia oil, $N = 1.606$; α-monobromnaphthalene, $N = 1.66$; and methylene iodide, $N = 1.74$. For permanent mounting, Canada balsam ($N = 1.54$) is most convenient. By evaporating the balsam at a gentle heat until a minute drop taken out on a pin point and chilled on the thumb nail is hard rather than pasty, it is made ready for use. Or a solution of balsam in xylol may be used; the xylol gradually evaporates, leaving balsam of proper consistency. To prepare a permanent mounting, it is best to cover the center of the glass slide with a layer of balsam and scatter the fragments upon it; then add a cover glass whose lower surface has a thin coating of liquid balsam. In this way the fragments can be scattered somewhat uniformly and not crowded together on the slide.

When many fragments are wanted they are best prepared by pounding the sample to powder on an anvil, rather than by grinding. The largest fragments that pass a 240-mesh sieve are suitable for use, being about 0.06 millimeter in thickness. The sieve should be of accurate construction, so that the openings are of known and uniform size. For most of the purposes of a petrographic laboratory, it should also be of small size, such as the 3-inch (diameter) size made by the Tyler Company of Cleveland, or by the Multimetal Company of New York.

Occasionally it is desirable to prepare thin sections of fragments. This may be done by embedding them in balsam on a cover glass which is itself cemented by balsam to a thicker glass plate. The mineral fragments should be pressed deep into the balsam. After the latter is well hardened, the surface is ground off until the fragments are reached and given a smooth polish. After thorough cleaning, the cover glass is removed by rapid heating of the glass plate and cemented in inverted position to a second glass plate previously given a thin layer of balsam. While cooling, the cover glass should be under moderate pressure so as to push the polished mineral surfaces down upon the glass plate. After grinding away the cover glass, the fragments are given second surfaces parallel to the first ones, and are carefully ground until sufficiently thin. Then they are cleaned and made ready for study by simply cementing a cover glass over them. Directions for grinding are given more fully in the following paragraphs.

Preparation of thin sections.—Fragments of rocks or minerals to be used in making thin sections may be either broken from the main mass or sawed from it. Commonly the fragment is obtained by breaking off a " chip " with a small hammer. The chip should be thin and flat and about an inch in diameter. Except when a study of alteration products or processes is to be made, the chip should be taken from the freshest and firmest part of the mass. If it is necessary or desirable to saw off a slice, this may be done by the use of a continuous wire moving over rotating wheels and supplied with fine emery or Carborundum;[1] or it may be accomplished by the use of a thin metal disk charged on the edge with diamond dust or Carborundum and properly mounted to rotate on an axle. The diamond disk saw is better than the endless wire saw for most purposes.

When a suitable fragment has been obtained, it is necessary to make a plane surface on one side of it by grinding. For this purpose the fragment is usually held in the fingers and pressed gently against a horizontal metal plate or " lap," rotating on a vertical spindle. The lap is sometimes of lead or copper, but soft cast iron is better, because the copper is so soft that the upper surface soon becomes uneven or curved. The grinding material is emery, or preferably Carborundum. At first, coarse grinding powder may be used; after a surface is obtained, it must be polished by using finer, and then very fine powder. In changing from one size of powder to a finer, the lap and fragment

---

[1] "Carborundum" is the patented trade name for silicon carbide, manufactured by the Carborundum Company.

must be thoroughly cleaned, since a single grain of coarse powder will prevent successful polishing. It is convenient to have two laps, one for coarse grinding, and one for use with fine powder. The final polishing may be done on a stationary plate, which may be a thick piece of ground glass. It is important to avoid wearing the plates to an uneven surface; therefore, the fragment should be kept constantly in motion and not held steadily in one place.

When a polished surface has been produced, the fragment is thoroughly cleaned with a stiff brush, in water, and then dried by warming to about 90°–100° C. The polished surface of the fragment is then cemented firmly to a glass plate, about 1 to $1\frac{1}{2}$ inches square and about $\frac{1}{4}$ inch thick. Canada balsam is a good cement; if it is viscous when cool, it must be evaporated until a drop on a pin point hardens when chilled; if the evaporation is carried too far the balsam becomes too brittle and may turn yellow. Solid balsam, previously evaporated to the right condition, is convenient; it is easily melted for use, but must not be further evaporated. Such balsam, dissolved in xylol or ether, may be used without heating; in this case time must be allowed (about two weeks) to permit the solvent to evaporate and the balsam to harden. When cementing the fragment all air bubbles must be excluded, since they prevent firm adhesion and frequently result in the loss of the whole section, or a part of it, in the later work. While the balsam is hardening, the fragment should be pressed as close to the glass plate as possible.

After the rock fragment has received a polished surface, by which it is cemented to its glass holder, it is ready for further grinding. The second grinding is intended to produce a second surface exactly parallel to the first one; the process is similar to the first grinding, but constant care must be used to keep the new surface parallel with the first one produced. As the grinding reduces the thickness, the fragment should be examined frequently, and if one part is thicker than another, the thicker part should be placed toward the periphery of the lap and a little more pressure put on this part. As soon as the thickness is reduced, so that the section becomes translucent, it should be examined at frequent intervals under the microscope after the surface has been covered with a drop of water and a cover glass. As soon as the section becomes as thin as 0.15 mm., such minerals as quartz and feldspar show bright interference colors between crossed nicols. The grinding should now proceed more slowly, with very fine Carborundum, and frequent microscopic examination.

When the highest interference colors of quartz and feldspar are grayish white, the section is reduced to standard maximum thickness, namely, 0.03 mm.   The last of the grinding is often done with flour emery, and the final polishing on a ground-glass plate with the finest Carborundum.

The section must now be mounted. For this purpose it is thoroughly cleaned with a soft brush and alcohol, and then loosened by gradually heating the glass plate. By adding a little additional warmed balsam the section may be freed completely from the glass plate and rendered readily mobile. It may now be transferred, while constantly immersed in balsam to avoid all strain, to an adjacent glass plate of suitable size, previously coated with warmed balsam.   A clean cover glass is then placed over the section, one edge being placed in position first and the glass gently lowered into position so as to avoid enclosing any air bubbles. Pressure on the cover glass with a dull point or pencil will drive out the surplus balsam.   After cooling, the excess balsam may be removed by alcohol or xylol.

Glass slides for thin sections should be about 26 by 46 mm., and the cover glasses either about 24 mm. in diameter or about 24 mm. square, leaving space at each end of the glass slide for labels or for writing on the glass with a diamond point.

CHAPTER IX

MICROSCOPIC STUDY OF REFRINGENCE

THE refringence of a substance is its power to produce refraction of light; it is measured by its index of refraction.

The most accurate method of measuring the index of refraction is by means of a prism cut from the substance and used to produce deviation in the path of a ray of light. When the prism is so adjusted as to produce minimum deviation, the angle of incidence on the first face is equal to the angle of refraction from the second face of the prism. If m equals this minimum angle of deviation, c equals the angle between the two faces of the prism, and N is the index of refraction; then

$$N = \frac{\sin \frac{1}{2}(m+c)}{\sin \frac{1}{2}c}.$$

Microscopic methods for direct measurement of the index of refraction are not as accurate as others, but they are more important in petrographic work. However, microscopic methods for comparing the indices of refraction of two substances in contact are of a high order of accuracy, and they may be used indirectly to determine indices, as will be described below. The accuracy of the method of the Duke de Chaulnes, for direct measurement of the index, depends upon the accuracy of focus and the correct measurement of the thickness of an object.

Chaulnes method.—Suppose a minute particle to be in the focus of the objective at the point O, in Fig. 90, nothing but air separating the point from the objective. If now a transparent plate of any medium (M) be placed over the particle between it and the objective, it will be necessary to raise the objective somewhat to bring the object again into focus. This is due to the fact that all rays from O are refracted away from the normal on emerging from

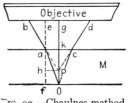

FIG. 90.—Chaulnes method.

the transparent plate, as illustrated in the figure for the two rays Oab and Ocd. Consequently, the objective must be raised the distance OP to bring the particle into focus.

Let ef be perpendicular to ac at a; it is, then, parallel to Og. Then Oaf is the angle of incidence of the ray Oab, and bae ($=Pah$) is the angle of refraction for the same ray. Then, in the right triangles Ofa and Pha:

$$\tan Oaf \quad \text{or} \quad \tan i = \frac{Of}{af} = \frac{ak}{Ok},$$

and

$$\tan Pah \quad \text{or} \quad \tan r = \frac{Ph}{ah} = \frac{ak}{Pk}.$$

By division

$$\frac{\tan i}{\tan r} = \frac{Pk}{Ok}.$$

Since, for small angles, the ratio between the tangents is sensibly the same as the ratio between the sines:

$$\frac{Pk}{Ok} = \frac{\tan i}{\tan r} = \frac{\sin i}{\sin r} = N.$$

Since Pk equals the thickness of the plate, Ok, minus the change of focus, Op, the index of refraction of air as compared with the plate is equal to the apparent thickness of the plate ($Ok - OP$) divided by the real thickness (Ok), and the index of refraction of the plate as compared with air is equal to the thickness (Ok) divided by the apparent thickness (Pk); or

$$N = \frac{Ok}{Pk}.$$

The distances Ok and Pk can be measured microscopically by means of the micrometer screw (the fine adjustment screw).

As will be described later, it is possible to estimate the index of refraction of minerals in thin sections from their relief.

The relative refringence of transparent substances in contact can be determined with great accuracy by two microscopic methods, the method of normal illumination and the method of oblique illumination.

Normal illumination.[1]—When the contact between two substances

[1] The illumination best adapted for this method is " normal " in both senses; that is, it is normal or usual in contrast with the special illumination of the next method, and it is normal or at right angles to the plate (on the average) unlike the case of oblique illumination.

of unequal refringence is observed microscopically a narrow band of light, sometimes called the " Becke line," may be seen under favorable conditions. Such a contact is usually inclined more or less to the object glass so that each substance is thinner on the edge than away from it (toward its center); therefore, each edge acts like that of an imperfect lens to refract and concentrate the light on one side or the other of the boundary, depending chiefly upon the relative values of the indices of refraction of the two substances.

With powdered minerals immersed in liquids nearly all fragments are thinner on the edge than in the center and therefore act as imperfect lenses to refract the light, provided they differ in index from the liquid. If the mineral fragment has a higher index than the liquid it tends to bring parallel light to a focus above the fragment; consequently a slight *raising* of the objective from good focus on the grain causes brightness within the area of the fragment. If the mineral has a lower index than the liquid it produces a virtual focus of previously parallel light below the grain; consequently a slight *lowering* of the objective from good focus on the grain causes brightness within the fragment. In both cases the reverse motion of the objective causes a bright line of light outside the fragment while the grain itself is darker than the field in general.

In the special case in which the boundary between the two substances is normal (or nearly so) to the object glass total reflection is of some importance in producing the white line. Let Fig. 91 represent a vertical section through a thin section in which two minerals are in contact along the line yz, B having the greater refringence. Four rays of light, 1, 2, 3, 4, from the condenser strike the

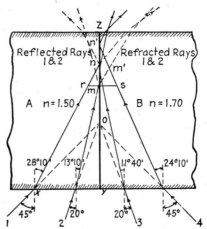

FIG. 91.—Normal illumination.
(After Hotchkiss.)

lower surface, xy, of the section at angles of 20° and 45°. If the refractive indices of A and B are 1.50 and 1.70 respectively, the rays 3 and 4 will be totally reflected at m' and n', while the rays 1 and 2 are partly reflected and partly refracted at m and n; therefore, there is more light from the surface to m' on the side of that mineral having the greater refringence.   On lowering the focus from the surface to m' the line of light narrows and brightens, moving toward yz.   Further lowering of the focus causes the bright line to appear on the other side of the line yz, since the rays 1 and 2 are nearer together, for example, at m, than the rays 3 and 4.   Therefore, the rule is that the bright line moves toward the mineral of higher index when the focus is raised and toward the mineral of lower index when it is lowered.

In using this method it is necessary to employ a medium, or preferably, a high-power, objective and focus accurately upon the line of contact; then lower the condenser enough to notably darken the field (if the condenser cannot be lowered enough the mirror may be shifted or a diaphragm partly closed) and a very fine line of white light, clearer and brighter than the mineral on either side may be seen very close to the line of contact. This bright line is the " Becke " line; it moves toward the mineral of higher index when the focus is very slightly raised.   The plane of contact should be normal or nearly normal to the plane of the section for the best results.

Oblique illumination.—By the use of oblique illumination the same phenomenon may be made clearer, so that differences of index as small as .001 may be detected promptly under favorable conditions.   It is only necessary to insert the condenser and shade part of the field so that the boundary being studied is in the half-shadow portion of the field of view.   The shading or darkening of part of the field may be accomplished by tilting the mirror, or by intercepting part of the light from the mirror in any way—most easily by interposing the finger.   If the boundary is inclined it causes refraction much as the edge of a lens would do, as it does with normal illumination, and this effect is made more evident by using oblique illumination. If the boundary is normal to the object glass the effect is easily understood from Fig. 92 in which A is any mineral surrounded by a second mineral (or liquid) B and B'. An inclined beam of light passing from B' into

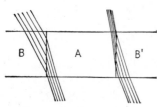

FIG. 92.—Oblique illumination.

A is made narrower or condensed since each ray is refracted away from the perpendicular to the contact plane, while a similar beam of light passing from A into B is widened or dispersed by refraction toward the perpendicular.   If the mineral is above the focus of the condenser when the edge appears bright (as in passing from B' to A) the mineral of higher refringence is on the side whence the light comes, and when the edge appears dark (as in passing from A to B) the mineral of lower refringence is on the side whence the light comes.

If the mineral is below the focus of the condenser the effects are reversed. The reversal of the effect is due to the fact that the change of condition is equivalent to inserting the shade above or below the focus of the condenser, and therefore the direction of inclination of the light is reversed. To determine whether the crystal is above or below the focus of the condenser it is only necessary to move the condensing lens up or down until the edge of the finger or object shading the mirror is in good focus; when the condenser is raised from this position the mineral is below the focus; when it is lowered from this position the mineral is above the focus.

In using this method it may be noted that the direction of inclination of the beam of light is reversed by the substage lenses and again reversed by the objective; hence the phenomena may be read as if no reversal took place.

With Leitz microscopes the ordinary method of cutting off the light with the finger to secure inclined illumination gives poor results; good results can be obtained by using the brass frame of a gypsum or mica plate (inserted in its usual place) to produce inclined illumination. Even better results can be obtained by employing a special shader, recently devised for use immediately below the condenser. In this case the effects are reversed as compared with using the finger with other microscopes, because the condenser must be removed and therefore the mineral is below the focus of the weak condensing lens which remains.

As compared with crystals or other solids, liquids in general have much greater dispersion, that is, they have much greater differences in indices for different parts of the spectrum. Therefore, if a crystal has exactly the same index of refraction as a certain liquid for yellow light, it will have greater refringence than the liquid for red light and less than the latter for blue light. Under these conditions if a fragment of the crystal is observed with inclined illumination in white light one edge of the fragment is colored by blue light and the opposite edge by red light. The blue edge will be on that side of the crystal away from the shadow (condenser being lowered), which is the side that is brightly illumined when the crystal is immersed in a liquid of higher refringence, or, without change of liquid, when monochromatic blue light is used instead of white light. Accordingly, the appearance of pale red and blue edges on opposite sides of a crystal is evidence that the fragment has a refringence equal to that of the liquid for some intermediate color. For some of the immersion liquids—notably cinnamon oil—the dispersion is very great and strongly colored borders are present even if the index for sodium light of the grain and the liquid differ in the second decimal place.

Immersion method.—Schroeder van der Kolk brought into prominence a method to determine the refringence of minerals in fragments or grains. It consists essentially in immersing the fragment in a liquid of the same refringence, as determined by the method of normal or inclined illumination, and then measuring the index of refraction of the liquid. A liquid of the same refringence may be

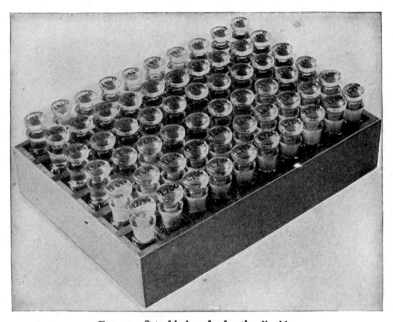

FIG. 93.—Set of index-of-refraction liquids.

obtained by reducing the index by dilution or raising the index by evaporation, or it may be obtained approximately by preparing beforehand a set of liquids whose indices differ by only a small amount, for example, by 0.01. Changes of temperature or of concentration through evaporation modify the refringence of liquids and should be avoided during use. The liquids recommended for this use by Larsen [1] are given on page 81. These liquids are selected partly because of relatively low dispersion. They may be kept conveniently in small dropping bottles with ground-glass dropper and cap, thus providing two ground joints to prevent evaporation. All the liquids, except as

[1] U. S. Geol. Survey Bull. 679, 1921, p. 15.

IMMERSION MEDIA AND THEIR PROPERTIES

Substance	N at 20° C.	$\dfrac{dN}{dT}$	Dispersion	Remarks
Water..............	1.333	Slight	....	Dissolves many minerals of low index.
Acetone.............	1.357	....	Slight	
Ethyl alcohol........	1.362	0.00040	Slight	Dissolves many minerals of low index.
Ethyl butyrate.......	1.381	....	Slight	
Methyl butyrate.....	1.386	....	Slight	
Ethyl valerate.......	1.393	....	Slight	
Amyl alcohol *.......	1.409	0.00042	Slight	Dissolves many minerals of low index.
Kerosene...........	1.448	0.00035	Slight	
Petroleum oil:†				
Russian alboline....	1.470	0.00040	Slight	
American alboline..	1.477	0.00040	Slight	
Valvolene ‡........	1.502	0.00040	Slight	Will not mix with clove oil.
Clove oil...........	1.531	0.00050	Moderate	Mixes with petroleum oil with difficulty; may be mixed readily with rape-seed oil, index of which is 1.471.
Cinnamon oil §......	1.585– 1.600	0.0003	Strong	
Cinnamic aldehyde...	1.615	0.0003	Strong	
α-Monobromnaphthalene ‖	1.658	0.00048	Moderate	
Methylene iodide.....	1.74±	0.00070	Rather strong	Expensive, discolors on exposure to light, but a bit of Cu or Sn will prevent this change.
Methylene iodide saturated with sulphur	1.778	....	Rather strong	
Methylene iodide, sulphur and iodides ¶.	1.868	....	Rather strong	
Piperine and iodides..	1.68– 2.10	....	....	
Phosphorus.........	2.05	....	....	
Sulphur and selenium.	2.0–2.	....	Very strong	
Selenium and arsenic selenide...........	2.72– 3.17	....	Very strong	

* Ordinary fusel oil may be used instead; it forms a milky emulsion with kerosene, which settles on standing, so that the clear liquid can be decanted off.

† Any of the medicinal oils may be used, such as Nujol.

‡ Any clean lubricating oil, such as used in automobiles, may be used.

§ Less expensive than cinnamic aldehyde, but the index of commercial oil is not definite.

‖ Mixtures of α-monobromnaphthalene with clove oil give liquids with less dispersion than those with cinnamon oil.

¶ To 100 grams of methylene iodide add 35 grams iodoform, 10 grams sulphur, 31 grams tin iodide (SnI₄), 16 grams arsenic iodide (AsI₃), and 8 grams antimony iodide (SbI₃), warm to hasten solution, allow to stand, and filter off undissolved solids. See H. E. Merwin: *Jour. Wash. Acad. Sci.*, III, 1913, p. 35.

noted, will form suitable mixtures in any proportions with those next above and below them in the table.   The index of refraction decreases with increase of temperature at the rate given (for 1° C.) in the column headed dN/dT.

A set of prepared liquids with a regular difference of index of 0.005 may be obtained from mineral dealers, such as Ward's. This set begins preferably at about 1.440 and continues to 1.740; the liquids above 1.740 change in index so rapidly that only the sulphur saturated methylene iodide (1.78) is desirable as permanent equipment. Such a set in bottles with ground-glass stoppers elongated as a glass rod below and having a flat top is shown conveniently arranged in a substantial tray in Fig. 93 on page 80.

A set of liquids convenient for approximate determinations, because preliminary measures of the indices of the liquids are unnecessary, is given below.   Most of these are easily obtained.   But for precise work the indices must be measured as different lots of the same material in some cases give results varying as much as 0.04:

Index	Liquid
1.33	Water
1.36	Ethyl alcohol
1.44	Chloroform
1.47	Glycerine
1.48	Castor oil
1.49	Xylol
1.50	Benzene
1.51	Cedar oil
1.53	Clove oil, or monochlorbenzol
1.54	Fennel oil
1.55	Nitrobenzene,* bitter almond oil, or anise oil
1.56	Monobrombenzene
1.59	Bromoform
1.60	Cassia oil
1.62	Monoiodobenzol
1.64	α-Monochlornaphthalene
1.66	α-Monobromnaphthalene
1.70	Cadmium borotungstate
1.74	Methylene iodide †
1.78	Methylene iodide saturated with sulphur

* Alters when exposed to light.
† The iodine which separates on exposure to light may be removed with copper.

Immersion methods can be made much more accurate and useful by taking advantage of the thermal or thermal and chromatic variation in index of liquids, as described in Chapter XX.

Refringence and relief in thin sections.—Thin sections are nearly always mounted in Canada balsam ($N = 1.54\pm$), and the constituent minerals are therefore in contact with that medium above and below the section. When the index of the crystal is nearly the same as that of the balsam, light passes through the two layers of the latter and the intervening section with very little refraction or reflection. The greater the difference between the refringence of the balsam and that of any crystal the more refraction and reflection occur at the surfaces of contact. When the refraction and reflection affect an appreciable part of the light, the section appears mottled with darker spots, because the polishing is never sufficient to make a surface which is not rough in its effect on light. At the same time the margins of crystals are marked by dark borders from which the light is refracted or totally reflected. The dark borders and mottling produce an appearance of relief within the section, as if certain crystals were raised above the level of the surrounding minerals. This relief may be used to estimate the difference between the refringence of the crystal and that of the balsam.

In using the relief as a means of estimating refringence, it is important to remember that the **apparent** relief is increased by (1) absorption, (2) inclusions, (3) disseminated alteration products, (4) cleavages or fractures, (5) imperfect polishing. It is necessary to make such allowances for any or all of these factors as may be proper. Finally, the visible relief depends also upon the adjustment of the microscope. The relief is seen more distinctly with the lower magnifications and with the field somewhat darkened. The refringence can be approximately estimated from the distance it is necessary to lower the condenser in order to make the relief perceptible. Or it can be estimated from the amount it is necessary to close the lower diaphragm to bring out the relief. At best, such methods serve only as approximations, and the following standard scale of refringence is therefore useful.

SCALE OF REFRINGENCE

1. Fluorite, $N = 1.434$. Negative distinct. $N < 1.48$.

   Limit: Natrolite, $N = 1.48\pm$. Castor oil, $N = 1.48\pm$.

2. Leucite, $N = 1.509$. Negative low. $N > 1.48 < 1.54$.

   Limit:
   - Microcline, $N_g = 1.529$. Clove oil, $N = 1.531 - 1.533$, or
   - Fennel oil, $N = 1.54$.
   - Quartz, $N_o = 1.544$. Canada balsam, $N = 1.533 - 1.541$.

3. Labradorite, $N_m = 1.557–1.567$. Positive low. $N > 1.53 < 1.59$.

Limit: Muscovite, $N_m = 1.59\pm$. Bromoform, $N = 1.589$.

4. Apatite, $N_o = 1.634$. Positive moderate. $N > 1.59 < 1.66$.

Limit: Enstatite, $N_m = 1.66\pm$. α-Monobromnaphthalene, $N = 1.65–1.66$.

5. Augite, $N_m = 1.71\pm$. Positive high. $N > 1.66 < 1.74$.

Limit: Staurolite, $N_m = 1.741–1.753$. Methylene iodide, $N = 1.742$.

6. Zircon, $N_o = 1.93–1.96$. Positive very high. $N > 1.74 < 2.00$.

Limit: Zincite, $N_o = 2.008$. Amorphous sulphur, $N = 1.998$.

7. Rutile, $N_\epsilon = 2.61\pm$. Positive extreme. $N > 2.00$.

It is very convenient to have these minerals mounted on a single slide for comparisons. They are also useful as a means of calibrating a microscope. Thus, with Nachet microscopes, orthoclase gives very slight negative relief when the condenser is lowered about 16 mm. (that is $1\frac{1}{2}$ turns of the screw, as far as it will go), muscovite gives slight positive relief when the condenser is lowered the same amount, enstatite gives positive relief when the condenser is lowered about 8 mm.; staurolite when it is lowered about 4 mm. If the mineral shows relief when the condenser is not lowered at all, the index is 2 or above. A similar calibration may be made for any microscope which has either a substage diaphragm or a device to permit lowering of the condenser. If the diaphragm is used in calibration, it is best to lower it as far as possible for all measures.

Whenever an unknown mineral is in contact with the common minerals of the scale of refringence, the relative refringence may be accurately determined by the method of normal, or of oblique illumination, even though the difference in the indices is slight. Furthermore, the same methods of comparison of indices will establish a limit for the refringence of any unknown mineral which is in contact with any known mineral.

DIRECTIONS FOR LABORATORY WORK

Determine the index of refraction of a cover glass or other glass plate by the method of the Duke de Chaulnes. If the glass plate, whose true thickness is known, is used, it is only necessary to measure the apparent thickness (PK of Fig. 90) to obtain the index by the relation $N = \dfrac{kO}{Pk} = \dfrac{\text{true thickness}}{\text{apparent thickness}}$.

If a glass of unknown thickness is used, its approximate true thickness may be obtained by focusing on a distinct point or scratch on a glass support, and then superposing the glass plate and focusing on its upper surface. But this measure is greater than the true thickness, since it includes the thickness of the air film between the glass surfaces. It can be used only in cases in which the thickness of the glass plate is so great that the thickness of the air film becomes negligible. For a thin glass plate of unknown thickness. the following method may be used.

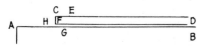

FIG. 94.—Measurement of index of refraction.

Let AB represent the upper surface of a slide supporting the cover glass CD, while between them there is an air film of indefinite thickness, as shown in Fig. 94.

If we focus on E and then on F, the distance through which the objective has been moved will be the *apparent* thickness of the cover glass. If we focus on E and then on H, the vertical distance will be the true thickness of the cover glass plus the thickness of the air film. By focusing on F and on G we get the true thickness of the air film. Therefore $N = \dfrac{EH - FG}{EF}$. The smallest dust particles usually serve as the best objects on which to focus.

Determine the relative refringence of two minerals or substances in contact by two different methods. In using the method of normal illumination it is necessary to focus sharply with a high-power objective on the contact to be studied, and then lower the condenser, or partly close the substage diaphragm, or both, producing poor illumination of the field. This will render visible a fine bright line, close to the contact. When the focus is slightly raised the bright line moves toward the mineral or substance of higher index. The contact between any two minerals in any thin section may be studied in this way, and differences of index as small as 0.002 may be detected. Still smaller differences may be distinguished by the method of oblique illumination. For this method, low power objectives are used; the condenser is slightly lowered, and one-half of the field is darkened by interposing the finger or other object above the mirror so as to cut off one-half of the beam of light. If the edge appears darkened, the mineral of lower refringence is on the side whence the light comes; if it appears brightened the reverse is true.

By immersing minute fragments in liquid, determine, by both of the preceding methods, whether quartz has a higher or lower index than (1) glycerine, (2) cinnamon oil or cassia oil.

Learn to estimate the refringence of minerals in thin sections by means of the relief. For this purpose the scale of refringence is very useful.

It is worth while to examine several sections illustrating each degree of refringence as follows:

Observe negative relief in fluorite.

Minerals showing distinct negative relief are not common.

Observe low relief (or absence of relief) in colorless quartz and orthoclase in oriented sections and sections of granite.

Observe moderate relief in green hornblende in oriented sections or sections of diorite.

Observe high relief in colorless olivine in oriented sections or sections of olivine gabbro or basalt.

Observe very high relief in titanite, zircon, or rutile, in any available sections, for example, sections of zircon syenite.

Finally, observe these differences as shown by the slide containing the scale of the refringence, and the slide containing the limiting minerals of the scale of refringence.

CHAPTER X

ISOTROPIC MINERALS

ISOTROPIC minerals include those which crystallize in the isometric system and those which are amorphous. Such minerals can be recognized microscopically by the fact that they are dark in all positions of rotation between crossed nicols, that is, when both nicol prisms are in their normal position in the path of light traversing the microscope. All other minerals, except when cut normal to an optic axis, are not dark in all positions between crossed nicols, but show interference colors and extinction positions.

DIRECTIONS FOR STUDY

The more important characters of isotropic minerals to be observed microscopically are as follows (each mineral does not necessarily have all these characters):

1. Crystal form.
2. Twinning.
3. Inclusions.
4. Alterations.
5. Cleavage; number of directions and relation to crystal form.
6. Color.
7. Refringence, usually estimated from the relief.
8. Optical anomalies, sometimes due to strain.
9. Associated minerals.
10. Textural relations.
11. Mode of occurrence.
12. Diagnostics.

Other characters, such as chemical composition, hardness, specific gravity, etc., should be learned from a study of the minerals by other methods, or by reference to descriptive textbooks. Microscopic study of minerals and rocks should be accompanied, as frequently as possible, by examinations of hand specimens.

Write a description of each important isotropic mineral on blanks similar to the sample on page 88. Since such blanks are adapted for use with anisotropic minerals, some of the spaces are not appropriate for isometric crystals.

Make one or more drawings of each mineral as seen microscopically. Make the drawings illustrate the chief characteristics and diagnostics. Study the common crystal forms assumed by each mineral; if they are unfamiliar, study models and make drawings.

The following relatively condensed statements of the characters of the more important isotropic minerals are intended merely for preliminary use. For more complete descriptions, refer to Part II of this work or any descriptive textbook of mineralogy.

The only important amorphous mineral is opal. The only isometric minerals of importance are pyrite, magnetite, fluorite, garnet, and leucite. Other isometric minerals, less abundant, include spinel, sodalite, analcite, sphalerite and galena.

Transparent minerals are studied microscopically by transmitted light, and opaque minerals by reflected light. Pyrite and magnetite are opaque; the other isotropic minerals to be studied are transparent in thin sections. In studying opaque minerals, the microscope should be adjusted near a window to receive light (not directly from the sun), on the upper surface of the thin section without using the reflecting mirror, so that the mineral will reflect it into a low-power objective.

Opal, $SiO_2 \cdot nH_2O$.—No crystal form, but sometimes mammillary, concretionary, banded. Colorless. Relief very low with an index (1.44) distinctly less than that of Canada balsam. Commonly found as coatings of cavities and in veins.

Pyrite, FeS_2.—In cubes, octahedrons, and pentagonal dodecahedrons, or in irregular grains. Opaque; yellow in reflected light; bright metallic luster. The yellow color in reflected light easily distinguishes it from the other opaque iron ores.

Magnetite, Fe_3O_4.—In octahedrons or in irregular grains. Opaque; bluish black in reflected light; distinct metallic luster. Is magnetic and is thus readily distinguished from most opaque black minerals. Its color in reflected light easily distinguishes it from pyrite and hematite, but not from ilmenite.

Fluorite, CaF_2.—Good octahedral cleavage; clear, transparent, bluish, or violet colored; very low index of refraction (1.435).

Garnet.—Silicate of Al, Fe''', or Cr with either Ca, Fe, Mn, or Mg. In crystals or in irregular grains. Transparent, frequently pinkish or red; high index of refraction (1.71). Hardness 7.0–7.5.

Leucite, $KAlSi_2O_6$.—In crystals, usually trapezohedrons, thus giving 4-, 6-, or 8-sided sections. Transparent, colorless; very low index of refraction (1.508); frequently with dark inclusions zonally arranged. In larger crystals, especially when examined with the sensitive tint, doubly refracting lamellæ can sometimes be distinguished.

(Sample blank for notes on microscopic study of minerals.)

Name of mineral

1. Comp.,
2. Cryst. syst.,   3. Cleavage,
   Habit.,
4. Twinning,   5. H =   G =
6. Indices,   7. Birefringence,
                            Max. interf. color (0.03 mm. thick)

8. Optic sign, $\begin{cases} 2E= \\ 2V= \end{cases}$ 9. Optic orientation,
                          $X\|$ $Y\|$ $Z\|$
   Dispersion,
10. Extinction angles,   11. Direction of elongation,
                           Sign of elongation,
12. Color in mass,   13. Color in thin section,
14. Pleochroism,   15. Inclusions,
   Absorption,
16. Alterations,   17. Associated minerals,
18. Mode of occurrence,   19. Similar minerals,
20. Diagnostics,

(Space below reserved for one or more drawings; remember that the field of view of most microscopes is at least six or seven inches in diameter and make drawings to correspond.)

CHAPTER XI

OPTICAL PROPERTIES OF UNIAXIAL MINERALS

Combination and resolution of simple harmonic motion.—If two simple harmonic motions affect the same particle at the same time, the result will be a regular periodic motion whose character depends upon the directions, phases, periods, and amplitudes of the two motions. Thus, if the two are equal in period and amplitude and the same in direction and phase, the resultant will be a vibration of double the amplitude of either alone. If they differ by half a phase the resultant is no motion. If they are in the same phase and equal in period and amplitude, but take place at right angles to one another, the resultant is simple harmonic motion along the diagonal (*EOG* in Fig. 95) of the square made from lines (*AOC* and *BOD*) representing twice the amplitudes of the component motions, (assuming that *B* and *C* are at the + ends of the two motions). If they differ by half a phase the resultant motion will be along the other diagonal of the same square. If the two component motions differ by one-quarter of a phase, the resultant motion is along the circle *ABCD*. Finally, if they differ in phase by any amount not a

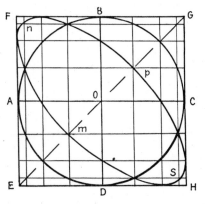

FIG. 95.—Combination of simple harmonic motions.

multiple of one-quarter of a phase, the resultant motion is along an ellipse, such as *mnps*, which represents the motion for a difference of phase of three-eighths.

In general, any harmonic motion may be combined with any other, and the resultant motion is a regular periodic one, either circular, elliptical, or rectilinear. Further, it is apparent by reversing the process, that any regular periodic motion may be resolved into two component simple harmonic motions at right angles to each other. The effect of crystals upon monochromatic light may be explained by these principles.

When simple harmonic motions of different periods are combined, the resultant motion is a complex periodic curved motion. Such motions may evidently be resolved into component parts which correspond to vibrations of light of different colors. The effect of crystals upon white light is analogous to such a resolution of a highly complex periodic motion into two harmonic motions acting at right angles.

Combination, or " interference," of wave motions.—If two waves are traveling along the same path and vibrating in the same plane, they will combine or " interfere " to form a wave whose character depends upon the wave lengths, the periods, the amplitudes, and the phases of the component waves. The resultant wave is easily constructed for any simple case.

If the component waves have the same wave lengths, the same periods, and the same phases, the resultant wave will have an amplitude equal to the sum of the amplitudes of the component waves, as in Fig. 96.

If the two waves are alike, except that they have a difference of phase of half a wave length, the resultant wave will have zero amplitude, and there will be no light, as in Fig. 97.

If the two waves have a phase difference of half a wave length and are unequal in amplitude, the resultant wave will have an amplitude equal to the difference (or algebraic sum) of the amplitudes of the component waves, as in Fig. 98.

If the two waves are alike, except that they have a difference of phase of one-eighth or one-quarter of a wave length, the resultant wave will have an amplitude equal to the algebraic sum of the component waves, as in Figs. 99 and 100.

If the two waves have the same amplitude and different wave lengths, the difference of phase will vary along the path, and the resultant wave will vary in amplitude, and be poorly defined as to wave length, as in Fig. 101.

In more general form, the wave resulting from the combination, or " interference," of any two waves may be formed by drawing each with its proper wave length, amplitude, and phase, and constructing the resultant wave from the points determined by taking the algebraic

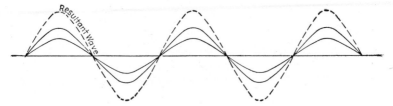

Fig. 96.—Two waves differing only in amplitude.

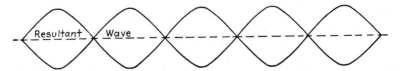

Fig. 97.—Two waves differing only in phase (by a half wave length).

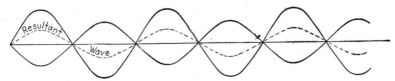

Fig. 98.—Two waves of unequal amplitude and half a wave length difference of phase

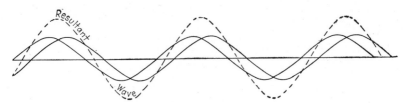

Fig. 99.—Two waves with one-eighth wave length difference of phase.

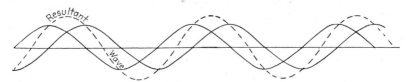

Fig. 100.—Two waves with one-quarter wave length difference of phase.

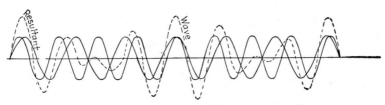

Fig. 101.—Two waves with different wave lengths.

sum of the corresponding ordinates of the component waves at different points along the path, as in Fig. 102. The construction and form of the resultant wave become more complicated with more than two component waves. Hence, the wave of white light is extremely complicated, since it is composed of waves of a great variety of lengths. This complex form of wave is present in all ordinary light, including that derived from the sun.

Just as any two harmonic motions may be combined to form another, often more complex, so any single harmonic motion may be resolved into component harmonic motions vibrating in planes making any angle with each other. Certain crystals, when properly oriented, resolve the complex vibrations of white light into vibrations acting in two planes, at right angles to one another. Such light is said to be

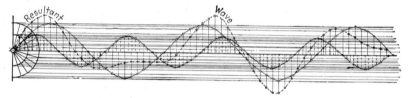

FIG. 102.—General case, showing method of construction.

plane polarized. Light whose vibrations take place in a circle or an ellipse is called **circularly** or **elliptically polarized** light. Such light is produced by certain sections of a few crystals of inferior grade of symmetry.

Polarization.—The process of resolving the extremely complex vibrations of ordinary light into vibrations taking place in definite directions or in definite planes is called polarization. Light may be polarized in several different ways:

Polarization by isotropic substances.—When ordinary light, which is vibrating in all directions normal to the direction of propagation, strikes obliquely the surface of an isotropic medium, it is divided into a refracted and a reflected ray, both of which are partly polarized. It seems to be true that those vibrations of the incident light which are most nearly perpendicular to the surface of the medium penetrate it most easily, while those vibrations which are most nearly parallel to the same surface are reflected most abundantly. Also, vibrations of an intermediate position seem to be more or less completely resolved into two components, one vibrating parallel to the surface and being reflected, the other vibrating at right angles to the first and being refracted. The amount of the incident light which is polarized in this way varies with the angle of incidence; it should be none at all for absolutely normal incidence, and it increases to a maximum at that angle of incidence at which the reflected and refracted rays are at right angles.   Therefore, at that angle of incidence which gives maximum polarization, $N = \tan i$.

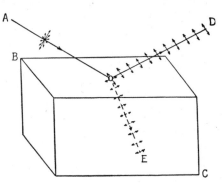

FIG. 103.—Polarization by reflection and refraction.

In Fig. 103, the incident ray AO is vibrating in all directions normal to the ray; upon striking the surface of the new medium BC at the angle which gives maximum polarization, it is divided into a reflected ray OD, vibrating parallel to the surface and normal to the ray, and a refracted ray OE, vibrating at right angles to the former and normal to the ray.

Polarization by anisotropic substances.—The single plane surface of an isotropic substance produces polarization, which is commonly partial, but the innumerable regular layers of atoms of anisotropic substances produce complete polarization both in the reflected and refracted rays, except in a few special cases.   In most cases, crystals produce plane polarized light, the position of the planes of vibration having a definite relation to the atomic structure of the substance. In some cases crystals produce circularly polarized or elliptically polarized light. Anisotropic crystals not only polarize the reflected and refracted rays, but they also generally divide the refracted light into two parts traveling at different rates and along different paths, and polarized in planes at right angles to each other.   This division of the refracted light into two rays is called double refraction, and the ability of a crystal to separate the two refracted rays is measured by its birefringence.   All anisotropic crystals produce double refraction, but only a few have sufficiently strong birefringence to make the double refraction easily visible to the naked eye.

Experimental double refraction.—If a small dot is viewed through a superposed cleavage piece of clear calcite, two images of the dot are seen; on rotation of the calcite one image remains stationary while the other revolves about the first.   The light which produces the fixed image is called the ordinary ray, O, since it travels through the calcite just as it would through a piece of glass. The light which produces the movable image is called the extraordinary ray, E, since it does not travel through the calcite as though it were glass. The paths of the two rays of light through the calcite are shown in a vertical section in Fig. 104, in which A is the object (or dot), B is the fixed image produced by the O ray, and C is the image produced by the E ray, which revolves about B. The two images have equal illumination, but are not at the same distance from the surface of the calcite. The O ray strikes each surface of the mineral at right angles and passes straight through; all the incident light is normal to the lower surface and yet part of it is refracted to form the E ray, which strikes the upper surface at an acute angle, but nevertheless leaves that surface

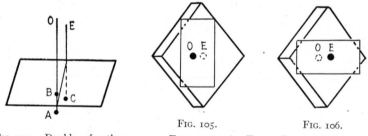

FIG. 105.   FIG. 106.

FIG. 104.—Double refraction.   FIGS. 105, 106.—Tourmaline over calcite.

at right angles. In short, the E ray is truly extraordinary in its apparent defiance of the law of refraction at each surface.

These two rays are completely polarized, so that they are vibrating only in two planes, the E ray in the plane of the paper and the O ray normal thereto, all vibrations being at right angles to the direction of propagation.[1] These facts may be verified by the use of a plate of tourmaline cut parallel with the vertical axis. Such a plate, like calcite, has the property of changing incident light (previously vibrating in all directions normal to its path) into two rays vibrating in planes at right angles to each other, and the additional property of absorbing, or being nearly opaque to, one of these rays, so that only light vibrating in a single plane (parallel with the vertical axis) is transmitted. If such a plate of tourmaline is superposed over the calcite with its vertical axis parallel with the long diagonal of the rhombic face of the calcite, only the image produced by the O ray is visible, as in Fig. 105; and if the tourmaline is turned 90°, only the

[1] Only approximately correct for the extraordinary ray, as explained on p. 97.

image due to the *E* ray is visible, as in Fig. 106. Therefore, the *O* ray is vibrating in the plane of the long diagonal of the calcite and the *E* ray is vibrating at right angles thereto, in a plane called the **principal section,** containing the ray and the vertical axis of the mineral.

Optic axis.—A detailed study of plates of calcite cut at various angles with the vertical crystallographic axis shows that one ray travels with constant velocity whatever the direction of transmission, while the other ray travels with different velocities in different directions, the variations being gradual and such that there is one direction (and only one) in which the velocities of the two rays are equal. This direction coincides with the vertical crystallographic axis, and

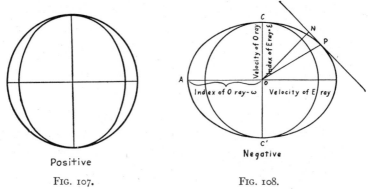

Positive

FIG. 107.

Negative

FIG. 108.

FIGS. 107, 108.—Wave-surfaces in uniaxial crystals.

is known as the optic axis. All the light traveling through the crystal exactly in this direction moves at the same rate, and, moreover, is not polarized. In crystals like calcite, the velocity of the *E* ray increases gradually from the optic axis until it reaches a maximum, which is the same for all directions of transmission normal to the vertical axis. The wave-surface of light traveling as extraordinary rays in such a medium is an ellipsoid of rotation, whose axis of rotation is its minor axis and coincides with the vertical axis of the crystal. The wave-surface of light traveling as ordinary rays in the same medium is a sphere which is tangent to the ellipsoid at the extremities of its minor axis. Crystals having wave-surfaces of this kind, the sphere being inside of the ellipsoid, as in Fig. 108, are called optically negative or −. In other crystals, like quartz, the velocity of the *E* ray decreases gradually from the optic axis until it reaches a mini-mum which is the same for all directions of transmission normal to the vertical axis. The wave surface of light traveling as extraordinary rays in such a medium is an ellipsoid of rotation whose axis of rotation is its major axis. In such crystals the ellipsoidal wave-surface is inside of the spherical wave surface, as in Fig. 107, and the mineral is said to be optically positive or $+$.

Isoaxial, uniaxial, and biaxial substances.—In all isotropic substances, light travels with equal velocity in all directions, so that the wave-surface is a sphere all axes of which are equal; such substances are therefore called **isoaxial**. Those anisotropic crystals in which one part of the light travels with uniform velocity and another part moves with a velocity varying in different directions are called **uniaxial**, since in them there is one " axis," or direction, parallel to which all the light travels with the same velocity. Those bodies in which both parts of the light travel with velocities which vary with the direction are called **biaxial**, because in them there are two " axes," or directions, parallel to which all the light travels with the same velocity.

Isometric crystals are isoaxial; tetragonal and hexagonal crystals are uniaxial; and other crystals are biaxial. Uniaxial crystals have one principal axis of symmetry which is the vertical crystallographic axis, parallel to which is the direction called the optic axis.

The index of refraction of a uniaxial crystal for the E ray varies with the direction of transmission, from equality with the index for the O ray in the direction of the optic axis, to its greatest deviation from this value in the direction normal to the vertical axis. The latter value is always implied when the index is referred to without statement of the direction; it is denoted by N_e, or by the Greek letter epsilon (ϵ). The index for the O ray is denoted by N_o, or by the Greek letter omega (ω).

The indices of refraction of two isotropic substances are inversely proportional to the velocities of light in them; also, the two indices of a uniaxial crystal are inversely proportional to the velocities of the two rays in that substance. Therefore, in negative crystals, in which the E ray travels faster than the O ray, the index of refraction for the O ray is more than that for the E ray, or $\omega > \epsilon$. In positive crystals, in which the O ray travels faster than the E ray, the index of refraction for the O ray is less than that for the E ray, or $\omega < \epsilon$.

In a negative crystal, the velocity of the E ray traveling at right angles to the optic axis is represented by OA, half the length of the major axis of the ellipse, and that of the O ray is represented by OC, half the length of the minor axis, or by the radius of the circle in Fig. 108. Further, OA is the direction of transmission and also represents the velocity of the E ray which vibrates in the direction OC and for which the index of refraction is represented by OC (which is proportional to $1/OA$). Similarly, OC is the direction of transmission and also represents the velocity of the ray which vibrates in the direction OA, and for which the index of refraction is represented by OA (which is proportional to $1/OC$).

Finally, an extraordinary ray traveling in an indefinite direction, such as OP, has a velocity represented by OP, but its index is the reciprocal of the velocity measured in the direction of the wave-normal; that is, it is $1/ON$, if NP is a tangent to the ellipse at the ·point P, and ON is a normal to this tangent from the point of origin, O. The tangent represents the wave-front of the light and a direction at right angles to this is known as the wave-normal. It is believed that the direction of vibration of any extraordinary ray is at right angles to its wave-normal and therefore not exactly normal to the ray.

Since one axis of the ellipse is equal to the diameter of the circle, all parts of the wave-surfaces are known if the ellipsoid alone is constructed, as may be done directly from the indices of refraction. Such a figure is called the index-ellipsoid or indicatrix.

Double refraction in uniaxial crystals.—By proper use of the wave-surfaces, the paths of the ordinary and extraordinary rays may be constructed for light of any known angle of incidence on any crystal surface. Beginning with the simplest case, the light may be incident normally upon the basal plane, for example, of a negative crystal. Since the optic axis is a direction and not a line of fixed position, the line representing the optic axis in the figure of wave-surfaces may always be assumed to meet the surface at the point of incidence of any ray; and, since the light will be assumed to be moving forward and not in both directions from a point, the surface of incidence may be assumed to pass through the center of the figure of wave-surfaces. Then, in Fig. 109, a beam of parallel rays, including R and R', strikes the basal plane, AB, at right angles, and each ray moves onward without division and without refraction, since the ordinary and extraordinary wave-surfaces coincide for these rays and CD is the wave-surface of all the transmitted light within the crystal. The condition of light transmitted in this way is shown in Fig. 110.

Second, assuming that the light is incident at right angles upon a vertical face of a positive crystal, a beam of light, RR', strikes the

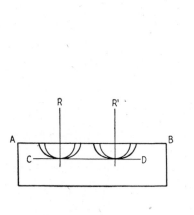

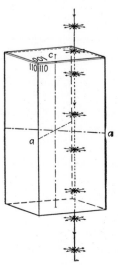

FIG. 109.—Light incident normally on a basal plane.

FIG. 110.—Ray parallel to the vertical axis.

prism face, AB, normally, as in Fig. 111. The wave-surface figures show that while the O and E rays follow a common path with no refraction they travel at unequal velocities; they are vibrating in

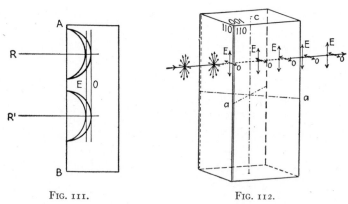

FIG. 111.

FIG. 112.

FIGS. 111, 112.—Effect of a positive uniaxial crystal on light striking a vertical plane at right angles.

single planes at right angles to each other, as shown in Fig. 112. Neither ray is " extraordinary " in the sense of not obeying the ordinary law of refraction at the surfaces, but the E ray has a velocity not equal to that of the light traveling parallel to the vertical axis in the preceding case.

Third, assuming that the light is incident at right angles upon a face of indefinite orientation of a negative crystal, in such a way that the plane of incidence is parallel with the optic axis, a beam of light, RR', strikes the pyramidal surface, AB, normally, as in Fig. 113. The wave-surface figures show that, while the ordinary light passes through without refraction, the extraordinary rays are refracted. The refraction of the E rays renders them less nearly parallel with the optic axis than the O rays in negative crystals, as in Fig. 113, and more nearly parallel in positive crystals. The two rays travel with

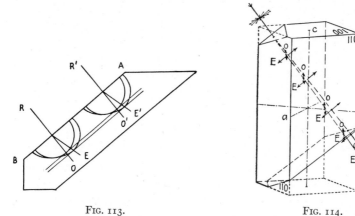

Fig. 113.   Fig. 114.

FIGS. 113, 114.—Effect of a negative uniaxial crystal on light striking a pyramidal surface at right angles.

unequal velocities and are polarized in planes at right angles to each other, as shown in Fig. 114.

Fourth, if a beam of light, RR', is incident obliquely on the basal plane, AB, of a positive mineral, in such a way that the plane of incidence includes the optic axis, as in Fig. 115, the paths of the refracted rays may be found by the use of Huyghen's construction, as before. The wave-surface of the O ray in the crystal, from the point C at the moment the ray $R'e$ reaches e, is found by drawing the section of a sphere whose radius is to de as the velocity of light in the mineral is to its velocity in air, and drawing a tangent from e to this circle. The wave-surface of the E ray in the crystal is similarly found by constructing the section of an ellipsoid of rotation whose shorter axis is at right angles to the optic axis, and whose two axes are given by

the proportion, $cf : cg = V_e : V_o = \dfrac{1}{N_e} : \dfrac{1}{N_o}$, and then drawing a
tangent from e to this ellipse. The paths of the two rays, their rela-

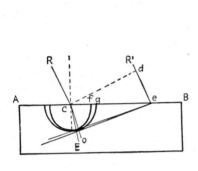

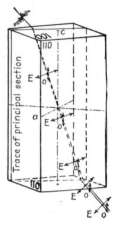

FIG. 115.

FIG. 116.

FIGS. 115, 116.—Effect of a positive uniaxial crystal on light striking a basal plane obliquely, the plane of incidence being parallel to the optic axis.

tive velocities, and their directions of vibration are shown in Fig. 116 for a positive mineral.

Fifth, assuming that a beam of light, RR', strikes obliquely a vertical plane, AB, of a negative mineral, in such a way that the

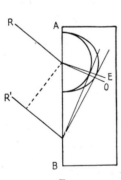

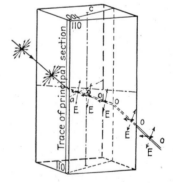

FIG. 117.

FIG. 118.

FIGS. 117, 118.—Effect of a negative uniaxial crystal on light obliquely incident on a vertical plane, the plane of incidence being parallel to the vertical axis.

plane of incidence is parallel with the vertical axis, as in Figs. 117 and 118, or normal to the optic axis, as in Figs. 119 and 120, the paths of the two rays produced may be constructed in a manner wholly similar to that used in the last case. The double refraction, relative velocities, and polarization of the two rays in planes at right angles to each other are shown in Figs. 118 and 120. In Fig. 119 the optic

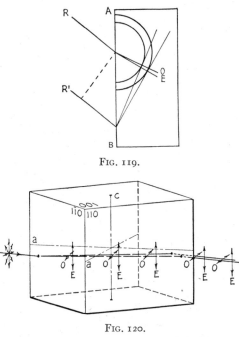

FIG. 119.

FIG. 120.

FIGS. 119, 120.—Effect of a negative uniaxial crystal on light obliquely incident on a vertical plane, the plane of incidence being normal to the optic axis.

axis is normal to the plane of the paper; therefore the sections of both wave surfaces are circles. It may be noted that the E ray is refracted more than the O ray in Fig. 117 and less than the latter in Fig. 119, though both figures represent negative crystals. It is evident that at some intermediate position of the plane of incidence the E ray must be refracted at the same angle as the O ray. It does not follow that the two rays will in this case coincide; they do not coincide because the E ray is refracted out of the plane of incidence in which the O ray remains.

Sixth, assuming that a beam of light, RR', is incident obliquely on a surface, AB, of indefinite position on a negative crystal, in such a way that the plane of incidence is parallel with the optic axis, as in Fig. 121, the paths of the two rays may be constructed by the same methods. The double refraction, relative velocities, and polarization of the two rays in planes at right angles to each other are shown in Fig. 122.

Seventh, if the plane of incidence is not parallel with the optic axis, the plane of the drawing will not cut the ellipsoidal wave surface of the extraordinary ray symmetrically, and therefore the point of tangency of the plane wave-surface with the ellipsoid will not lie in the plane of incidence which is the plane of construction in which the O ray lies. In such a case a three-dimension figure is needed to determine the path of the E ray.

As previously stated, the extraordinary ray does not obey the law of refraction; but the wave-normal of the extraordinary ray always occupies such a position that the index of the crystal for the extraordinary ray in the given direction is equal to the sine of the angle of incidence divided by the sine of the angle between the wave-normal and the normal to the surface.   That is, if ϵ' is the index for the extraordinary ray in a special direction and R is the angle between the wave-normal of that ray and the normal to the surface:

$$\epsilon' = \frac{\sin i}{\sin R}.$$

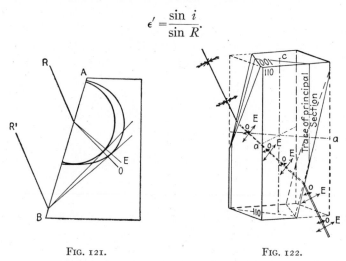

FIG. 121.   FIG. 122.

FIGS. 121, 122.—Effect of a negative uniaxial crystal on light obliquely incident on a surface of indefinite position, the plane of incidence being parallel with the optic axis.

Absorption and pleochroism.—Isoaxial crystals reduce by absorption the amount of light of various wave lengths reflected or transmitted, and the proportion of the light absorbed has no relation to crystalline form or direction.   If the amount of absorption is sufficient to be perceptible the crystal is darkened and usually colored.

Uniaxial crystals may modify the amount and kind of light transmitted or reflected, and the modification may be quite different for the two rays into which the transmitted light is divided.   The crystal may absorb much more of one ray than the other; the fact is most briefly expressed by an " absorption formula "; for example, tourmaline absorbs the O ray more than the E ray, or, in tourmaline, $O > E$.   Also, the kind of light absorbed in the two rays may differ; thus, the unabsorbed part of the O ray from one variety of tourmaline is dark green, while the unabsorbed part of the E ray is reddish violet.   This is expressed in a " pleochroism formula " as follows: $O =$ dark green, $E =$ reddish violet.

The extraordinary ray in a uniaxial crystal vibrates in the principal section, that is, in a plane containing the incident ray and the optic axis, while the O ray vibrates in a plane at right angles to the principal section. Also, all incident light vibrating in the principal section passes through the crystal as extraordinary rays. Therefore, if white light vibrating in a single plane before incidence passes through a crystal of tourmaline, the color of the transmitted light depends upon the relative position of the plane of vibration of the incident light and the optic axis of the mineral.

DIRECTIONS FOR LABORATORY WORK

Construct the path of vibration of a particle affected by two simple harmonic motions of the same amplitude differing by 5/8 of a phase, and at right angles.

Observe double refraction by looking through a cleavage piece of calcite. Look at a single dot; rotate the calcite. Notice the relation between the line connecting the two images and the shorter diagonal of the rhombic face. Find the optic axis of the calcite. Assuming that the rhombic faces are of equal size, the vertical axis connects the two trihedral solid angles. Is the principal section parallel or at right angles to the shorter diagonal of the rhombic face? Do both images revolve? Is the distance between the dots related to the thickness of the calcite? How? Superpose another piece of calcite over the first, and, on rotation (avoiding scratching of the pieces), notice that four images are visible in many positions. Explain this fact by one or more drawings. Draw a vertical section through the calcite, showing the paths of the two rays and also the position of the optic axis. Is the extraordinary ray refracted so as to be more or less nearly parallel with the optic axis than the ordinary ray?

CHAPTER XII

THE NICOL PRISM

THE most important and most distinctive feature of a petrographic microscope is the device for changing ordinary light into light polarized in a single plane. This instrument, called a Nicol prism, or simply a nicol, because it was first constructed and described by William Nicol (in 1828), consists of a cleavage rhombohedron of trans-

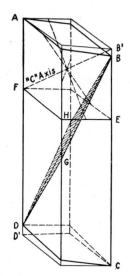

FIG. 123.—Nicol prism in perspective.

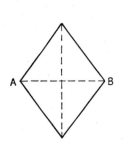

FIG. 124.—End view of Nicol prism.

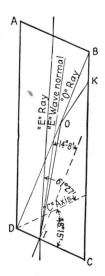

FIG. 125.—Vertical section of Nicol prism.

parent calcite cut into two parts and then cemented together again with Canada balsam. In its original form the nicol is about three times as long as it is thick, and the natural angle of 70° 52′ between the end faces and the obtuse vertical edges is changed by artificial means to 68°—that is, the natural form, $AB'CD'$, is changed to the shape $ABCD$ of Fig. 123. It is then carefully sawed into two parts along the plane $BHDG$, which is perpendicular to the shorter diagonal of the end face. After polishing, the cut faces are cemented together in their original position. The prism faces are then covered by a black coating of some kind, and the nicol is ready for use. The top view of the nicol is given in Fig. 124, in which AB is the shorter diagonal.

If a ray of light parallel with the prism edges enters the lower end of the nicol, as at I in Fig. 125, it is immediately divided into two rays. The index of refraction of Canada balsam is about 1.54; the index of calcite for the O ray is 1.6585; therefore this ray, which strikes the layer of balsam at O at an angle of 76° 57′, will be totally reflected to, and absorbed in, the black coating of the prism K, since the angle of incidence is greater than the critical angle. The index (ϵ') of calcite for the E ray varies with the direction in the crystal, being 1.4864 at right angles to the vertical axis and equal to ω (1.6585) parallel thereto. In the direction taken by the E ray from the incident light mentioned, the index of calcite is 1.534, which is so nearly equal to that of balsam that the extraordinary ray passes through the cementing layer with practically no change in direction. The vibrations in the E ray are in the plane containing the ray and the shorter diagonal of the end face of the prism.

Nicol prisms are sometimes made of different shape; thus, they may have the rhombic vertical edges ground off, so that the cross section becomes a rectangle whose sides are parallel to the diameters of the rhomb; such prisms usually have the end faces at right angles to the vertical edges and may be much shorter than Nicol's type in proportion to their width. Several other forms are occasionally used. A given microscope may have its two nicols of unlike construction, but the complete polarization of the transmitted light in one plane is accomplished in all cases.

Every petrographic microscope has two such artificial prisms; one is placed below the stage, in the axis of the microscope, and is called the **polarizer;** the other, above the objective, is called the **analyzer.** The essential quality of these nicols consists in their power to eliminate one ray and to allow the passage of the other, vibrating in one plane. They are inserted in their places in such a way that the lower, and sometimes also the upper, can be easily rotated horizontally on its axis. One or both can, without difficulty, be entirely removed from the path of the light.

DIRECTIONS FOR LABORATORY WORK

Having given the angle between the basal plane and the rhombohedral cleavage plane in calcite as $44°\ 37'$, calculate, by the aid of the description of the nicol prism, the angle between the vertical or optic axis and the end face of the nicol.

From the indices of refraction of calcite and of Canada balsam, calculate the angles which give the path of the O ray in the nicol, assuming the incident light to be parallel with the vertical edges of the prism.

To find the path of the extraordinary ray:

Assume that the wave-normal of the E ray coincides with the path of the O ray after the first refraction in the calcite; this assumption is not correct, but it may serve as an approximation, the error in which may be reduced by later calculation to a negligible quantity. It may be shown that the index, ϵ', in any special direction in a uniaxial crystal may be calculated from the values of ω and ϵ and the angle (denoted by A) between the optic axis and the wave-normal of the given E ray, by means of the formula:

$$\epsilon' = \frac{\epsilon\omega}{\sqrt{\omega^2 \sin^2 A + \epsilon^2 \cos^2 A}}.$$

Calculate the index for the E ray on the assumption stated. From the index thus obtained, derive the angle of refraction, R, of the wave-normal of the E ray from the equation:

$$\epsilon' = \frac{\sin i}{\sin R}.$$

From this value of R, calculate a new value of A. With this value of A, calculate a new value of ϵ' by means of the first equation; from the new value of ϵ', a new value of R may be obtained; and the process may be continued until the error in the first assumption is reduced to any desired limit. To reduce the error to less than $1'$ it is only necessary to go through the cycle twice.

When the correct angle, R, has thus been obtained, the position of the E ray may be readily derived from the equation:

$$\tan A = \frac{\epsilon^2}{\omega^2} \tan B,$$

in which B is the angle between the optic axis and the E ray.

It is, of course, possible for light to strike the layer of balsam at such an angle that the O ray would not be totally reflected, or at such an angle that the E ray would be totally reflected; in either of these cases the nicol would not accomplish its purpose properly. It may be useful to determine the limiting angles of incidence within which the nicol does its work. The angle between these positions is the angular aperture of the prism.

For this purpose, calculate the angle of incidence at which the O ray would strike the balsam at the critical angle. By tracing this ray back to its path outside the nicol, one of the limiting angles may be found. Then assume an angle of incidence of $11°\ 35'$, and determine the index and the path of the E ray. It will be found to be very near its critical angle. What is the angular aperture of the nicol?

Determine the direction of vibration of the ray emerging from the lower nicol, first, by observing the direction of the shorter diagonal of the end face;[1] and second, by the use of a section of a mineral of known absorption, such as biotite. In a section of biotite showing distinct cleavage lines, these are parallel with the vibration plane of the lower

[1] In some microscopes the lower nicol is not rhombic in cross-section, but made as described on p. 105; the second method may be used.

nicol when the mineral shows maximum absorption, since the ray vibrating parallel with the cleavage in biotite is absorbed more than the ray vibrating normal thereto. When the lower nicol in your microscope is turned so as to produce darkness with the upper nicol in place (" crossed nicols "), is the plane of vibration of the lower nicol from front to rear (" N–S ") or from right to left (" E–W ")?

Determine the value of the index of refraction of calcite for the ordinary and for the extraordinary ray. Use the Chaulnes method on cleavage fragments. Since the E ray vibrates in the principal section, this must be parallel to the vibration plane of the lower nicol when the index for that ray is obtained. This method will not give the minimum value of the index for the E ray. Why not? What values do you obtain?

Study the effect of calcite on light of normal incidence when the light travels (1) parallel to c, (2) normal to c, (3) oblique to c. For this purpose use oriented sections and notice the following points: No double refraction (only one image, or, more strictly, one image directly over another)[1] and no polarization (dark between crossed nicols) in the first case (basal sections of calcite are often light and colored between crossed nicols because the light is not all traveling parallel to the optic axis; to obtain parallel light remove all sub-stage lenses, leaving only the polarizer); no double refraction (one image directly over another)[2] and double polarization (light between crossed nicols) in the second case; both double refraction and double polarization in the third case.

Determine the absorption formula in tourmaline. This may be expressed as $c>a$ or $c<a$, referring to the rays vibrating parallel to the crystallographic axes, or it may be expressed as $O>E$, or $O<E$, referring to the ordinary and extraordinary rays. Finally, it may be expressed in terms of the axes of the ellipsoid as $X>Z$ or $X<Z$ (X is equivalent to a and to N_p; Z is equivalent to c and N_g). Notice that there is no differential absorption in sections cut normal to c. Why?

Determine the pleochroism formula of tourmaline. This may be expressed as $c=$ some color, $a=$ some color, or $O=$ some color, $E=$ some color; but it is most commonly expressed in terms of the axes of the ellipsoids, that is, X and Z.

Observe absorption in tourmaline tongs. The tongs consist of two plates of tourmaline cut parallel to c. Each transmits the E ray while absorbing practically all of the O ray. If one piece is revolved over the other, a position will be reached where no light passes through. Why?

[1] All light traveling exactly along the optic axis moves at the same velocity, but two images are produced because a cone of light is necessary for a focus, and this involves some light not exactly along the optic axis; one image is determined by the curvature of the wave front of the O ray and one by the curvature of the wave front of the E ray.

[2] Two images are produced because the light travels with two velocities; that of the E ray is imperfect because the wave-front is not symmetrical about this direction.

CHAPTER XIII

UNIAXIAL MINERALS IN PARALLEL POLARIZED LIGHT

THE addition of a nicol to produce polarized light increases the usefulness of the microscope for petrographic studies many fold. For certain purposes a condensing lens must be used above the polarizer to render the polarized light either convergent or divergent. But for many other purposes no such lens is necessary, and for certain work it is imperative that it be removed, and the light taken from a distant source, such as the sky, so as to be as nearly parallel as possible.

It is important to understand fully the action of the petrographic microscope upon parallel polarized light. If a section or fragment of the uniaxial mineral is in place between crossed nicols, the light is, in general, doubly refracted and plane polarized three times. These facts are illustrated diagrammatically in the vertical section and plan of Figs. 126 and 127. After reflection from the mirror M, the ray of light enters the lower nicol, IJ, where it is doubly refracted, and completely polarized, one ray (the extraordinary) vibrating in the principal section, which is the plane of the paper in the drawing, and the other ray vibrating normal thereto. The E ray vibrates in the direction PP' of the plan and the O ray in the direction of AA'. The O ray is totally reflected by the Canada balsam to the black surface at W; only the E ray passes through the polarizer.

When this ray strikes an anisotropic mineral section, as SS', cut in an indefinite direction, it is, in general, divided into two rays, which may be called the ordinary (O') and extraordinary (E') rays for this crystal. In the drawing the mineral is supposed to be uniaxial and the O' ray is not refracted, since the incidence is normal. In general, in biaxial crystals, both rays are refracted. The rays O' and E' vibrate in planes at right angles to each other, the E' ray vibrating in the principal optic section of the mineral, which may be assumed to be in the position BB' in the plan, while the O' ray vibrates in the direction CC'. These two rays pass upward to the analyzer RT, where the third double refraction produces two rays from each of them. In the vertical sec-

tion, the portion above XY is a section at right angles to the lower portion and in the direction AA' in the plan. If DO be taken to represent
the vibration of the E ray after passing the polarizer, the two rays, O'
and E', produced by the mineral have vibrations that may be represented by OG and FO respectively.
In the upper nicol the ordinary
ray (O'') derived from O' has a
vibration represented by NO, and
that (O''') derived from E', a vibration represented by HO. Also
the extraordinary ray (E'') derived
from O' has a vibration represented by LO, and that (E''')
derived from E', a vibration represented by KO. Now the two
ordinary rays (O'' and O''') are
totally reflected to the dark wall
of the upper nicol; therefore their
vibrations, NO and HO, disap-
pear. But the two extraordinary
rays (E'' and E'''), whose vibrations are represented by LO and
KO, pass through the analyzer;

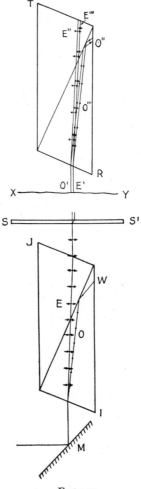

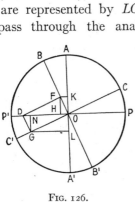

FIG. 126.   FIG. 127.

FIGS. 126, 127.—Effects of a petrographic microscope on light.

and, since their vibrations are in the same plane and have a fixed
phase relation, they "interfere" or combine. In monochromatic
light this interference produces variation in the intensity of the light,
depending upon the difference of phase of the two rays. As explained
later, if the rays have no difference of phase, or if one is retarded an

integral number of wave lengths behind the other, the amplitude of the resultant wave is zero, and darkness results. If the rays have a difference of phase of one-half wave length, or any uneven multiple thereof, the interference doubles the amplitude and quadruples the intensity. In white light, since the different colors constituting the light have different wave lengths, the retardation which one ray suffers has different relations to the different colors, causing some to be in opposite phase and others to differ by an integral number of wave lengths; therefore, interference reduces the intensity of some colors (even to zero, as a limit), while increasing the intensity of others; thus, interference produces colors from white light. The color produced depends upon the difference of phase, or the relative retardation, and this in turn depends upon the birefringence of the mineral concerned, the direction in which the light travels through the crystal with respect to the optic axis (or optic axes), and the thickness of the section or fragment.

In the simple combination of two light waves (without the microscope), darkness results when the phase difference is half a wave length, as in Fig. 97, but when monochromatic light passes through crossed nicols and through a crystal plate between them, darkness results when the phase difference produced by the crystal is one wave length. This fact needs explanation. In Fig. 128

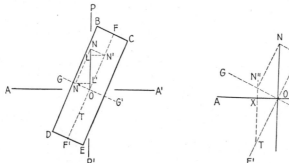

FIG. 128.—Vibration directions.   FIG. 129.—Vibrations in the analyzer.

let PP' represent the plane of vibration of light which passes through the lower nicol or polarizer; upon entering a crystal section $BCDE$, whose planes of vibration are FF' and GG', the vibration of a particle at O, which may be assumed to be at its crest at N, is resolved into two components, ON' and ON''. If these two waves pass through the crystal so as to have, at emergence, no difference of phase, or a difference of phase of any integral number of wave lengths, the wave

ON'' will be at its crest N'' when the wave ON' is at its crest, N'. If, in passing through the crystal, they acquire a difference of phase of half a wave length, or any uneven multiple thereof, the wave ON'' will be at N'' when the wave ON' is at its trough, T.

Whatever the difference of phase which results from the difference in path and difference in velocity of the two waves in the crystal, when they enter the upper nicol, whose vibration plane is AA', each will be resolved into two components one of which, in the plane PP', will be totally reflected and absorbed in the walls of the analyzer, while the other, in the plane AA', will pass through the upper nicol. If they have a difference of phase of one wave length, the components which will be absorbed may be represented by OL and OL'. The more important components which pass through the analyzer are shown in Fig. 129 at OX and OY, which will be their positions if the phase difference is any integral number of wave lengths. It is clear that OX and OY are equal and opposite in direction; therefore these two waves will destroy each other and darkness will result if monochromatic light is being used. Also, if the difference of phase is half a wave length (or an uneven multiple thereof), when the wave vibrating in the plane GG' is at N'' the wave vibrating in the plane FF' will be at T, and the components of these waves vibrating in the plane AA' will be two waves (each OX) of equal amplitude and acting in the same direction; therefore, the resultant wave will have double the amplitude.

Whenever the difference of phase is neither a wave length nor a half wave length (nor a multiple thereof), the components in the plane AA' will be unequal, and the resultant will always have some amplitude varying between the limits named.

The difference of phase produced by any crystal depends upon the difference in velocity and the difference in path of the two waves within the crystal, and the latter varies with the thickness of the section (or fragment). Accordingly, a wedge-shaped section of a crystal will produce a difference of phase varying from zero at the thin edge to any desired amount at the other end. Hence, a wedge will alternately produce darkness and light upon its gradual insertion between crossed nicols, when monochromatic light is used. In Fig. 130, the relation between the thickness of the wedge and the difference in phase is shown; the difference in phase D, is expressed in terms of fractions of the wave length, λ, of the light used. The thickness necessary to produce a given difference in phase varies with the mineral used, and also depends upon the way in which the wedge is cut, that is, the relation in position between the path of the light and the optic axis in the wedge.

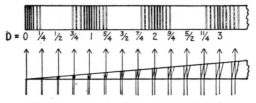

FIG. 130.—A wedge between crossed nicols.

When white light is used, the difference of phase must be measured in some other unit than the wave length, because the white light has no definite wave length, but consists of waves whose length varies

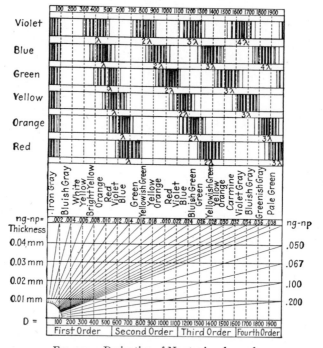

FIG. 131.—Derivation of Newton's color scale.

from about 380 to about 760 millionths of a millimeter, sometimes expressed as 380 to 760 millimicrons, or 380 to 760 mμ. In Fig. 131, the difference of phase, D, is given in millionths of a millimeter. The same figure shows the effect of any difference of phase from zero to

2000 mμ on various kinds of monochromatic light. For each color a medium value of the wave length is chosen as follows: violet, 410 mμ; blue, 460 mμ; green, 510 mμ; yellow, 565 mμ; orange, 620 mμ; red, 690 mμ. When white light is used, the effect produced depends upon the relation of the difference of phase to the wave lengths of all parts of the white light; all these parts are approximately represented by the colors selected. Accordingly, the effect may be inferred by a study of the upper part of Fig. 131; it is modified somewhat by the fact that the intensity of various parts of the spectrum varies considerably, being greatest for yellow and least for violet. With no difference of phase, all parts of white light destroy each other in the upper nicol, as illustrated in Fig. 129, and darkness results. From the same figure it is clear that the intensity of the light increases as the difference of phase increases; accordingly, as D varies from 0 to 260 mμ, the effect varies from darkness to white light; at 300 mμ yellow light is produced, since yellow is near its maximum ($\frac{1}{2}$ λ for yellow) and violet is partly destroyed. At 400 mμ violet is wholly destroyed and blue and green are much weakened; yellow is considerably past its maximum, but on account of its greater relative intensity it dominates over red; for the same reason orange is found at 450 mμ and red at 530 mμ. At 575 mμ violet is produced, since green, yellow, and orange are practically destroyed, and the red and blue simply combine to increase the intensity of violet.

Another method of obtaining an understanding of the way in which interference produces colors from white light is by studying Fig. 132, which represents certain wave lengths of each important color of white light in their proper relations. By making a tracing of this drawing and then moving the point 0 of the tracing to points such as 1, 2, 3, etc., of the drawing, it is possible to see the effect on each color of various amounts of retardation.

A model,[1] such as shown in Fig. 133, is useful in studying the effect of a petrographic microscope on light. The vertical rod is divided into several parts, which may be rotated independently. The lowest celluloid plate represents the vibration plane of the lower nicol with a ray of light represented on it. The transverse plate next above represents the stage of the microscope carrying a mineral section; it may be rotated to bring the vibration planes of the mineral into any desired relation to that of the polarizer. The celluloid plates next above represent the vibration planes of the mineral and the rays

[1] See F. E. Wright: *Am. Jour. Sci.*, CLXXVI, 1908, p. 536.

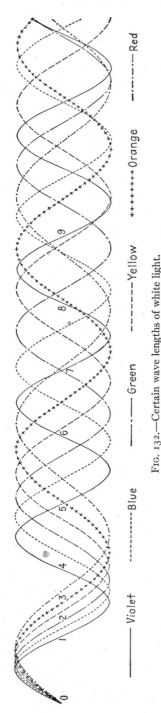

FIG. 132.—Certain wave lengths of white light.

vibrating in them; they rotate together, remaining at right angles; one is set half a wave length ahead of the other, but can be set at any other small amount; the four celluloid plates near the top represent four rays in the analyzer, only two of which pass through; they rotate together, and

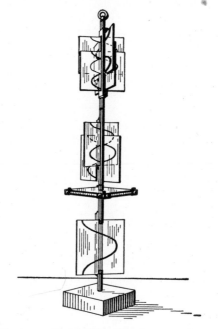

FIG. 133.—Model illustrating the effect of a petrographic microscope on light.   (After Wright.)

two are shown half a wave length ahead of the other two. The way in which the microscope introduces the equivalent of half a wave length retardation is readily seen by the use of this model.

The colors from darkness to the first violet are known as colors of the first order; and violet at the " upper " end of the order is called the sensitive tint, because a slight change in difference of phase produces, in this region, a decided change of hue, to which the eye is very sensitive. At 660 mμ, blue is produced, since yellow, orange, and red are nearly extinguished and green and violet combine to reinforce the blue, which is near its maximum. At 750 mμ, green is produced, violet and red being nearly destroyed and blue and orange merely adding to the green. Yellow, orange, and red follow in order. At 1125 mμ, the second violet marks the upper limit of the second order. From this point the colors are repeated in the same order: violet, blue, green, yellow, orange, red. The colors of the third order are somewhat paler than those of the second, and in the fourth order they are still less distinct, being mixed with white; above the fourth order, pale greenish and reddish grays mark the transition to white of the higher order, not readily distinguishable from ordinary white light. This white results from the fact that as the difference of phase increases it gradually reaches values which are uneven multiples of one-half the wave length of colors in all parts of the spectrum, the intensities of which are therefore increased; a mixture of waves taken regularly from each color of the normal spectrum produces light closely similar to white. To illustrate, if the difference of phase is 5300 mμ, it is equal to:

15 times $\frac{1}{2}$ of 707 mμ, a wave length in red.

17 times $\frac{1}{2}$ of 623 mμ, a wave length in orange.

19 times $\frac{1}{2}$ of 558 mμ, a wave length in yellow.

21 times $\frac{1}{2}$ of 505 mμ, a wave length in green.

23 times $\frac{1}{2}$ of 461 mμ, a wave length in blue.

25 times $\frac{1}{2}$ of 424 mμ, a wave length in violet.

Abnormal interference colors are produced by uniaxial crystals in various ways. If the crystal absorbs part of the light so as to be colored when the upper nicol is not in use, the color observed when it is seen between crossed nicols will be due to the combined effect of the interference color and the color due to absorption. Further, the birefringence of any anisotropic mineral is not exactly the same for all parts of the spectrum; for most minerals the differences in the birefringence for different parts of the spectrum are not sufficiently great to produce noticeable effects; but in a few minerals these differences result in very peculiar interference colors. Thus, if a mineral has zero birefringence for one color and appreciable birefringence for other colors, the former color will be lacking in all the interference colors produced by the mineral, no matter what its thickness may be. For example,[1] melilite is often nearly isotropic for yellow light, and the interference color is a dark blue, called ultra blue. It may be distinguished from blue of the normal series of interference colors by superposing a mica plate or sensitive tint plate, the method of using which will be described later. It will be found that the ultra blue color is produced although the difference of phase is only 100 mμ, to 200 mμ, instead of 660 mμ or 1175 mμ. In biaxial minerals abnormal interference colors may also result from the fact that the extinction position is not exactly the same for all colors, or from the fact that the crystal is uniaxial for some special color and biaxial for all others.

Factors determining interference colors.—The interference color produced by any crystal plate depends directly upon the difference of phase produced by the plate, and this, in turn, depends upon three factors, namely, (1) the birefringence of the mineral, measured by the difference between ω and ϵ; (2) the thickness of the plate, and (3) the direction in which the section is cut with reference to the optic axis. If light travels in a crystal at right angles to the optic axis, the relative velocities of the two rays are inversely proportional to the indices, ω and ϵ; accordingly, the difference of phase for a given thickness varies directly with the difference between the indices. If the two rays travel at unequal velocities through a greater thickness, it is evident that the difference of phase is increased. Finally, if light travels through a plate at an acute angle with the optic axis, the extraordinary ray has an index, ϵ', nearer to ω in value than is ϵ; therefore, the difference of phase produced by a given thickness is less than when the light travels at right angles to the optic axis, since the difference of phase is proportional to the difference between the indices.

Further, if parallel light is incident at right angles upon a basal section of a uniaxial mineral, all parts have the same index, since ϵ' is equal to ω, as shown in Figs. 109 and 110, and the light is not doubly refracted nor polarized, but passes through the section as it would through an amorphous or an isometric substance. Therefore, such sections are dark between crossed nicols in all positions of rotation; light from the lower nicol does not have its vibration plane changed, and is all cut off by the analyzer.

Determination of order of interference color.—Any given color, except gray at the lower end of the first order, is found at least twice

---

[1] Another example is furnished by torbernite (air dried) which is isotropic for green light and weakly birefringent for other colors (+ in red and − in blue light) giving abnormal purple (red to blue) interference colors (N. L. Bowen: *Am. Jour. Sci.*, XLVIII, 1919, p. 195).

in the color scale, but only once in any single order. The precise shade of a color, say red, in one order is not exactly the same as in another order, but this difference is not sufficient to enable the order to be distinguished, especially by the beginner. There are two methods of determining the order to which a color belongs; one is by means of the quartz wedge, the other is by means of a beveled edge.

The quartz wedge is a wedge-shaped plate of quartz, like Fig. 130, cut with its vertical axis parallel with the glass plates between which it is mounted. It is usually marked " quartz wedge," or " compensator "; the arrow at one end indicates the direction of vibration of the slow ray. When the quartz wedge is to be used to determine the order of an interference color, the mineral producing the color should be turned to a position at 45° from extinction, and the wedge should be inserted, thin edge forward, in the path of the light above the mineral. This will cause a series of changes in the interference color observed, due to an increase or a decrease in the retardation produced by the mineral. It is convenient to call the ray which is more retarded in any anisotropic substance the slow ray, or the Z ray, in that medium, and to call the other ray the fast ray, or the X ray. If the slow ray in the mineral is the slow ray in the wedge, as in Fig. 135, the colors observed will be in the order obtained by reading the colors of Newton's scale (Fig. 131) from left to right, and the colors are said to " rise," since they pass to higher orders. If the slow ray in the mineral is the fast ray in the wedge, as in Fig. 134, the colors obtained will be in the reverse order. If the first result is secured, the wedge should be removed and turned over, if the microscope is of French design, or the stage should be turned 90°, if the microscope is of American or German design; then the insertion of the wedge as before will give the second result. When this is obtained the wedge should be inserted far enough to cause the colors to " fall " to the dark gray at the lower end of the first order. Since this color occurs in only one place in the scale the order to which it belongs is not in question. To obtain the order of any other interference color it is only necessary to find its relation to this dark gray. This may be done by listing the interference colors, as they are observed, from the original color, produced by the mineral alone, to the dark gray, or *vice versa*. Thus, if the list reads: red, yellow, white, dark gray, the interference color, red belongs to the first order, while if it is: red, orange, yellow, green, blue, red, yellow, white, dark gray, the original color belongs to the second order, as may be readily seen by studying the series in Newton's scale (Fig. 131).

When the darkest (gray) color is obtained, the retardation of one

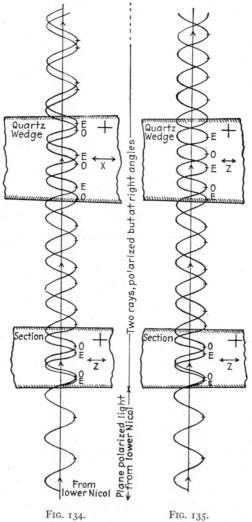

FIG. 134.   FIG. 135.

FIGS. 134, 135.—Diagrams showing the action of the quartz wedge.

ray caused by the mineral is balanced by the acceleration of the same ray produced by the wedge, and the wedge is said to **compensate** the mineral; the wedge is said to be at the **compensation point.** If the two plates in this position could be viewed separately between crossed nicols, they would be found to produce the same color, and the same luminous intensity, if equally transparent.

The beveled edge, when present, is a simpler means of determining the order of an interference color. It can only be used when the mineral under examination has, somewhere along its border, an edge (in contact with balsam or a substance of weak birefringence) sufficiently beveled to produce a series of colors similar to those caused by an artificial wedge. It is only necessary to observe the relation between dark gray of the first order and the interference color produced by the full thickness of the mineral, as shown by the series of colors between them on the beveled edge, to determine the order to which the given color belongs. For example, if the mineral, a in Fig. 136, gives a yellow interference color over the surface where it is

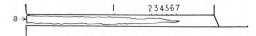

Fig. 136.—Magnified section through a mounted mineral section.

of full thickness, as at 1, and if it produces a series of colors on a beveled edge that are as follows: 2, green; 3, blue; 4, red; 5, yellow; 6, white; 7, dark gray, the yellow interference color found over the main surface belongs to the second order. Frequently, the beveled edge is very narrow, so that it is impossible to distinguish all the colors; but, since red is the highest color of each order, if a single red band can be seen on the bevel, the color of the main surface is of the second order (or higher); if two red bands can be seen on the bevel, the main color is of the third order (or higher). If the bevel is not at the edge of the rock section, care must be taken to allow for the effect of the adjacent mineral, which occupies part of the thickness of the section along the bevel. This is easily done with minerals of weak birefringence. If the adjacent mineral is one of strong birefringence it is usually necessary to use the quartz wedge to determine the order of the color. Of course, the wedge must be used whenever the mineral has no beveled edge.

Measurement of birefringence.—The birefringence of a mineral is always measured by the difference between its greatest and least indices of refraction, that is, with uniaxial minerals, the difference between ω and ϵ. The extraordinary ray has the index ϵ, only when it is traveling at right angles to the vertical or optic axis. When propagated in any other direction it has an index, ϵ' nearer to ω than ϵ is. Therefore, a section of a uniaxial mineral must be parallel to the optic axis in order that the indices of refraction for light passing through normal to the surfaces may be ω and ϵ. The birefringence of a given crystal or grain, as cut in a section, is less than the birefringence of the mineral of which it is a sample, except when the given crystal or grain is cut parallel with its optic axis (or, in biaxial crystals, parallel to both optic axes) and with the same exception it is measured by the difference between ω and ϵ', which is always less than the difference between ω and ϵ.

The difference between the two indices, ω and ϵ, may be determined by accurate measures of those indices themselves, or it may be estimated from its effect in producing an interference color. The interference color produced by a given crystal or grain depends upon (1) the direction in which the crystal or grain is cut with reference to the optic axis, (2) the birefringence of the mineral, (3) the thickness of the section. In a given thin section of uniform thickness, the crystals or grains which are cut exactly parallel with the optic axis produce the highest interference color shown by any crystals or grains of a given mineral. Therefore, in any thin section of uniform thickness, those crystals or grains of any given mineral which produce the highest interference colors exhibited by that mineral are cut parallel to the optic axis (and in them the color is due to the difference between ω and ϵ, and not to the difference between ω and ϵ'), provided there are crystals or grains of all orientations present. Since this condition is satisfied at least approximately in most rock sections for all the minerals which are present in abundance, it is possible to use the interference colors exhibited by various minerals to determine either the birefringence of the mineral (the thickness of the section being known) or the thickness of the section (the birefringence of the mineral being known) by confining attention to those crystals or grains which produce the highest interference color for the given mineral.

Minerals which are useful in determining the thickness of sections must be (1) abundant, (2) fixed in composition so as to be also fixed in birefringence, (3) colorless, or nearly so, in thin section. Quartz satisfies all these requirements very fully and is in common use for this purpose. The birefringence of quartz is 0.009, and, as may be seen from Fig. 131 (or from Michel Lévy's table of birefringences, which is a large colored chart similiar to Fig. 131), a rock section, in which the highest interference color given by quartz is pure white, has a thickness of 0.03 mm., or, more exactly, 0.032 mm. If quartz gives even the palest yellow as its highest interference color, the section has more than the standard thickness (which is 0.03 mm., or less) and if it produces a red color the thickness is about twice the standard. All the feldspars (except anorthite, which is rare) have birefringences between 0.0065 and 0.008; if any common feldspar shows an interference color above grayish white the section is thicker than the standard; if any common feldspar gives an orange interference color the section has twice the standard thickness. Occasionally olivine may be used to determine the thickness, because, although not fixed in composition, its birefringence varies very little for the ordinary variations in composition. The birefringence of olivine is about 0.036; if the highest interference color shown by olivine is second order yellow, the section is about 0.025 mm. thick; if olivine gives any interference color in the third order the section has more than the standard thickness.

A few of the more important rock-forming minerals have **maximum** interference colors in sections of standard thickness (0.03 mm.) as follows:

1. Dark grays: leucite, penninite, vesuvianite, apatite.
2. Light gray to white: nepheline, zoisite, antigorite, feldspar, quartz, enstatite, corundum, gypsum, cordierite.
3. Yellow to red: cordierite, topaz, staurolite, andalusite, clinochlore, hypersthene, wollastonite, cyanite.
4. Blue to green of second order: tourmaline, sillimanite, augite, hornblende.
5. Yellow to red of second order: diopside, tourmaline, humite, olivine.
6. Blue to red of third order: muscovite, biotite, acmite.
7. Grays and whites of higher orders: zircon, titanite, calcite.

It is impossible, for many reasons, to obtain highly accurate measurements of birefringence from interference colors, but approximate determinations are easily made and very useful. For this purpose it is necessary, first, to estimate as closely as possible the thickness of the section, and then to ascertain the exact position in the color chart of Michel Lévy of the highest interference color given by the mineral. The thickness of the section may be determined by the method just described, or it may be measured as described in connection with the description of the Chaulnes method for estimating the index of refraction. For this purpose, a very high power objective should be focused first on a dust particle in contact with one surface of a known mineral and then on a particle in contact with the other surface. The change from one focus to the other must be accomplished by means of the fine adjustment, and the difference in position of the two focal points may be read from the graduated screw head of the fine adjustment. For accuracy, several readings should be taken. It is also useful to use a strong source of light and filter the light through red glass. Brilliant diffraction circles then appear about the dust particles when

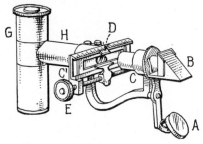

FIG. 137.—Michel Lévy comparator.

above or below their focal points. The distance thus measured is the apparent thickness of the section; by multiplying by the index of refraction of the known mineral, the true thickness may be obtained.

When the thickness of the section is known, the approximate value of the birefringence is easily read from Fig. 131, or from Michel Lévy's table of birefringences. For example, if the thickness is 0.03 mm., and the interference color is yellow of the second order, the birefringence is found to be 0.030 by tracing to its upper end the diagonal line which passes through the intersection of the horizontal line of 0.03 mm. and the vertical line of yellow (second order) color. This determination may be made somewhat more accurate by the use of Michel Lévy's comparator, shown in Figs. 137 and 138. This instrument consists of a small mirror, A, from which a ray of light is sent by reflection from B through the crossed nicol prisms, C and C', into the

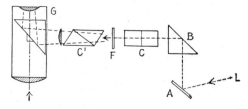

FIG. 138.—Diagram of a Michel Lévy comparator.

ocular, G, which is inserted in the microscope in the usual manner. Between the nicols the ray passes through a quartz wedge, F, which may be moved by the screw, E, any desired amount, which is read at the vernier, D. In the ocular the light meets another reflector which turns it upward to the eye. This reflector has a small aperture so situated that light from a thin section placed on the stage of the microscope between crossed nicols passes through it to the eye. Thus the interference color produced by a crystal or grain in a thin section may be compared directly with the color produced by a quartz wedge at a measured position.

Wright's [1] combination wedge is much simpler, but can be used only with a special ocular; it is used to compensate the retardation produced by any given mineral. Compensation produces a dark line across the wedge, and the position of this line, as read on a graduated scale on the surface of the wedge, gives the difference of phase produced by the mineral and compensated by the wedge in millionths of a millimeter. As may be seen in Fig. 139, the slow ray (Z) of the plate is the fast ray (X) of the wedge. When the wedge is correctly constructed, the retardation of the slow ray in the plate is exactly

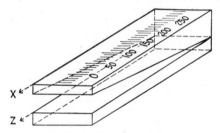

FIG. 139.—Wright graduated combination wedge.

compensated by the wedge at the thickness marked zero, and colors rise in both directions from this line. When this wedge is used to compensate the difference of phase produced by a crystal or grain on the stage of the microscope, the dark line of compensation moves along the scale to a position at which the scale gives directly the compensated phase difference. As before, the birefringence may be found from Fig. 131, or from Michel Lévy's chart by tracing to its upper end the diagonal line which passes through the intersection of the horizontal line expressing the thickness and the vertical line expressing the retardation.

Scale of birefringence.—For purposes of comparison and of classification it is useful to establish a scale of birefringence. The birefringence of a uniaxial mineral is measured by the difference between its indices, ω and ϵ. Either of these indices may be the greater index; it is convenient to have symbols for the greater index and the smaller index. The greater index is represented by N_g, and the smaller index by N_p, the subscripts referring to " great " and " petty " or small. When the light travels at right angles to the optic axes, so

[1] F. E. Wright: *Am. Jour. Sci.*, XXIX, 1910, p. 415. Also *Jour. Geology*, X, 1902, p. 33.

that the two rays have their maximum difference of velocity, the index of refraction for the slow ray is N_g and that for the fast ray is N_p.

A scale of birefringence may be drawn up as follows:

No.	Mineral	Birefringence		Interference Color in Sections 0.03 mm. Thick	
1	Leucite	Very weak	$N_g - N_p < 0.0035$	Dark grays	First order
2	Orthoclase	Weak	$N_g - N_p > 0.0035 < 0.0095$	Light gray to white	First order
3	Hypersthene	Moderate	$N_g - N_p > 0.0095 < 0.0185$	Yellow to red	
4	Augite	Rather strong	$N_g - N_p > 0.0185 < 0.0275$	Blue to green	Second order
5	Tourmaline	Strong	$N_g - N_p > 0.0275 < 0.0365$	Yellow to red	Second order
6	Muscovite	Very strong	$N_g - N_p > 0.0365 < 0.0545$	Blue to red	Third order
7	Titanite	Extreme	$N_g - N_p > 0.0545$	Gray to white	Higher orders

Relative velocities of transmitted rays.—Light passing through any uniaxial crystal not parallel with the optic axis is divided into two rays (if the crystal is not at extinction) which vibrate in planes at right angles to each other and travel with unequal velocities. The retardation of the slow (Z) ray as compared with the fast (X) ray determines the interference color produced between crossed nicols, as already explained. If the retardation of the slow ray be increased, the interference color " rises " in the color scale, that is, it changes in the direction of the higher orders of the scale. If the retardation be decreased, the interference color " falls," that is, it changes toward darkness, which is considered the bottom of the scale. If a plate, in which the direction of vibration of the slow ray is known, is superposed over a section so that the vibration planes coincide, the interference color rises, provided the plane of vibration of the slow ray in the section is parallel with the plane of vibration of the slow ray in the plate, so that the same ray which is retarded in the section is further retarded in the plate. The interference color falls, provided the plane of vibration of the slow ray in the section is parallel with that of the fast ray in the plate, so that the ray which is retarded in the section is advanced in the plate. Consequently, by properly superposing such a plate over any mineral section, the position of the plane of vibration of the slow ray can be distinguished from that of the fast ray. This may be accomplished by means of: First, the quarter undulation mica plate; second, the sensitive tint plate; or third, the quartz wedge. In all these plates the arrow marks the position of the plane of vibration of the slow ray. The mica plate consists of a thin cleavage film of colorless mica of such thickness as to produce a retardation of a quarter of a wave length of yellow (sodium) light, that is, about 150 mμ. It is usually mounted between glass plates and marked " mica " or $\frac{1}{4}$ λ. Except with crystals producing very low or very high interference colors the mica plate is very convenient. For crystals giving very low interference colors the sensitive plate is most useful, while for those exhibiting very high interference colors the quartz wedge must be used. These plates are sometimes mounted with their vibration planes parallel with one edge of the glass plate and sometimes with their vibration planes at 45° with the edges, but in all cases they must be used with their vibration planes not parallel with the planes of the nicols.

Elongation and flattening.—Many crystals are much longer in one direction than in any other direction, and such a direction of elongation is easily seen microscopically. Thus, apatite and rutile are commonly elongated in the direction of the vertical axis, and fibrous minerals are still more elongated. Nearly all uniaxial crystals, which exhibit elongation, have the vertical axis parallel to their long direction. Whenever a mineral under examination exhibits distinct crystal outline with one direction several times as long as any other, this direction may be used as a basis of reference, and the relation to it of the vibration directions of the fast and slow rays may be determined. Whenever the vibration direction of the slow ray (Z) is exactly parallel, or more nearly parallel, than that of the fast ray (X), to the direction of elongation, the elongation is said to be positive. If the fast ray is more nearly parallel to the elongation, the sign of elongation is said to be negative.

Another crystal habit which is very common in some minerals consists in an elongation in all directions parallel to a given face, or in a flattening parallel to that face. This is well illustrated by lamellar minerals, like tridymite and calomel. In uniaxial minerals, flattening is, in nearly all cases, parallel to the basal pinacoid. Sections of such minerals across the plane of flattening appear to be elongated in directions in that plane which are determined by the intersection of the plane of the section with that of the flattening. As in the preceding case, whenever the direction of vibration of the slow ray is more nearly parallel to the direction of apparent elongation (in the plane of flattening) the sign of elongation is said to be positive, and when X occupies this position the sign of elongation is said to be negative. Since the direction of apparent elongation is indefinite in this case (being any direction in a plane), the sign of elongation may be better described as positive when the fast ray vibrates more nearly at right angles to the plane of flattening than the slow ray, and as negative when the slow ray vibrates in this direction.

Extinction position.—If the crystal plate in Fig. 128 be supposed to be rotated about an axis perpendicular to the paper at O, a study of the figure shows that the component waves in the plane AA' have their maximum amplitude when the vibration planes (FF' and GG') of the crystal bisect the angles between the vibration planes (PP' and AA') of the nicols, and their minimum (zero) amplitude when the vibration planes of the mineral coincide with the vibration planes of the nicols. With zero amplitude of the waves vibrating in the plane of transmission of the analyzer, no light passes through, and darkness, or **extinction** of light, takes place.

It is evident that the rotation of the crystal plate, just described, may be conveniently accomplished by rotating the stage of the microscope carrying the plate. Four times in a complete rotation the vibration planes of the crystal coincide with the vibration planes of the nicols, and darkness, or extinction, results. The angle between successive positions of extinction is necessarily 90°, since the vibration planes of the crystal and those of the nicols are at right angles.

An approximate position at which a given crystal is at extinction may be recognized at once on rotation of the stage. But it is not always easy to determine the exact position of extinction, since the crystal often appears to be dark through a rotation of several degrees; that is, the eye is not sensitive to the difference between no amplitude and a very small amplitude of vibration or intensity of light. Several methods have been devised to permit more accurate determination of the position of extinction. The methods of special importance are described herewith.

1. **Parallel polarized light.**—The ordinary method of observing the position of maximum darkness without accessory apparatus is sufficiently accurate for many purposes.

For this method and all others, it is necessary that the microscope be in accurate adjustment in order to secure correct results. The nicols must be accurately crossed, and (except when convergent light is used) the light must be as nearly parallel as it is possible to make it. To test the angle between the vibration planes of the nicols, remove all the lenses, ocular, objective, and condenser, from the microscope, and point it directly at the sun, the rays from which are parallel and so intense that the light passing through the nicols on account of a rotation of less than 1' from the position of total extinction is readily visible. If either nicol has inclined end-surfaces complete extinction is impossible, because the inclined incidence causes a slight rotation of the plane of polarization. In such a case the test can be made more satisfactorily if the microscope has substage and upper diaphragms and they are closed. To obtain parallel light take the light from the open sky (or from a cloud) and remove the condenser.

With any method of determining the extinction position, the probable error of a single measurement may be reduced to any desired limit by sufficiently increasing the number of measurements and taking the average. It is also desirable to measure the position when rotating the stage clockwise, and again when rotating it counter-clockwise.

2. **Sensitive tint plate.**—A plate of gypsum (or other colorless mineral) cut to such a thickness as to produce a violet interference color (at the upper limit of the first order) between crossed nicols, is called a sensitive tint plate, because the eye is especially sensitive to slight changes of tint in this part of the color scale. It is usually mounted between narrow glass plates and marked " sensitive tint," " red 1st order," or " gypsum "; the arrow at one end indicates the direction of vibration of the slow ray in the plate. The plate should be used in most cases with the arrow in a position at 45° with the vibration planes of the nicols. It produces no effect when the arrow marking a plane of vibration in the plate is parallel with either nicol. It is inserted in a slot or other opening in the tube of the microscope, between the objective and the analyzer. When a crystal (or grain) not surrounded by other crystals occupies part of the field of the microscope, and is rotated exactly to the extinction position, it has no effect on the light, and the two nicols cause darkness. If the sensitive tint plate is interposed between the nicols, the whole field is colored in violet. If the stage is rotated slightly the crystal is no longer at extinction, and it changes the planes of vibration of the transmitted light, and causes a slight change in the color of that part of the field occupied by the crystal. Therefore, when there is no difference in color between that part of the field unoccupied and that part occupied by the crystal, the latter is at extinction.

3. **Bertrand ocular.**—It is necessary that part of the field of view be unoccupied, in order that the sensitive tint plate may be used

satisfactorily.   Furthermore, this plate is not well adapted to use with colored minerals, nor with those which produce interference colors above the first order.   The device of Bertrand is more complicated, but also more useful.   It consists of four plates of quartz cut parallel with the base, two cut from right-handed quartz alternating with two from left-handed quartz.   All the plates serve to produce circular polarization and to rotate the plane of polarization, the right-handed plates rotating the plane to the right (clockwise) and the others rotating it to the left.   They are shaped as quadrants and placed in a special ocular, in which their rectangular edges correspond to cross hairs.   This ocular must be used between crossed nicols; therefore, a nicol must be superposed above the ocular, and the ordinary analyzer removed.   When the nicols are exactly crossed the four quadrants are of the same pale greenish-blue color.   If a

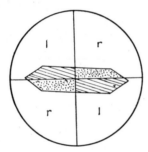

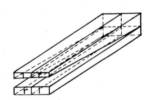

FIG. 140.—Bertrand ocular.   FIG. 141.—Wright biquartz wedge.

thin section or grain of an anisotropic crystal is put on the stage in the focus of the microscope, not at the extinction position, the quadrants are differently colored, opposite quadrants being of the same tint, as in Fig. 140.   When the stage is rotated, the quadrants become alike in color at the exact position of extinction.   The vibration planes of the mineral then coincide with the principal planes of the nicols.

4. **Wright's biquartz wedge.**—There are several other devices sometimes used to determine accurately the extinction position; the most important of these is the biquartz wedge plate of F. E. Wright;[*] in this instrument two plates of quartz cut normal to the axis and of proper thickness, one right-handed and the other left-handed, are combined with two wedges of quartz selected to rotate the plane of polarization in the reverse direction, as shown in Fig. 141.   The effect of

[1] *Am. Jour. Sci.*, XXVI, 1908, p. 377.

this combination is to produce zero rotation in each half wedge, where the plate and wedge have the same thickness. It is used at the focal plane of the ocular, which must be cut so as to permit its insertion; a nicol must be used above the ocular, as with the Bertrand plate. The biquartz wedge divides the field into two halves, which are equally illuminated if no crystal is in the path of the light, or if a crystal in the field on the stage is at extinction. If the crystal is turned even a very small angle from extinction, the intensity of illumination in the two parts of the field is rendered unequal.

Extinction angles.—The angles between extinction positions and various crystallographic directions are called angles of extinction, or extinction angles. It is only necessary to measure from one extinction position to any given crystallographic direction, since extinction positions are always 90° apart. Usually the angle measured is that between a cleavage, crystal boundary, or twinning plane and the nearest extinction position. But in some cases the extinction angle is measured from a crystal plane to the plane of vibration of the fast (or the slow) ray.

Optic sign of uniaxial minerals.—In uniaxial minerals the optic axis is parallel with the vertical crystallographic axis, c; the ordinary ray always vibrates at right angles to the optic axis; and the extraordinary ray vibrates in the principal section, which includes the incident ray and the vertical axis; when the light is traveling normal to the optic axis, the E ray vibrates parallel thereto. In certain minerals the ordinary ray travels faster than the extraordinary ray; such minerals are said to be positive or $+$; in this case the (O) ray vibrating normal to the principal section has greater velocity than the (E) ray vibrating in that plane. It is true for all substances that the greater the velocity the less the refraction and the smaller the index of refraction. Therefore, in positive crystals ω is less than ϵ, the index of E ray is N_g, and that of the O ray is N_p. In other minerals the extraordinary ray travels faster than the ordinary, and these minerals are said to be negative or $-$; in this case the ray vibrating in the principal section has greater velocity than the ray vibrating normal thereto; also, in negative crystals ω is greater than ϵ, the index of the E ray is N_p, and that of the O ray is N_g, while in positive crystals the index of the E ray is N_g, and that of the O ray is N_p.

There are various ways to determine whether a uniaxial mineral is positive or negative, that is, to determine its optic sign. One method is to make accurate measurements of ω and ϵ; but this cannot be done without special apparatus, and is not in common use.   Other methods involve the use of convergent light and will be described later.   Finally, there are methods by which the velocity of the ray vibrating parallel with the vertical axis is compared, in parallel polarized light, with the velocity of the ray vibrating normal thereto.   This can be done only in case the position of the vertical crystal axis can be recognized or determined in some way, usually by means of the crystal outline.   It is only necessary to find the vertical axis, and then determine, by means of superposing a plate, whether the ray vibrating parallel with this axis is the fast ray or the slow ray.   In the latter case the mineral is positive;   in the former case it is negative.

To determine the relative velocity of the ray vibrating parallel with the vertical axis, which is the E ray for the crystal, any one of the methods already described may be used.   If the crystal gives an interference color lower than white of the first order, the sensitive tint plate should be used;   if the color is higher, but below the fourth order, the mica plate is preferable, if the color is still higher, the quartz wedge is commonly employed.   The crystal should be turned 45° from extinction and the proper plate superposed with the arrow marking the plane of vibration of its slow ray also at 45° from the planes of the nicols.   If the interference color rises, the arrow gives the direction of vibration of the slow ray in the crystal;   if the color falls, the arrow is parallel with the direction of vibration of the fast ray in the crystal.   In Fig. 142 a uniaxial crystal whose vertical axis is parallel with the elongation is shown in two positions, producing a red interference color between crossed nicols.   If a mica plate is superposed the interference color rises to blue when the arrow of the plate is parallel with the vertical axis, and falls to yellow when the two are at right angles;   therefore, the crystal is positive.   In Fig. 142a a uniaxial crystal producing a dark gray interference color is shown in two positions.   When the gypsum sensitive tint plate is superposed, the color changes to blue in one position and red in the other, and it might be inferred that the color had risen (from gray) in both cases. But the red is lower than the sensitive tint (with which the new color may better be compared in using this plate) and is produced by the action of the plate in lowering the interference color of the crystal to darkness and then raising it to red.   In other words, the red color is produced by the addition of a plus and a minus quantity, while the blue color is produced by the addition of two plus quantities.   Since the color rises when the arrow is parallel with the vertical axis, the slow ray vibrates in that direction and the crystal is positive.

Occasionally the superposition of a plate causes changes in color such that it is not easy to decide whether the change is to a higher color or to a lower color; thus, the change when a mica plate is used may be from green of the second order to red, when the slow ray of the plate is parallel with the elongation, and also when they are at right angles. One of these red colors is red of the first order and the other

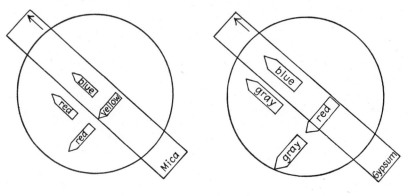

FIG. 142.   FIG. 142a.
FIGS. 142, 142a.—Uniaxial positive crystals with superposed plates.

is red of the second order, but it may be very difficult to determine which one belongs to either order. In some cases it is possible to solve the difficulty by compensating one of the red colors by using the quartz wedge. In some instances it is possible to determine the order of one of the red colors by observing a beveled edge. If any part of the mineral section, acting alone, produces an interference color other than green (because of varying thickness) a test of that part may give results which are easily understood. Again, a sensitive tint plate or a quartz wedge may be used in place of the mica plate and the results may be satisfactory. Finally, if the mineral section has a beveled edge, the direction of motion of the interference colors on that edge may be used to determine whether the main surface color is rising or falling. This is illustrated in Fig. 143, in which a long, smooth bevel is represented as producing colors from gray to red of the second order. Now, if a mica plate (or other plate) be superposed over this so that the main surface color falls, it is evident that the red surface color has been replaced by one of the colors formerly on the beveled edge. Therefore, when a given color, for example, white, moves up a beveled edge, the main surface color has fallen in the New-ton color scale; and when a given color moves down on a beveled edge, the main surface color has risen.

A convenient combination quartz wedge and sensitive tint plate has been devised by Johannsen.[1]   In it the quartz wedge is improved

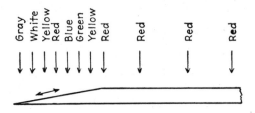

FIG. 143.—Movement of interference colors on a beveled edge.

by the addition of a mica plate adjusted so as to exactly compensate the thin edge of the quartz wedge, giving the effect of an infinitely thin edge.   A short space separates the wedge from a gypsum plate in the same carriage.   When not in use it is unnecessary to remove the carriage from the microscope; it is convenient to move it merely so that the light passes through the space between the gypsum plate and the wedge; it is shown in this position in Fig. 144, with the gypsum plate to the left and the quartz-mica wedge to the right.

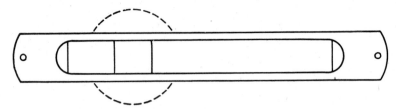

FIG. 144.—Johannsen quartz wedge—gypsum plate.

The Berek compensator (see Fig. 144*a*) is an improved device to measure retardation accurately; it is also convenient for the determi-nation of the position of the fast and slow rays, thus permitting the recognition of the optic sign.   The device consists of a plate of calcite, 0.1 mm. thick, cut normal to the optic axis, and mounted on an axis of rotation in the plane of the plate which is held in a metal frame for

[1] *Amer. Jour. Sci.*, XXIV, 1910, p. 436.

insertion in the tube of the microscope, like a sensitive tint plate or quartz wedge. The angular position of the calcite plate is measured

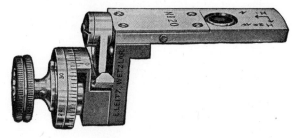

FIG. 144a.—Berek compensator.

on a drum attached to the axis of rotation. This position may be determined by the aid of a vernier reading to tenths, which may be

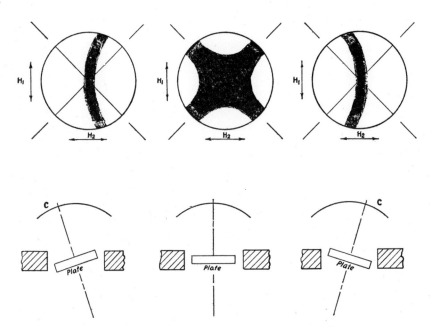

FIG. 144b.—The use of the Berek compensator. After Rogers and Kerr: Thin Section Mineralogy, 1933, p. 75.

calibrated in degrees. The compensator is used in a position at 45° with the vibration planes of the nicols. It is marked with two arrows:

H_1, parallel to the axis of rotation, is the vibration-direction of the slow ray; H_2, at right angles to this, is the trace of the optic axis of the calcite (when inclined), and therefore the vibration direction of the fast ray. The calcite plate is horizontal when the drum reading is about 30; inserted between crossed nicols in this position it produces a large dark cross; when this cross is centered the plate is horizontal, but this "zero point" (at about 30) is not used because compensation points can be read on the narrow line of compensation much more accurately, as illustrated in Fig. 144b.

Directions for use of the compensator are supplied with each instrument, and these include such tables as are needed. It is convenient

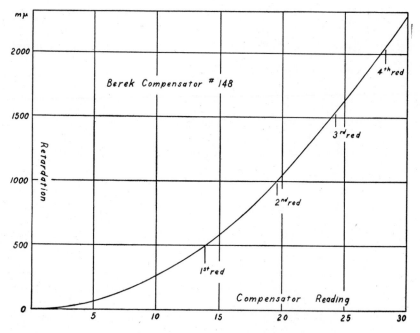

FIG. 144c.—The relation between compensator reading and retardation in Berek compensator No. 148. After R. C. Emmons.

to construct a curve such as shown in Fig. 144c to replace the tables; this must be done for each instrument since it depends upon the constant of the apparatus.

In the use of the Berek compensator the student must take two precautions not needed in using other accessories, such as the quartz wedge.   He must be careful to

1. Bring the crystal to be studied exactly to the center of the field.
2. Turn the crystal exactly 45° from extinction.

Of course the crystal must be turned from extinction in that direction which will permit compensation.   If compensation is not produced on rotation in one direction, it is only necessary to rotate the crystal the other way.   In the proper position, a rotation of the drum of the compensator either way lowers the interference color.   By observing the amount of rotation in both directions necessary to produce compensation two readings (a and b) are obtained.   One half of the difference between these readings is the amount of the rotation measured from the zero position.   Using this value, the curve gives directly the retardation in mμ.   From this value the birefringence is easily obtained by the use of the interference color chart, provided the thickness of the section is known or can be measured.   If the thin section contains quartz (or any mineral of known birefringence) the thickness of the section can be obtained by measuring accurately the retardation produced by this mineral of known birefringence.

DIRECTIONS FOR LABORATORY WORK

Newton's color scale.—Study the effect of the quartz wedge between crossed nicols on monochromatic light.   (By burning table salt in a Bunsen burner flame, an intense yellow light may be obtained.   Nearly monochromatic red or blue light may be obtained from ordinary light by filtering it through very deeply colored red or blue glass.)   Then study the effect of the wedge on white light.   Color the lower part of Fig. 131 as accurately as you can, making each color pass gradually into the next one.   Use the colors produced by the wedge in white light as a guide, and compare the result with Michel Lévy's table of birefringence.   Make a tracing of Fig. 132 and study the effect on each color when o of the tracing is over, 1, 2, 3, etc., of the drawing.

Factors determining interference colors.—The interference color depends (1) upon the birefringence of the mineral.   Prove this experimentally by examining thin sections of gabbro, and noticing the difference in the interference colors produced by plagioclase and those produced by augite, although the section is of uniform thickness, and both minerals are cut in all sorts of directions.   The plagioclase is colorless and has no distinct relief;   between crossed nicols it is usually striped because of twinning;   its interference colors are confined to the grays, unless the section has more than the standard thickness.   The augite is nearly colorless and has distinct cleavages and high relief;   its interference colors vary from gray or yellow to blue or green of the second order, if the section has the standard thickness. Prove that the interference color depends (2) upon the thickness of the section, by again examining the quartz wedge. Prove that it depends (3) upon the direction in which a section is cut, by examining the different crystals or anhedra (an anhedron is a single crystalline individual without crystal boundaries, which are essential to a crystal) of a single mineral in any thin section. For example, the various anhedra of augite in a section of gabbro exhibit different interference colors, although they are all sections of a single mineral and of uniform thickness.

Determine the order of the interference color of sections of olivine and muscovite, by means of the quartz wedge. Also determine the order of the interference color of the same or other sections giving high colors, by studying the color bands on beveled edges.

Estimation of thickness of thin sections.—Select a thin section of granite containing muscovite, and estimate its thickness by means of the highest interference colors given by anhedra of quartz. (Quartz is the colorless mineral, without relief, cleavages, or twinning, and usually very transparent.) Then measure the apparent thickness by means of focusing first on one surface and then on the other, and noting the exact amount of rotation of the fine adjustment screw necessary to make the change from one focus to the other. Calculate the real thickness from the apparent thickness and the index of the mineral through which the observation was made (use that index of the mineral which was used in observing the apparent thickness). The two methods of estimating the thickness should give approximately the same result, but identical results should not be expected, since neither method is extremely accurate.

Estimation of birefringence.—After careful study, select the anhedron of muscovite, in the granite just examined, which produces the highest interference color. Muscovite is a colorless mineral, with fine continuous, parallel cleavage lines and distinct relief. It commonly has a mottled appearance between crossed nicols. By means of the thickness of the section, as already determined, find the approximate birefringence of muscovite from Fig. 131 or from Michel Lévy's table of birefringences. Use the same section to estimate the birefringence of orthoclase. (Orthoclase is a colorless mineral whose two cleavages are usually only seen under favorable conditions, that is, with analyzer removed and condenser much lowered; it is often cloudy with alteration products, sometimes simply twinned, and has no relief.)

Scale of birefringence.—It is worth while not only to study the colors produced by the quartz wedge and those that are printed on Michel Lévy's table, but also to observe the colors produced by common minerals selected so as to form an ascending scale of birefringence. In order that the student may become familiar with each degree of this scale, the following minerals composing it should be examined microscopically between crossed nicols.

Leucite may be found in leucite phonolites; it is isometric and isotropic above 560° C., but at lower temperatures it is often very weakly birefringent.

Orthoclase is common in granite; it has no relief, is often simply twinned, frequently cloudy from alteration products, and has two cleavages, not always easily seen.

Hypersthene is found in some norites and andesites; it is weakly pleochroic in green and brown tints, and has distinct prismatic cleavages at an angle of about 93°; it has high relief.

Augite is common in gabbro and in basalt; it is nearly colorless and has distinct prismatic cleavages nearly at right angles; it has high relief, and large extinction angles.

Diopside is found especially in contact metamorphic rocks formed by the action of magmas on dolomite. It is colorless, and resembles augite very closely.

Muscovite is common in some kinds of granite; it is colorless and has distinct relief, extinction sensibly parallel to fine parallel cleavages, and a mottled appearance between crossed nicols.

Titanite is rather sparsely distributed, even when most abundant; it is found especially in syenites and diorites. It is grayish or reddish or nearly colorless, with very high relief, often in narrow doubly wedge-shaped forms. **Calcite,** seen well in marble, illustrates still stronger birefringence, and is very common.

Determination of relative velocities.—To determine the relative velocities of the two rays transmitted by any mineral section not at extinction, turn the section 45° from extinction, or simply turn it to the position of maximum illumination, since accurate orientation is unnecessary. Note the interference color produced and the order to which it belongs. Superpose a mica plate, sensitive tint plate, or quartz wedge, with its vibration planes bisecting the angles between the nicols and therefore parallel with the vibration planes of the mineral section. Note the interference color now produced, and determine the order to which it belongs. If the interference color has risen, the slow ray in the mineral has passed through the superposed plate as the slow ray, and its direction of vibration is shown by the arrow on the plate. Note that the mica plate makes a change of interference color amounting to about one and a half of the major divisions on the table of Michel Lévy, while the sensitive tint plate moves the interference color about five and a half of the major divisions, or just one order; the quartz wedge produces a change the amount of which depends upon the thickness of the part of the wedge in use at any given position. Use these plates in determining the relative velocities of transmitted rays in anhedra of quartz, of muscovite, and of augite.

Determination of sign of elongation.—The sign of elongation of uniaxial minerals is + in those minerals in which the slow ray is parallel with the axis of elongation and − in those in which the fast ray occupies this position. Since the elongation of uniaxial minerals is usually parallel with the vertical axis, the sign of elongation of such minerals is usually the same as the sign of the mineral. If the elongation is parallel with the basal pinacoid, the sign of elongation is the reverse of the sign of the mineral. Tourmaline is a mineral formed by the action of igneous vapors on silicates; it is found in some granites, pegmatites, and veins. It is a mineral showing strong absorption when the long axis is at right angles to the plane of vibration of the lower nicol. Find a section of tourmaline and determine its sign of elongation.

Determine the extinction position in quartz by each method for which you have the necessary equipment. To test the relative accuracy of the various methods, take the average of several readings of the position as determined by each. Try the methods in the following order: First: Simple contrast of dark and light between crossed nicols in parallel polarized light. Find the position of maximum darkness. Second: With the sensitive tint plate find the position at which the quartz is colored exactly like the color produced by the plate alone. Third: With the Bertrand ocular remove the upper nicol and replace it by a nicol placed above the ocular. See that this nicol is exactly crossed with the lower nicol so as to cut off all light when no crystal intervenes. When the Bertrand ocular is in position and the nicols are crossed, the quadrants are all colored alike in a pale greenish-blue tint. Find the position at which the quartz section does not modify the equality of color of these quadrants. Fourth: With Wright biquartz wedge plate use a superposed nicol, as with the Bertrand ocular. See that the nicols are crossed and find the position at which the intensity of illumination in the two parts of the wedge is equal.

Determine the extinction angle in muscovite and in augite. The extinction angle is the angle between the extinction position and some crystallographic direction, in this case, cleavage planes. Turn the section till the cleavage lines are parallel to one of the cross hairs. The angle from this position to the nearest extinction position is the extinction angle; take the average of several readings of this angle. In muscovite the angle is very near zero degrees; in augite it is large. Select crystals or anhedra of augite showing only one direction of cleavage. These are in the vertical zone. Why?

Determination of optic sign.—Those uniaxial minerals are positive in which the vertical (and optic) axis is the direction of vibration of the slow ray, and those are negative in which it is the direction of vibration of the fast ray. Thus, the sign of the mineral can be determined by the methods giving the relative velocities of transmitted rays whenever the direction of the vertical crystal axis can be determined in any way, as, for example, by a study of the crystal form or the cleavage. Use, first, sections of known orientation and determine the sign of quartz and apatite from vertical sections. Then determine the sign of tourmaline or apatite in rock sections.

CHAPTER XIV

UNIAXIAL MINERALS IN CONVERGENT POLARIZED LIGHT

Uniaxial crystal plates in convergent polarized light.—Every petrographic microscope is provided with a strong converging lens, which may be readily turned into or away from its position directly beneath the thin section. When this lens is not in use, the polarized light is nearly parallel, and its effects may be regarded as produced by parallel waves, the effect of the crystal being the same on one ray as upon each other ray. But when the converging lens or condenser is in use, the different rays of light travel in distinctly different directions and the crystal produces effects upon them which depend upon their direction, and its relation to the optic axis of the crystal. If a uniaxial mineral section is examined in the usual way between crossed nicols in parallel polarized light, and the condenser is then introduced, the first effect that is noticed is concentration of light, so as to illuminate the mineral more brightly; if a low power objective is in use, the condenser will also reduce the size of the field, because it cuts off the light from the outer portion of the field and concentrates it in the center. Also, if the section is turned to the extinction position, the extinction is not as complete as it is without the condenser, because all parts of the light are not extinguished. This is due to the fact that all parts are not parallel, and therefore are not vibrating in the same pair of planes as they pass through the crystal. A uniaxial mineral section parallel to the base is dark (or " at extinction ") in all positions of rotation between crossed nicols, if the light used is parallel and travels through the mineral parallel with the optic axis. But if a basal section of a uniaxial mineral (for example, calcite) is in the path of convergent light, it is dark in no position of rotation between crossed nicols, nor is there any position of maximum illumination; the amount of light passing through depends upon the birefringence of the mineral, and the power of the lenses above and below the section, and is the same in all positions of rotation.

When the microscope is used in the ordinary manner, only average or mean effects produced by convergent light can be observed, as described in the preceding paragraph.   A simple modification of the microscope makes it possible to see the exact effect of the crystal upon light of any given angle of inclination to the optic axis, provided such light is passing through the microscope.   As ordinarily adjusted, the microscope magnifies an image of the object on the stage.   The condenser and objective also produce an image (telescopic) of the source of light at a spot higher above the objective lens than the image of the mineral.   The lenses of the microscope are adjusted to magnify the image of the mineral and are therefore not in the proper position to magnify the telescopic image of the source of light.   But this image may be observed directly at a short distance above the objective by simply removing the ocular.   Or a magnified image of the telescopic image may be observed by inserting a properly adjusted lens (called a Bertrand lens) below the ocular.   Such telescopic images of the source of convergent light, which has passed through an aniso-tropic crystal between two nicols, are called interference figures.

Uniaxial optic axis interference figure.—A basal section of a uniaxial mineral produces the simplest and most important interference figure obtainable from that mineral.   There are two kinds of lines in interference figures; namely, those which are colored (when observed in white light) and have a form unchanged by rotation of the section, and those which are dark in white light between crossed nicols (or white between parallel nicols) changing in form on rotation of the nicols in all figures except those produced by basal sections of uniaxial crystals.   The first are called isochromatic curves, or simply, colored curves; the second are called isogyres, or, from their form, the dark cross of uniaxial optic axis figures, and the hyperbolas of biaxial interference figures.

The color curves are produced by interference, just as the color bands of the quartz wedge are produced.   Thus, in Fig. 145, the light passing through the basal section at O corresponds to light passing through an infinitely thin edge of a wedge where no difference of phase is produced.   The light passing through at O is parallel with the optic axis, and it is not doubly refracted nor polarized; there-fore, it is cut off in the upper nicol and darkness results at the center of the interference figure.   At a little distance from the center, the path of the light is slightly inclined to the optic axis; therefore, it is doubly refracted into two rays traveling at unequal velocities and polarized in two planes, the E ray vibrating in the principal section, and the O ray at right angles thereto. That is, at any point, as R or R', the E ray vibrates in the plane whose trace is formed by connecting R or R', with the center of the figure (which is the projection of the optic axis) and the O ray vibrates in a plane whose trace is at right

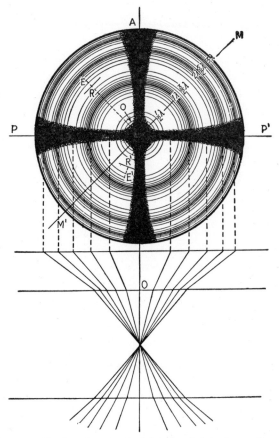

FIG. 145.—Explanation of uniaxial optic axis interference figure.

angles to the former plane. At a greater distance from the center, the light is more inclined to the optic axis, and, therefore, the two rays produced travel at more unequal rates and also travel a greater distance in passing through the section; therefore, a point is finally reached at which the difference of phase is half a wave length of any kind of monochromatic light. If such light is in use, the intensity along any radius (except the directions AA' and PP'), as OM, reaches a maximum where the difference of phase is $\frac{1}{2}\lambda$ (or an uneven multiple thereof), and decreases to darkness in passing from such a point to a spot where the difference of phase is one wave length (or a multiple thereof). If white light is in use, this series of concentric light and dark circles is replaced by concentric circles of color, which exactly reproduce, along a given radius, the whole or a part of the color scale of Newton; the point at the center always corresponds to the bottom of the scale; the successive colors may be wide and plain, or, with thick plates of minerals of strong birefringence, so narrow as to be indistinct; some bands may even be invisible.

The color curves are closer and closer together outward from the central axis, because the inclination of the rays and the length of path in the crystal increase with the distance from the center. The distance from the optic axis (at center) to the first (or any given) curve depends upon several factors, especially: (1) the birefringence of the mineral, (2) the thickness of the section, (3) the angle of aperture of the condenser and objective. It is, of course, increased if the image is magnified, as by the use of the ocular and Bertrand lens; it also increases with the mean index of refraction of the mineral.

The isogyres, or dark lines forming the black cross, are the locus of points at which the transmitted rays have zero amplitude of vibration. In more detail, at a point R, in Fig. 146, there emerges a ray of light whose vibration in the polarizer may be represented by Rb; upon entering the crystal this vibration is resolved into two components, Re and Ro, vibrating in the principal section and normal thereto. Assuming that the crystal produces a difference of phase, in this direction of transmission, of half a wave length, upon leaving the crystal, if the vibration of the O ray is at o, that of the E ray will be at e'. When the two vibrations, Ro and Re' enter the analyzer, each one will be divided into two parts; those components which vibrate in the plane of the polarizer will be totally reflected and absorbed; the other components will be two rays, the vibration of each of which is represented by Ra. By a similar construction, as at R', R'', and R''', it may readily be seen that the length of the line Ra, which measures the amplitude of vibration of the transmitted light, decreases regularly in both directions from the position $45°$ from either nicol, and becomes zero when the point R is on either line AA' or PP'. In Fig. 147 it is supposed that there is a difference of phase of one wave length at the point R; an inspection of the figure shows that the length of the line Ra, which measures the amplitude of vibration of a transmitted ray, decreases from a maximum at $45°$ from the nicol to zero parallel with either nicol. In the same way it can be shown that the amplitude (and intensity) of the transmitted light decreases to zero parallel with the nicols, no matter what may be the difference of phase produced by the crystal. Therefore, no light is transmitted at any point along the lines AA' and PP', and they are lines of darkness. By a similar construction it may be shown that they are lines of light when the nicols are parallel instead of crossed.

On rotation of the stage, an interference figure from a basal section of a uniaxial crystal exhibits no change whatever, since the optic axis suffers no change in position; furthermore, lateral movement of the section produces no change in the interference figure, so long as

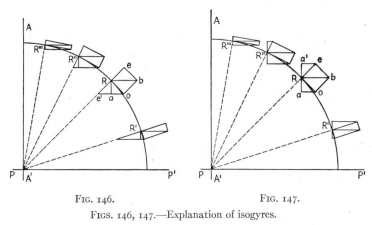

FIG. 146.   FIG. 147.

FIGS. 146, 147.—Explanation of isogyres.

the field of view is still occupied by the same crystal of constant thickness.

Uniaxial interference figures from vertical sections.—A vertical section of a uniaxial mineral produces an interference figure quite different from that given by a basal section. In such a figure the isogyres are visible only at and near the extinction position; in all other positions of rotation the figure consists of color curves only. The latter are not circular, but (nearly) hyperbolic, and arranged in four quadrants, as in Fig. 148. The number of curves which are distinguishable in white light is less than the number produced in monochromatic light (see Fig. 148), because in white light the separate curves are replaced by white of the higher order beyond the curves representing four to seven orders—the exact number seen depending upon the mineral, the perfection of the lenses, the quality of the eyes of the observer, etc. In many instances, only the central portion of

Fig. 148 (within the small circle) is visible, as in Fig. 149, because the section is thin, or the crystal has weak birefringence, or both. In such a case, the central color (for example, red) is the interference color seen when the crystal itself is observed between crossed nicols.

Two opposite quadrants have a lower interference color than the center of the field, and the other two quadrants have a higher color

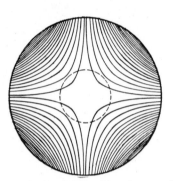

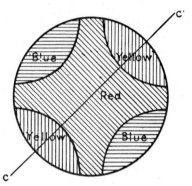

FIG. 148.—Interference figure from vertical section of calcite at 45° with nicols in monochromatic light.

FIG. 149.—Interference figure from vertical section of quartz at 45° with nicols in white light.

than the center. If the plate is thick, or the birefringence greater, so that the interference figure resembles Fig. 148, the same condition exists, though in that case it may be less easily observed. The optic axis always lies in those quadrants which have a lower interference color than the center.

The isogyres of this interference figure are broad and poorly defined; they move rapidly as the section is rotated; when the extinction posi-

FIG. 150.—Isogyres of a vertical section of quartz at extinction.

tion is reached they form a black cross occupying a large portion of the field of view, as in Fig. 150. When the section is rotated this black cross separates promptly into two hyperbolic curves which leave the field of view in opposite quadrants within a small angular rotation. As the next position of extinction is approached, the isogyres again enter the field as hyperbolic curves in the same pair of opposite quadrants, form a cross, and leave the field in the other pair of opposite quadrants. The isogyres move so rapidly that this interference figure is sometimes called the "flash figure." The optic axis always lies in those quadrants in which the isogyres enter, and in which they leave the field.

Uncentered uniaxial interference figures.—A uniaxial interference figure is centered when the center of symmetry of the figure is in the center of the field of view, like those hitherto described.   All sections of uniaxial minerals, which are not either exactly parallel or exactly normal to the optic axis, produce uncentered interference figures. Since such figures are therefore very common, it is important to understand them.   In Fig. 151 the optic axis is inclined forward in the N—S plane, so that its pole is near the south edge of the field.   After rotation of the crystal clockwise about 22°, the interference figure

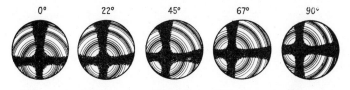

FIG. 151.   FIG. 152.   FIG. 153.   FIG. 154.   FIG. 155.

FIGS. 151–155.—Uncentered uniaxial interference figures, the optic axis near the center of the field.   Rotation clockwise.

appears as in Fig. 152; Figs. 153, 154 and 155 show the same interference figures after rotation in the same direction of about 45°, 67°, and 90°.   In Figs. 156 to 160 a similar series of drawings of an interference figure is given; in this case the section is inclined so much from the base that the optic axis is outside of the field of view.

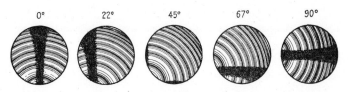

FIG. 156.   FIG. 157.   FIG. 158.   FIG. 159.   FIG. 160.

FIGS. 156–160.—Uncentered uniaxial interference figures, the optic axis outside the field. Rotation clockwise.

The isogyres are the most important part of any interference figure, because are always present, while the color curves are absent when the section is very thin and the birefringence weak.   The isogyres of the basal section do not change form or position on rotation; the isogyres of the vertical section rapidly change both form and position on rotation.   The isogyres of sections only a little inclined to the base rotate about the center of the field of view as a black cross, with very slight changes in form.   As the inclination of the section to the base increases, so also does the amount of change of form of the isogyres on rotation, and at an increasing rate.   In all cases in which the optic axis is in or near the edge of the field, the isogyres change form so little that they are commonly described as straight lines. No matter how great the inclination of the section may be, the isogyres are absolutely straight and parallel with the planes of the nicols when they pass through the center of the field.   On rotation in either direction they curve so that the convex side is toward this straight-line position.   Thus in Fig. 162 the isogyre is straight, passing through the center of the field.   Turning to the right (clockwise) the isogyre moves also to the right, the lower part moving a little faster than the

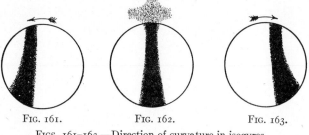

FIG. 161.   FIG. 162.   FIG. 163.
FIGS. 161–163.—Direction of curvature in isogyres.

upper part, and the whole showing a slight curvature downward to the right, so that the convex side is toward the position formerly occupied by the straight line, as in Fig. 163.   Turning to the left from the first position, the curvature (Fig. 161) is again such that the convex side is toward the straight-line position.   But if the optic axis (at the center of the black cross) had been below the field in Figs. 161 to 163 instead of above it, the isogyre would have moved to the left when the stage was rotated clockwise, and to the right when the stage was rotated to the left.

The approximate position of the optic axis may be inferred from a study of the isogyres in any section of a uniaxial mineral; the optic axis is always on the straight line made by an isogyre as it passes through the center of the field; the direction of motion of the isogyre on rotation of the stage reveals on which side of the stage the optic axis is, since the latter always moves around the center of the field at the rate and in the direction of rotation of the stage.   The approximate distance from the edge of the field to the optic axis may be inferred from the amount of curvature and from the rate of motion of the isogyre; the amount of curvature and the rate of motion both increase at an increasing rate as the distance increases.

In general, interference figures of uniaxial crystals (except flash figures), in which the optic axis is more than the radius of the field outside of the field, are not used, because they are not easily distinguished from certain biaxial interference figures. For the same reason, flash figures are unsatisfactory for some uses.

Interference figures from crystals producing rotary polarization.— A few uniaxial crystals of a low grade of symmetry produce rotary polarization. In general, the effects resulting are only visible from sections much thicker than those used for ordinary purposes, and therefore it is unnecessary to describe them at length. A thick basal section of a mineral causing rotary polarization rotates the plane of polarization of the light transmitted by the lower nicol through a small angle, the size of which varies with the mineral and with the thickness. The amount of rotation is also commonly quite different for different colors; for example, in quartz, extreme violet is rotated two and a half times as much as the red end of the spectrum. The direction of rotation depends upon the symmetry of the crystal, being to the right in right-handed quartz and to the left in left-handed quartz.

On account of this rotation of the plane of polarization, a thick basal plate of quartz in parallel monochromatic light between crossed nicols appears light. When one nicol is rotated through the proper angle, the section becomes dark. In parallel white light between crossed nicols, such a section gives an interference color, which changes gradually as one nicol is rotated so as to compensate, successively, the rotation produced by the crystal for various wave lengths. In convergent light an interference figure is produced the center of which (inside the first color curve) is occupied uniformly by an interference color produced by rotary polarization. Inside the first color curve the isogyres are absent; outside this curve the interference figure is approximately normal.

Uses of uniaxial interference figures.—Uniaxial interference figures are useful for three chief purposes, namely:

1. They serve to determine the crystal system of any mineral producing them as either tetragonal or hexagonal. They distinguish, thus, between basal sections of uniaxial crystals (which are dark in all positions between crossed nicols) and sections of isoaxial crystals

which give no interference figures. They also distinguish uniaxial from biaxial crystals; to make this distinction with certainty the section must, in most cases, show the optic axis within the field of view. The difference between uniaxial and biaxial figures will be described later.

2. They serve to determine, more or less accurately, the location of the optic and vertical axis, and thus to orient the section and the crystal. Under favorable conditions this may lead to the measurement of crystal angles and the establishment of crystal habit, and of axial ratios. It more frequently leads to recognition of crystal faces and cleavages, and distinctions between tetragonal and hexagonal crystals.

3. They serve to determine the optic sign (or character) of the crystal. This is one of the most important uses of interference figures. The optic sign of a mineral can be determined in parallel polarized light without the use of interference figures only in case:

(a) The mineral is known to be uniaxial, and
(b) The direction of the vertical axis can be determined from the crystal form.

These two conditions are only rarely satisfied; therefore, the optic sign is nearly always determined from interference figures. The methods are described below.

Uniaxial interference figures are, in rare cases, useful for still other purposes. For example, if the thickness of the plate and the power of the lenses are known, the birefringence of the mineral may be estimated from the distance between the optic axis and the first color curve, or from the number of color curves within the field of view.

Determination of sign from basal sections.—The light which produces an interference figure may be considered as made up of a cone of rays; any point of the figure represents an E ray and an O ray, the former vibrating in the principal section and the latter at right angles thereto. Since each plane including the optic axis is the principal section for the light rays in that plane, all radii of the interference figure are vibration directions for the E rays. The tangents perpendicular to the radii are the vibration directions for the O rays, as in Fig. 164. In any mineral the E ray is either the slow ray or the fast ray, whatever be its direction of vibration. Therefore, the slow ray in a crystal, which is producing an interference figure, is vibrating in directions which average N.W.—S.E. in two quadrants, while it is vibrating in

directions which average N.E.—S.W. in the other two.   If the slow
ray is the E ray, it is vibrating in directions N.W.—S.E. in quadrants 2 and 4 and in directions at right angles thereto in quadrants
1 and 3.   Let any one of the accessory plates (mica plate, sensitive
tint plate, or wedge) be superposed
over such an interference figure.
In such a plate, light vibrating in a
given direction, say N.W.—S.E.,
passes through either as the slow
ray or the fast ray, quite independent of its position in one quadrant or another of the field—therefore, the slow ray of the basal section passes through the accessory
plate as the slow ray in two quadrants, and as the fast ray in the other
two.   The retardation is increased
and the interference color rises at

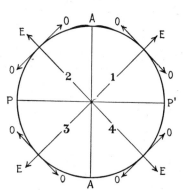

FIG. 164.—Vibration directions in a
uniaxial figure.

all points in the first pair of quadrants; the retardation is partly (or
wholly) compensated and the interference color falls at all points in
the second pair.   For example, Fig. 165 is a view of the interference
figure from a thick basal plate of apatite.   Upon superposing a mica
plate, as in Fig. 166, the dark cross is replaced by a grayish-white
cross and the color curves are displaced outward in the N.W. and S.E.

FIG. 165.   FIG. 166.
FIGS. 165, 166.—Determination of sign of a negative mineral.

quadrants and inward in the N.E. and S.W. quadrants; furthermore,
two dark spots appear at the two places where the retardation produced by the mineral section is just compensated by the action of the
mica plate.   In Fig. 166 the mineral is negative; with a positive mineral the two dark spots appear in the other two quadrants.

It is very easy to remember how to interpret the effect of the mica plate when it is noticed that a line joining the two dark spots makes a plus sign with the arrow of the plate when the mineral is positive, and a minus sign when it is negative. In case a sensitive tint plate is used, the dark cross is changed to a cross of violet, and the color between the arms and close to the cross falls from the sensitive tint to yellow

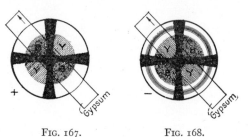

FIG. 167.   FIG. 168.

FIGS. 167, 168.—Determination of sign with sensitive tint plate.

in two quadrants, and rises to blue in the other two. It should be noticed that the yellow quadrants correspond to the dark spots produced by the mica plate, and may be used in the same way to deduce the sign of the mineral, as in Figs. 167 and 168. Finally, if the quartz wedge is used (see Figs. 169, 170), the color curves move toward the center in two quadrants, and away from it in the other two, as the

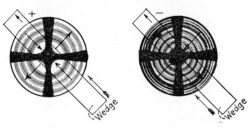

FIG. 169.   FIG. 170.

FIGS. 169, 170.—Determination of sign with quartz wedge.

wedge is gradually inserted, thin edge forward. Those quadrants in which the color curves move away from the optic axis correspond to the quadrants in which the dark spots appear when the mica plate is used, and may be used in the same way to obtain the sign of the mineral.

Determination of sign from vertical sections.—Uniaxial interference figures from basal sections are much more useful than those obtained from vertical sections, because the latter are not distinguishable from certain biaxial interference figures. They may, nevertheless, be used to determine the sign, and the determination is correct, not only for a uniaxial mineral, but also for any biaxial crystal which gives a flash figure. The sign may be determined from a flash figure either by finding the position of the optic axis and testing in parallel polarized light the relative velocities of the transmitted rays, or more directly, by the use of the quartz wedge, provided it is thick enough to produce compensation.

The position of the optic axis may be learned from the flash figure either by observing in which quadrants the hyperbolas enter and in which they leave the field, or by studying the distribution of the color curves. The optic axis is always in those quadrants in which the hyperbolas enter and leave the field, and it is in those quadrants occupied by the lowest interference colors of the flash figure.

When the position of the optic axis has been determined the ocular is replaced, the condenser removed, and the mineral observed in parallel polarized light. The relative velocities of the transmitted rays are then tested by the methods previously described. If the ray vibrating parallel with the optic axis is the slow ray, the mineral is positive; if it is the fast ray, the crystal is negative.

To determine the sign by means of the quartz wedge, the section is turned 45° from the position of the momentary black cross, so that the optic axis bisects the angle between the planes of the nicols. The quartz wedge is then inserted, thin edge forward. If the color of the center of the interference figure rises, turn the stage or the plate 90° and insert again. When the wedge is thick enough and properly oriented, a color of the interference figure is compensated, the compensation causing a dark hyperbola in the interference figure. If this dark curve appears when the optic axis of the mineral is normal to the slow ray of the wedge, the mineral is positive. If it appears when the two are parallel, the mineral is negative.

Determination of sign from other sections.—If the section is inclined to the base less than 20° (or even 25° with objectives of large angular aperture) the optic axis is within the field of view, and the methods described for basal sections may be employed to determine the sign. If the section is inclined more than 25° to the base, but the optic axis is still not more than the radius of the field outside thereof, the same methods can still be used, since the approximate position of the optic axis can be fixed, and the effect of an accessory plate observed upon that quadrant of the interference figure which is within the field of view. For example, with or without the use of the color curve, the crystal may be turned until the optic axis is S.E. of the field and at 45° with the nicols, as in Fig. 171; then, when a mica plate is superposed, a dark spot appears in the field of view, if the crystal is negative. The dark spot may be anywhere in field, depending upon the inclination and rotation of the section, the birefringence of the mineral, etc. With a sensitive tint plate a yellow area appears if the mineral is negative. As a confirmation of the test the optic axis may be rotated to a position S.W. of the field, as in Fig. 172; when a mica plate is superposed, the interference colors rise at all points in the field of view and no dark spot appears, if the mineral is negative.

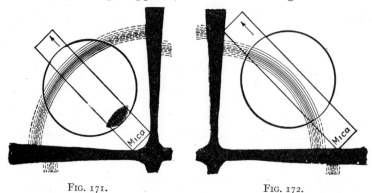

FIG. 171.　　　　　FIG. 172.

FIGS. 171, 172.—Determination of sign, the optic axis being outside the field of view

If the section is inclined much more than 30° to the base and does not give the flash figure, it is impossible to determine the sign unless it is known that the mineral is uniaxial. If one is dealing with uniaxial crystals only, any section whatever suffices to determine the sign. It is only necessary to turn the section until an isogyre passes through the center of the field; the dark line then marks the trace of the optic axis. Turn the stage 45°, noting into what quadrants the optic axis is rotated. Change to parallel polarized light, and superpose a plate; if the color rises when the slow ray of the plate is parallel with the optic axis, the mineral is positive; if the color falls, the crystal is negative.

DIRECTIONS FOR LABORATORY WORK

Uniaxial optic axis interference figures.—Any section of any anisotropic crystal gives some kind of an interference figure, but only basal sections of uniaxial minerals give centered uniaxial optic axis figures. To see the interference figure it is necessary to focus on the section between crossed nicols, introduce the condenser so as to have convergent light, and remove the ocular or insert the Bertrand lens. For minerals of weak birefringence it is necessary to use a high-power objective; for other minerals such an objective is not indispensable, but gives the best results.   Study the interference figure produced by basal sections of known uniaxial minerals.   The Bertrand lens is used to magnify the interference figure.   In many microscopes it is in the tube above the analyzer and in focus when inserted.   In French microscopes it is inserted at the base of the tube below the analyzer and focused by means of the upper screw.   Usually the interference figure is more distinct without the Bertrand lens.

Note that the isogyres are always present, while the color curves may be present or absent; the former are therefore the most important part of the figure.   In basal sections the isogyres are parallel to the vibration planes of the nicols; in other sections they are parallel to the same planes in any position in which one of them passes through the center of the field.

Notice that the distance from the center of the black cross to the first colored ring depends upon: [1] (1) the birefringence of the mineral, (2) the thickness of the section, and (3) the angular aperture of the objective and condenser.   To observe the influence of the birefringence, examine the interference figure of quartz (weak birefringence), of tourmaline (strong birefringence), and of calcite (extreme birefringence).   Use oriented basal sections which are about equal in thickness.   To see the effect of the thickness of the section, examine the figure of a thin basal section of quartz and of a thick plate of quartz. Use oriented sections and plates.   To observe the effect of the objective, examine any interference figure having colored rings, and notice the effect of changing the objectives.

Make drawings of the axial interference figure from thin and thick sections of quartz and calcite.   Compare the colors of the colored rings with those in Fig. 131 and Michel Lévy's table of birefringence.

Uniaxial interference figures from vertical sections.—Study the interference figure produced by a vertical section of quartz and at least one other uniaxial mineral, such as apatite, tourmaline, or calcite.   Notice the distribution of color and find the position of the optic axis from it; the optic axis is always in those quadrants in which the lowest colors are found.   If the stage is turned slowly, the isogyres are usually too indistinct to be understood.   By turning the stage rapidly, determine in which quadrants the isogyres leave the field at a given position, and thus determine the position of the optic axis.

Determination of optic sign.—Axial interference figures furnish a ready means to determine the optic sign.   Determine the sign of quartz and of calcite by means of the mica plate and by means of the sensitive tint plate.   Make drawings of axial interference figures after the plates have been superposed, and mark in your drawings the direction of vibration of the slow ray in the plate.   With the quartz wedge, those quadrants in which the colors move away from the center can be used, like the dark spots, to make a plus or minus sign with the axis of the wedge, but the preceding methods are usually more satisfactory

Learn how to find axial interference figures in a rock section.   Use sections of granite. An anhedron (which means a single crystalline individual having no crystal faces and therefore not properly called a crystal) which gives such a figure is cut so as to be normal to the optic axis, and is therefore dark between crossed nicols in all positions of rotation. This character should be used in hunting for anhedra of the desired orientation.   Absolute darkness in all positions is never obtained, because it requires a section exactly normal to the optic axis, perfect nicols, no condenser, a flat mirror, and exactly parallel light.

Study the appearance of uncentered optic axis interference figures.   Such figures are obtained from anhedra which are nearly dark in all positions of rotation.   The center of the

---

[1] It depends also, of course, upon the amount of magnification as, for example, by means of a Bertrand lens.   Finally, it varies somewhat with the mean index of refraction of the mineral.

interference figure, from a section which makes an angle of about 75° with the optic axis, is inside the field of view, but near the edge; it rotates in the same direction and with the same speed as the stage, while the isogyres move, but always remain nearly straight and parallel with the vibration planes of the nicols. Determine the sign from such an interference figure.

In sections inclined about 60° to the optic axis, the center of the black cross is outside the field, but not far away; and its position can be determined by studying the movements of the black lines which cross the field. Determine the sign from such an interference figure. Notice that the black lines in such a figure do not remain exactly straight in all positions, but are very nearly so. When a bar crosses the center of the field it marks the trace of the optic axis. Make drawings showing different positions of the axial figure during rotation, and indicate what part of it is in the field of view. Illustrate by a drawing the effect of a mica plate upon such a figure.

In sections considerably inclined to the optic axis the axial interference figure is some distance outside the field. Note that the black lines do not remain exactly straight on rotation, but that they are straight when they cross the center of the field. In this position, which is the position of extinction in parallel light, the black line marks the trace of the optic axis. This fact may be used to determine the sign by the methods with parallel light already described. Make such a determination.

In sections which are parallel to the optic axis, the black lines are much curved. They come in from two opposite quadrants as approaching hyperbolas, form an indistinct momentary black cross at the center, and then go out as separating hyperbolas in the other two quadrants. Prove that the hyperbolas are always in the quadrants containing the trace of the optic axis, by study of oriented sections; and use this fact to determine the sign by the methods with parallel light already described.

In rock sections, anhedra which are cut parallel to the optic axis can be recognized in two ways: (1) they have the highest interference color produced by the given mineral; (2) they give the interference figure already described (the flash figure). Find such anhedra. The sign should be determined by finding the position of the optic axis and testing in parallel polarized light the relative velocities of the transmitted rays, and also by the use of the quartz wedge. Why does the dark curve of compensation appear when the optic axis of a positive mineral is normal to the slow ray of the wedge? Make a drawing illustrating the effect of the wedge in this case.

CHAPTER XV

UNIAXIAL MINERALS

A. Directions for Study

It is advisable to study the microscopic characters of minerals in the order in which they have been considered here. The characters of uniaxial minerals will then be studied as follows:

I. In ordinary light (that is, without either nicol).

1. Determine the crystal system. This is possible only in case crystal outlines or two or more cleavages are present. Remember that elongation is nearly always vertical. Cross sections of elongated crystals are especially useful.
2. Study twinning. This is frequently done to better advantage between crossed nicols.
3. Study inclusions.
4. Study alterations.
5. Study the cleavage, determining the number of directions and the angles between cleavages.
6. Observe the color.
7. Estimate the index of refraction from the relief.
8. Study textural relations to adjacent minerals. This is frequently done to better advantage between crossed nicols.

   Note: All these characters can be studied equally well in parallel polarized light, using the lower nicol, and it is therefore rarely removed. The color of a pleochroic or absorptive mineral varies on rotation in parallel polarized light, but the color observed midway between the positions of greatest variation in absorption or pleochroism may be taken as nearly the same as the uniform color that would be seen in ordinary light.

II. In parallel polarized light with lower nicol.

9. Determine absorption formula.
10. Determine pleochroism formula.

III. In parallel polarized light between crossed nicols.

11. Determine the extinction angle. In uniaxial minerals this angle is always 0° (that is, extinction is parallel) when measured on prismatic or basal faces or cleavages. But it is not 0° when measured on other cleavages, for example, rhombohedral cleavages, as in calcite.
12. Determine the highest interference color, which will be shown by sections cut parallel with the optic axis. Since other sections of the same mineral

will show all lower interference colors, the highest color is the only one which is significant.

13. Determine the birefringence from the highest interference color, assuming that the section is 0.03 mm. thick, by the use of Fig. 131 or Michel Lévy's table of birefringence. Later this can be determined without any assumption by determining the thickness of the section by means of the same figure or table and some known mineral.

14. Determine the optic sign. If crystal outline or cleavages serve to locate the vertical axis, the sign can be determined in parallel light. Usually this is not possible.

15. Determine the sign of elongation.

IV. In convergent polarized light between crossed nicols.

16. Determine the optic sign. This is always possible if crystals or anhedra are large enough to give interference figures. The colored rings of the interference figure also afford a means of estimating the birefringence.

After the mineral has been identified by means of all its characters, the associated minerals should be noted, as well as the petrologic mode of occurrence. Other characters, such as chemical composition, specific gravity, behavior with reagents, etc., may be obtained from descriptive text-books.

B. Tetragonal Minerals

Tetragonal and hexagonal minerals present the same general characters between crossed nicols, and the minerals of one system are not readily distinguished from those of the other, except by the cleavages or crystal outlines, which, in cross section in tetragonal minerals, show four- or eight-sided figures, and in hexagonal minerals, three-, six-, or twelve-sided figures.

None of the tetragonal minerals is of prime importance in the composition of rocks, except scapolite and melilite in certain extremely rare rocks. Rutile and zircon are common accessory constituents in many rocks. Cassiterite is an important ore mineral.

The following descriptions of minerals merely mention some of the more important characters as a guide in preliminary study; they should be supplemented by the study of the descriptions in descriptive text-books.

Scapolite group.—Aluminum silicates of Ca or Na with Cl. Rectangular prismatic cleavage distinct. Negative with negative elongation. Usually colorless. Refringence low (1.55 to 1.59); birefringence varies from 0.010 to 0.037, increasing with increase of Ca.

Rutile, TiO_2.—Usually in capillary or acicular crystals. Yellowish brown to deep red, or even opaque. Geniculated twinning frequent and rather characteristic. Positive. Refringence very high. (2.71); birefringence extreme (0.287).

C. Hexagonal Minerals

Besides the minerals to be studied in detail, the following may be mentioned as important; graphite, corundum, tridymite, cancrinite, dolomite, magnesite, siderite, rhodochrosite, and smithsonite.

Quartz, SiO_2.—In crystals and irregular grains. No cleavage. Uusually colorless. Many small inclusions, frequently bubbles, etc. Frequently shows undulatory extinction. Refringence low (1.547); birefringence weak (0.009), Positive.

Calcite, $CaCO_3$.—In crystals and irregular grains. Rhombohedral cleavage pronounced. Polysynthetic twinning common. Usually colorless. Mean refringence moderate (1.601); birefringence extreme (0.172). Negative.

Apatite, $Ca_4(CaF)(PO_4)_3$.—Usually in hexagonal prisms, elongated vertically. Usually colorless. Refringence moderate (1.637); birefringence very weak to weak (0.002–0.005). Negative.

Nephelite, $NaAlSiO_4$ (with K and excess SiO_2).—In short hexagonal prisms and in irregular grains. Colorless. Cleavage, $10\overline{1}0$ and 0001, not well marked. Refringence low (1.540); birefringence weak (0.005). Negative.

Tourmaline.—An aluminous silicate of boron, with Li, Mg, or Fe. Usually in prisms. From almost colorless to blue, red, or green. Transparent to nearly opaque. No cleavage, but irregular cross fracturing about normal to c. Refringence moderate (1.635); birefringence strong (0.03±). Negative. Absorption very marked: $O > F$.

Hematite, Fe_2O_3.—Usually not in crystals. Rarely in very thin scales, sometimes transparent and red to yellow in transmitted light. Usually opaque. Red in reflected light.

Ilmenite, $FeTiO_3$.—Usually not in crystals. Opaque iron black with tinge of brownish in reflected light. Difficult to distinguish from magnetite except by the alteration products.

CHAPTER XVI

OPTICAL PROPERTIES OF BIAXIAL MINERALS

As previously stated, isometric crystals are isoaxial; tetragonal and hexagonal crystals are uniaxial, and all other crystals (orthorhombic, monoclinic, and triclinic) are biaxial; in these there are two directions parallel to which all the light travels with the same velocity.

Experimental double refraction in biaxial crystals.—The optic axis of a uniaxial mineral is parallel with the vertical axis, and all light of normal incidence passes through a basal plate with the same velocity and without polarization or refraction. In general, in biaxial crystals, neither optic axis is parallel with the vertical axis, and light of normal incidence on a basal plate is divided into two parts or rays traveling at unequal velocities and completely polarized in planes at right angles to each other. If the crystal is orthorhombic, like sulphur, neither ray is refracted at the surface of a basal section; but both are " ordinary " rays in the sense of obeying the ordinary law of refraction. If such a section be placed over a small particle, two images of the particle are produced at unequal distances, directly above the object. In order to see these images separately it is necessary to use polarized light. A section of sulphur parallel to either the macro- or brachypinacoid produces exactly the same effects. All pinacoidal sections of an orthorhombic crystal act on light of normal incidence in the same way as vertical sections of uniaxial minerals; that is, two rays are produced which obey the ordinary law of refraction at the surfaces, but travel at unequal rates and vibrate in planes at right angles to each other, as in Fig. 173.

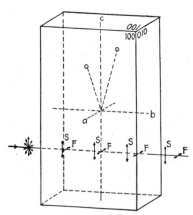

FIG. 173.—Effects of sulphur on light striking any pinacoid at right angles.

The velocity of light in a given substance is inversely proportional to its indices of refraction; by measuring the indices of refraction of sulphur for each pinacoidal plate, the following results may be obtained:

INDICES OF REFRACTION OF SULPHUR

From Plate Parallel to	For Ray Vibrating Parallel to the Crystal Axis		
	a	b	c
Basal pinacoid..............	1.95	2.04	....
Macropinacoid..............	....	2.04	2.24
Brachypinacoid.............	1.95	....	2.24

It is evident from this table, not only that the indices are different for two rays of light traveling in the same direction, but vibrating in different directions, but also that the indices are the same for rays traveling in different directions, but vibrating in the same direction. The direction of vibration, and not the direction of transmission, determines the index of refraction.

If the indices of refraction are then measured in several plates, all of which are parallel to the vertical axis, c, but make various angles with a and b, it is found that in each plate the mineral has the index, 2.24, for light vibrating parallel to c, and an index varying between 1.95 and 2.04 for light vibrating at right angles to c and at varying angles to a and b; indeed the index of the crystal varies gradually from 1.95 to 2.04, as the angle between the plate and the axis a, and the consequent angle between the direction of vibration of this ray and the axis a varies from 0° to 90°. The two paths and the unequal velocity of light incident normally on a vertical surface of sulphur are illustrated in Figs. 174 and 175, in which the plane of incidence is at right angles to the vertical axis. The construction of these figures is similar to that of similar figures for uniaxial crystals. (Figs. 109–122.)

Light incident normally on any surface of sulphur, the surface being parallel to one and only one crystal axis, and not normal to an optic axis, is divided into two rays polarized at right angles and traveling at unequal velocities, one of which is refracted, like an " extraordinary " ray and the other not refracted, like an " ordinary " ray.

In all biaxial crystals, the direction of vibration of the fast ray, having the smallest index, is designated as the axis X, that of the slow ray, having the largest index, as the axis Z, and that of the ray of intermediate velocity and intermediate index as the axis Y. In general, the ray vibrating parallel to Y has an index which is not half way between the indices of the rays vibrating parallel to X and Z, but may be nearer to either. The axes, X, Y, and Z, are at right angles to each other in all biaxial crystals.

The relative velocities of the two rays traveling in all directions at right angles to c in sulphur are represented in Fig. 176, in which

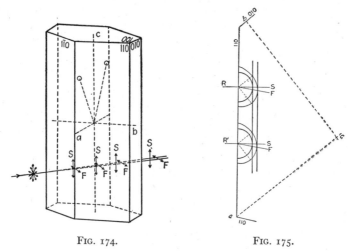

FIG. 174.   FIG. 175.

FIGS. 174, 175.—Effects of sulphur on light incident at right angles on a prism.

the light is supposed to originate at the center, and move outward in all directions in the plane of the paper. It is thus traveling at right angles to the vertical axis, which is assumed to be normal to the paper at the center of the figure. Of the two rays traveling parallel to a, the slow ray, vibrating parallel to Z (which is parallel to c in sulphur) reaches the point S at the same time that the intermediate ray, vibrating parallel to Y (which is parallel to b in sulphur), reaches the point I; at the same time, also, the fast ray traveling parallel to b and vibrating parallel to X (which is parallel to a in sulphur) arrives at the point F. The wave-surface of the slow ray is a circle of radius inversely proportional to 2.24, since for all directions of propagation the vibration direction is the same; the wave-surface of the other ray is an ellipse whose axes are inversely proportional to the indices, 2.04 and 1.95.

Measures of the indices of refraction of sulphur in plates parallel to a and making various angles with b and c establish the facts that the crystal has the index, 1.95, for light vibrating parallel to a in each plate, and an index varying gradually from 2.04 to 2.24 for light vibrating at right angles to a, and at gradually decreasing angles with c. The wave-surfaces of the two rays propagated in all directions at right angles to the axis a in sulphur are represented in Fig. 177, in which the wave-surface of the fast ray is a circle of radius inversely proportional to 1.95 wholly outside of the wave-surface of the other ray which is an ellipse whose axes are inversely proportional to the indices, 2.24 and 2.04.

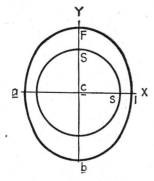

FIG. 176.—Wave-surfaces normal to vertical axis in sulphur, differences of velocities being exaggerated.

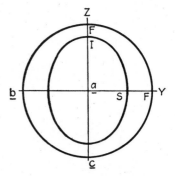

FIG. 177.—Wave-surfaces normal to axis a, in sulphur, differences of velocities being exaggerated.

Measures of the indices of refraction of sulphur in plates parallel to b and making increasing angles with a show that the mineral has a constant index, namely 2.04, for light vibrating parallel to b, and an index varying gradually from 1.95 to 2.24 as the plate (and, therefore, the directions of vibration of the ray vibrating at right angles to b) makes increasing angles with the a axis. Consequently, there is a direction in this zone in which the varying index is exactly equal to the constant index, 2.04, and all the light accordingly travels with the same velocity. The wave-surfaces of the two rays propagated in all directions normal to the axis b in sulphur are represented in Fig. 178, in which the wave-surfaces of the intermediate ray vibrating parallel to Y (that is, b in sulphur) is a circle of radius inversely proportional to 2.04, which is cut at four points by the wave-surface of the ray vibrating at right angles to the Y-axis.

A perspective drawing of the wave-surfaces in sulphur is given in

Fig. 179; in most biaxial crystals the relative velocities of the rays along the axes X, Y, and Z are much less unequal than shown in the figure, and the points, S and S', may be nearer to Z or nearer to X; but the general form of the wave-surfaces is the same in all. The relation in position between the axes X, Y, Z, and the crystal axes, a, b, c, is not fixed, and, in general, it is not the same as that shown in Fig. 179. It will be described later.

Measurements of the indices of refraction of sulphur, in any plate not parallel to a crystal axis, yield two values, both of which are greater than 1.95 and less than 2.24, one being greater and the other less than **2.04.** The exact values vary gradually with the angles between the

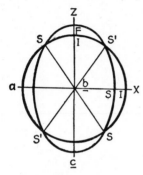

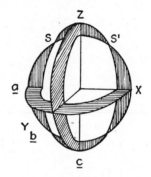

FIG. 178.—Wave-surfaces normal to axis b, in sulphur, differences of velocities being exaggerated.

FIG. 179.—Wave-surfaces in axial planes in sulphur, differences of velocities being exaggerated.

direction of vibration and the axes X, Y, and Z. Thus, the complete wave-surfaces are continuous surfaces intersecting in only four points; three rectangular sections of the surfaces are shown in perspective in Fig. 179.

All plates of any orthorhombic mineral not parallel to any crystal axis (nor normal to either optic axis), and all plates of any biaxial mineral not parallel to any one of the axes X, Y, Z (nor normal to either optic axis), divide light incident at any angle (including that incident at 0°) into two rays, both of which are refracted at the surface in directions which do not lie in the plane of incidence. The two rays are polarized at right angles and travel at unequal rates. Since they do not lie in the plane of incidence, it is impossible to construct their paths by means of plane figures; a diagram on three coordinates must be used. It is unnecessary, for practical purposes, to determine the precise paths of the refracted rays, and the subject need not be pursued further. But it is worth while to emphasize the fact that, in the general case, both rays are refracted (out of the plane of incidence), even though the light is incident at right angles; therefore, in general, in biaxial minerals both rays are " extraordinary " in the sense of not obeying the ordinary law of refraction.

Triaxial ellipsoid.—In general, in biaxial crystals, for any direction of propagation there are two velocities; for any direction of vibration there is only one velocity and one index of refraction. As with uniaxial crystals, all the velocities and all the indices of refraction for every direction of propagation and of vibration in biaxial minerals may be deduced from a single continuous surface, called an indicatrix, or index-ellipsoid. Such a surface is a triaxial ellipsoid, whose three symmetry axes are proportional to the three indices of refraction, namely, the greatest index, the least index, and the intermediate index of the mineral (the index for light vibrating at right angles to the directions of vibrations in the two preceding cases). The intermediate index of refraction is designated N_m, the subscript standing for mean, although the index is, in general, not a mean value of the other two, which are designated N_g and N_p, as in the uniaxial crystals. The general form of the triaxial ellipsoid of a biaxial crystal is shown in Fig. 180; this

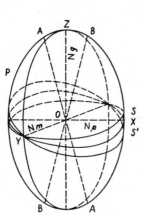

FIG. 180.—Triaxial ellipsoid.

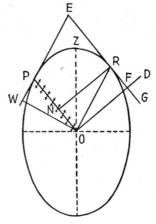

FIG. 181.—Derivation of index for a ray from triaxial ellipsoid.

is not an ellipsoid of rotation, since all three axes are unequal. The three planes, XY, XZ, and YZ, are planes of symmetry of the form, and there are no other planes of symmetry. All sections of the form passing through the center are elliptical; in two positions (YS and YS') the ellipses have their diameters equal and are circles. The two circular sections include the intermediate axis Y and are normal to the plane XZ. They must be equally inclined to Z (and also to X)

since, beginning with the section YZ, which has its long axis in the plane XZ, and rotating the section clockwise about Y, a position must be found before reaching the position XY in which the axis of the section in the plane XZ is equal to Y, inasmuch as this axis changes gradually from a length, Z, greater than Y to a length, X, less than Y; also, beginning with the same section and rotating anticlockwise, another circular section must be found at the same angular distance from Z, since the curves on either side of Z are alike. These circular sections are normal to AA and BB, which are known as the primary optic axes; as explained later, these axes do not coincide exactly with the directions SS and $S'S'$ of Fig. 178.

If light travels from the center, O, of the ellipsoid, in any direction in a symmetry plane, as XZO, meeting the surface of the ellipsoid at P (Figs. 180 and 181), it consists in general of two rays vibrating at right angles to each other and also at right angles to the direction of the wave-normal; the first ray vibrates parallel to OY and has an index represented by OY (or N_m), and a velocity represented by $1/OY$; the second one vibrates in the direction perpendicular to OY and to the wave-normal, OW. Expressed in another way, one ray vibrates in the plane XZO and at right angles to the wave-normal, while the other one vibrates at right angles to that plane and therefore at right angles to the ray and also to the wave-normal. If OR is constructed perpendicular to OW and meets the surface of the ellipsoid at R, then OR represents the index of the second ray, and $1/OR$ represents the velocity of this ray in the direction of the wave normal, OW. If the point N is found by dropping a perpendicular from R to OP, $1/RN$ represents the velocity of the second ray, OP, in its own direction. In all cases, the line which represents the index extends from the center to the surface in a direction perpendicular to the wave-normal.

Finally, if light travels in any direction whatever, not in a plane of symmetry of the ellipsoid, it consists, in general, of two rays whose wave-normals, vibration directions, velocities, and indices cannot be obtained from any two-dimension figure, but may be obtained from a three-dimension model as follows:

In Fig. 182 let OR [1] represent the direction of the rays. Construct a cylinder (of elliptical cross section) parallel to OR and tangent at all points of an ellipse (P_1P_2) to the indicatrix, and find the chief axes

[1] OR may be considered to be a ray from the center, O, of the triaxial ellipsoid (Fig. 180) to an indefinite point, R.

of its elliptical cross section; the half-lengths of these axes are the reciprocals of the velocities of the rays; the symmetry planes of the cylinder are the vibration planes of the rays. If P_1 and P_2 are the points of tangency of the tangent cylinder lying in these symmetry planes, OP_1 and OP_2 are the vibration directions of the rays. If ON_1 is normal to OP_1 in the plane P_1OR, and ON_2 normal to OP_2 in the plane P_2OR, then ON_1 and ON_2 are the wave-normals of the rays. The distances OP_1 and OP_2 are proportional to the indices of the rays transmitted along the direction OR. If perpendiculars are dropped from P_1 and P_2 upon OR (produced), these lines are inversely proportional to the velocities of these two rays, though OP_1 and OP_2 are inversely proportional to the velocities of these rays in the directions of the wave normals.[1]

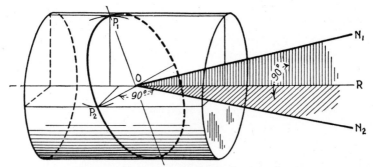

FIG. 182.—Derivation of index in the general case.

The directions of vibration of the light moving in a certain direction are always at right angles to the wave-normals and to each other; the traces of the positions of these directions in the plane normal to the ray are determined by the positions of the major and minor axes of the elliptical section of the triaxial ellipsoid cut through its center by the plane normal to the ray. These directions of vibration bisect the angles between the intersections of the plane normal to the ray and the two circular sections of the ellipsoid; they also bisect the angles between the intersections of the plane normal to the ray and the two planes each containing the ray and one optic axis; or, again, they bisect the angles between the projections of the optic axes on the section.

Optic axes.—The two directions normal to the circular sections of the triaxial ellipsoid are called the optic axes (primary) and are commonly denoted by the capital letters A and B. In orthorhombic

[1] For a more complete discussion and demonstration see L. Fletcher: The Optical Indicatrix, London, 1892, and F. Pockels: Lehrbuch der Kristalloptik, Leipzig, 1906, pp. 48–55.

crystals one optic axis is indistinguishable from the other, so far as its effects on light are concerned; in other biaxial crystals there is no necessary nor constant difference between them.   Since all diameters of the circular section are equal, all light rays whose wave-normals are parallel to either optic axis travel at velocities whose components in the direction of their wave-normals are equal; the rays in one cone have all possible directions of vibration (parallel to all diameters of the circular section).

There is a very small angular difference[1] of position between the directions AA and BB of Fig. 180, and the directions SS and $S'S'$ of Fig. 178; the former are distinguished as primary optic axes and the latter as secondary optic axes. The difference in position is 0° 12′ in orthoclase, 0° 15′ in barite, 0° 52′ in diopside, and is more than 2° only in crystals of large optic angle and very strong birefringence. For distinctness, this difference is exaggerated in Fig. 183, in which OP is the primary optic axis normal to the circular section of the triaxial ellipsoid at its center, and OR is the secondary optic axis, whose position is established as in Fig. 178.   Neither the primary nor the secondary optic axis is an axis of no double refraction, like the optic axis of a uniaxial mineral, but the wave-normal of light traveling along the primary axis suffers no change of direction.   The two axes are indistinguishable in common minerals by ordinary methods.   The plane bb' in Fig. 183 is tangent to the surface II at P, and also to the surface FS at D; furthermore, it is tangent to these surfaces along a continuous circular line of which P and D are the extremities of the diameter marking the intersection of the optic plane; the plane of the circle is normal to the plane of the paper.

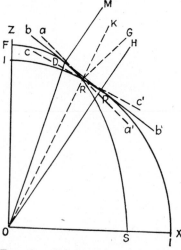

FIG. 183.—Interior and exterior conical refraction.

Interior conical refraction.[2]—A beam of light incident at O (Figs. 183 and 184) at right angles to a section of the crystal normal to OP (the primary optic axis) is changed

---

[1] See statement at bottom of p. 159.

[2] The descriptions of interior and exterior conical refraction were written by L. M. Scofield and N. H. Stearn. For a rigorous detailed discussion of conical refraction see W. Voigt: *Neues Jahrb. Min.*, 1915, I, p. 35.

into a hollow cone of light whose apex is at the point O and whose base is the circle of which DP is a diameter, the distance DP increasing with the thickness of the section, the size of the optic angle, and the birefringence of the mineral.   The various parts of this cone have their wave-normals parallel to OP, and their vibration directions parallel to all possible diameters of the circular section, the direction at any point on the circle DP being parallel to a line through that point and the point P, as shown in Fig. 186.   The formation of the cone is due to the fact that the incident light is not plane polarized, but is free to vibrate parallel to all diameters of the circular section; that portion vibrating normal to the plane of the paper travels out on the path OP with a circular wave-front II, while that portion vibrating parallel to the plane of the paper and normal to OP travels out (with an elliptical wave-surface FS) on the path OD, which is the direction of propagation of light having such a wave-surface with a wave-normal parallel to OP; and all other portions of the incident ray take paths within the crystal according to their vibration directions, so that they strike the plane bb' on a circle of which DP is a diameter; all

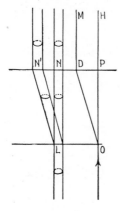

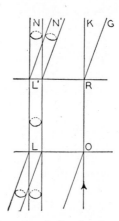

FIG. 184.—Refraction along
primary optic axis.

FIG. 185.—Refraction along
secondary optic axis.

portions of the light in the cone travel with equal speed in the direction of their wave-normals and so reach the circle DP at the same instant.   Upon emerging from the crystal through the plane bb', each portion is refracted toward the axis of the cone an amount equal to the refraction suffered upon entering the crystal (taking a direction parallel to the course of the incident ray) and so forming a hollow cylinder of light whose cross-section is the circle, DP.   This phenomenon of the formation of a cone of light within the crystal is termed interior conical refraction.

Exterior conical refraction.—All rays traveling parallel to the secondary optic axis travel with the same velocity and vibrate in various directions normal to their respective wave-normals; to obtain the presence of all possible vibration directions in this beam, special conditions must be set up to bring about accordance with the law of geometrical optics which states that a ray upon emergence from a plane plate is always parallel to its original direction before entering the plate.   Though the directions of propagation of all the rays described above are the same, their wave-normals are not, that of one coinciding with the ray, that of another being normal to the ellipse FS at R and those of all others being intermediate between these two limiting cases, and lying in the surface of a cone.   Upon emerging from a crystal cut normal to OR (or parallel to cc') these rays form a continuous hollow cone of light of which $L'N$ and $L'N'$ are rays at the extremity of a diameter. $L'N$ is the ray of circular wave-surface, and, since its wave-normal is normal to the surface of the section, it is not refracted upon emergence. $L'N'$ is the ray of elliptical wave-surface FS, and, since its wave-normal is not normal to the surface of the section, it is refracted away from the direction OR, and follows the direction determined by its wave-normal as a spherical wave upon emergence. All other rays are refracted an intermediate amount, following directions determined by their wave-normals as spherical waves upon emergence, thus forming a hollow cone of light outside the crystal.

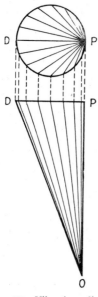

FIG. 186.—Vibration directions in interior conical refraction.

FIG. 187.—Model of wave-surfaces of a biaxial crystal.

The differences between the two phenomena may be summed up as follows:

	Interior Conical Refraction	Exterior Conical Refraction
Optic axis involved	Primary axis	Secondary axis
Locus of occurrence	At incidence	At emergence
Direction of rays within the crystal	Along all lines of cone one line of which is the primary optic axis	Parallel to secondary optic axis
Wave-normals of rays within the crystal	Parallel to primary optic axis	Along all lines of cone one line of which is the secondary optic axis
Wave-surface	Parallel to section	Variable
Emergence expression	Hollow cylinder of light parallel to primary optic axis	Hollow cone of light whose circular section is normal to its own axis

The directions [1] of the primary and secondary optic axes are so nearly the same that the effects of the two are combined in ordinary interference phenomena, and their blended effect serves merely to permit the passage of some light through sections normal to one of the biaxial optic axes, thus explaining the fact that they do not show as complete extinction as do uniaxial basal sections. Aside from explaining incomplete extinction in these sections the phenomena of interior and exterior conical refraction are of little practical importance to the petrographer.

Optic plane, optic normal, and bisectrices.—The optic axes lie in the plane of the greatest and least axes of the triaxial ellipsoid, which is called the plane of the optic axes, or, simply, the optic plane. The axis Y, being at right angles to the optic plane, is known as the optic normal. The axes X and Z bisect the angles between the optic axes, and are therefore called the bisectrices; the one which bisects the smaller angle between the optic axes is known as the acute bisectrix, and the other is designated the obtuse bisectrix. The acute angle between the optic axes is called the optic angle, and is denoted by $2V$.

Crystals in which Z is the acute bisectrix are said to be *positive*, for, if the angle between the optic axes be supposed to diminish to $0°$ (the limiting case), the two optic axes coincide, and the triaxial ellipsoid becomes an ellipsoid of rotation with its long axis coincident with the optic axis, which is the condition in a positive uniaxial crystal.

Crystals in which X is the acute bisectrix are said to be *negative*, for, if the angle between the optic axes diminishes to its limit, the triaxial ellipsoid becomes an ellipsoid of rotation with its short axis coincident with the optic axis, which is the condition in negative uniaxial crystals.

The angle between the optic axes is closely related to the relative values of N_g, N_m, and N_p; indeed, if this angle is represented by $2V$, the exact relation between it and the indices of refraction is given by the equation:

$$\tan V = \sqrt{\frac{1/N_p{}^2 - 1/N_m{}^2}{1/N_m{}^2 - 1/N_g{}^2}}.$$

The relation may be stated more simply as follows, if a close approximation is sufficient:

Positive Crystals	Negative Crystals
$\tan V = \sqrt{\dfrac{N_m - N_p}{N_g - N_m}}.$	$\tan V = \sqrt{\dfrac{N_g - N_m}{N_m - N_p}}.$

[1] The relation in position is given by the formula: $\tan V = \dfrac{N_g}{N_p} \tan W$, in which W is half the acute angle between the secondary optic axes of a positive crystal.

Also,   Positive Crystals   Negative Crystals

$$\sin^2 V = \frac{N_m - N_p}{N_g - N_p},\qquad\qquad \sin^2 V = \frac{N_g - N_m}{N_g - N_p},$$

$$\cos^2 V = \frac{N_g - N_m}{N_g - N_p}.\qquad\qquad \cos^2 V = \frac{N_m - N_p}{N_g - N_p}.$$

Optic orientation.—There is a remarkably close relation between the symmetry of crystals and their optical properties. Isometric crystals, which have three equal crystal axes that are commonly also principal axes of symmetry, have a wave front whose axes are all equal. Tetragonal and hexagonal crystals have one principal axis of symmetry, and equal crystal axes at right angles to it; optically, the principal axis of symmetry is an optic axis and all the axes of the wave front at right angles to it are equal. No other crystals have a principal axis of symmetry (that is, one in which like planes of symmetry meet), and no other crystals have only one optic axis. Orthorhombic crystals have three rectangular axes of binary symmetry coincident with the three unequal crystal axes, and the three unequal ellipsoidal axes are parallel with them; in orthorhombic crystals of various kinds, any one of the ellipsoidal axes may coincide with any one of the crystal axes. Monoclinic crystals have one axis of binary symmetry (the crystal axis, b), with which one axis of the triaxial ellipsoid coincides in all cases. There being no symmetry axes to fix their position, the other two ellipsoidal axes (always at right angles to each other and to the first ellipsoidal axis) have positions in the plane of symmetry containing the crystal axes a and c, which vary with variations of chemical composition, and also, in a single crystal, with the wavelength of the light. Finally, triclinic crystals have no axes and no planes of symmetry; in them the axes of the triaxial ellipsoid may occupy any position whatever, depending upon the composition of the crystal and the kind of light used, but always being at right angles to each other, and fixed in position for any kind of monochromatic light for all crystals of exactly the same composition of a given species.

Absorption and pleochroism.—All substances absorb more or less of the light which is reflected or refracted at their surfaces. In isometric crystals, the amount of absorption bears no relation to the crystal form; in uniaxial crystals it may vary with the direction of vibration of the light, and in cases of variation the absorption is a maximum or a minimum for light vibrating parallel to the optic axis, and a minimum or a maximum for light vibrating at right angles thereto. In biaxial crystals, the amount of absorption may vary similarly, and the variation may reach a maximum or a minimum foɪ light vibrating parallel to any one of the three ellipsoidal axes.   The facts in regard to absorption in biaxial crystals are not completely expressed without stating the absorption parallel to each of the ellipsoidal axes. Absorption formulas are commonly written in terms of these axes; thus, $X > Y > Z$ means that the crystal has the greatest absorption for light vibrating parallel to X and the least for that vibrating parallel to Z.

Crystals not only absorb various proportions of the total light as the direction of vibration changes; they also, in many cases, absorb unequally the various kinds (wave lengths) of light.   Therefore, the color of reflected or transmitted light may vary with the direction of vibration.   In biaxial crystals, such selective absorption may result in three different colors for light vibrating parallel to the three ellipsoidal axes.   A pleochroism formula is a brief expression of the color observed with light vibrating successively parallel to each of these axes.   For example, one kind of common hornblende has the following pleochroism formula: X, clear yellow, Y, dark brown, Z, dark brownish green.

DIRECTIONS FOR LABORATORY WORK

Make drawings similar to Figs. 174 and 175 showing the effects of sulphur on light incident at right angles on the face 011.

CHAPTER XVII

BIAXIAL MINERALS IN PARALLEL POLARIZED LIGHT

Biaxial crystal plates between crossed nicols.—In general, biaxial crystals affect parallel polarized light in the same way as uniaxial crystals. Except at the extinction position, a ray of polarized light is divided at the surface of the crystal into two rays which vibrate in planes which are at right angles to each other and are inclined to the planes of the nicols. The two rays are both refracted, and are refracted unequally, if the incidence is inclined; the same is true if the incidence is normal, provided the plate is not normal to a plane of symmetry of the triaxial ellipsoid. On account of the differences of phase of the transmitted light, interference colors are produced just as with uniaxial crystals. When a biaxial crystal plate is rotated between crossed nicols, monochromatic light is extinguished when the vibration planes of the mineral coincide with the vibration planes of the nicols. In most biaxial minerals, white light is extinguished under the same conditions; in a few the vibration planes of different colors are not coincident nor so close together that their separation produces no visible effect—in these crystals it is only possible to obtain extinction of one part of the spectrum at any given position.

Sections of uniaxial crystals normal to the optic axis cut off all the light between crossed nicols, provided the rays are strictly parallel and strike the sections at right angles. Under the same conditions plates of biaxial minerals normal to an optic axis do not cut off all the light, the amount passing through depending upon the birefringence, the dispersion, etc. This difference is due to several facts; the optic axes of biaxial minerals are not precisely the same in position for different parts of the spectrum; therefore no single section can be exactly normal to the optic axis for all colors; also, the effects of the primary and secondary optic axes are commonly blended, so that refraction occurs at each surface of the plate (interior and exterior conical refraction), and the vibration directions of part

172

of the light are so shifted as to allow a small portion to pass through the analyzer.

Extinction angles.—Isoaxial crystals are extinguished in all positions between crossed nicols and therefore have no extinction angles. Uniaxial crystals have extinction which is parallel to basal or prismatic faces or cleavages in all sections showing only one direction of cleavage; the extinction is, in general, not parallel to rhombohedral faces or cleavages. In common biaxial crystals, the most prominent faces and cleavages are either pinacoidal or prismatic. The extinction directions in such crystals bisect the angles between the projections of the optic axes on the section. In sections parallel to the vertical axis, extinction is parallel to pinacoidal or prismatic cleavage in orthorhombic crystals; it is inclined to such directions, except in orthopinacoidal sections, in monoclinic minerals, and is inclined to such directions in all vertical sections in triclinic crystals.[1]

In cross sections (that is, those normal to the vertical axis) extinction is parallel to pinacoidal cleavage in orthorhombic and monoclinic crystals, and inclined in triclinic minerals; in the same sections, extinction bisects the angles between prismatic cleavages (and is therefore called symmetrical) in orthorhombic and monoclinic crystals, and is inclined in triclinic.

In sections parallel to the side pinacoid (o1o), extinction is parallel to pinacoidal or prismatic cleavages in orthorhombic minerals, and inclined to those directions in monoclinic and triclinic crystals.

In general, extinction, measured on pinacoidal or prismatic cleavages or faces, is parallel or symmetrical in all sections parallel to one (or two) crystal axes in orthorhombic crystals; it is parallel or symmetrical in all sections parallel to the ortho-axis, b, and inclined in all other sections in monoclinic minerals; and it is inclined in all sections parallel to a crystal axis in triclinic minerals.

Extinction angles may be made more useful when they are expressed in terms of the relations between definite vibration planes and definite crystal directions. For example, it is true that the maximum extinction angle in the vertical zone in some types of hornblende is 20°, but it is much better to express this as the angle between the vibration direction of the slow ray (Z) and the direction of the vertical axis (c), thus, $Z \wedge c = 20°$. This makes the statement more exact, and thus doubles the possible range of extinction angles

---

[1] Parallel extinction is not impossible in triclinic minerals, but in them it would be merely a result of chance.

which can be measured. For instance, if the extinction angle in the vertical zone of augite is measured, it will be found to have a maximum value of 40° in one type. In this case the measure made is merely to the extinction position nearest the direction of the cleavage which marks the vertical axis. But if the measure is always made from the cleavage to the vibration direction of the slow ray Z, it is clear that 45° is no longer the greatest possible angle—this is now 90°. Therefore, augite, whose maximum extinction angle in the vertical zone is 40°, may be distinguished from another type whose maximum extinction angle is 50°.

The measurement of extinction angles, thus, to a specified vibration direction is useful if the orientation of the section is known. The orientation may be only imperfectly known, as illustrated by the measurements just cited *in the vertical zone;* in such a case, it is necessary to make several measures in differently oriented grains or anhedra (in the zone) and assume that the largest angle found is the true maximum of the zone. This assumption is justified as an approximation, because it is usually true that a large part of the zone gives an angle varying only a little from the maximum. This is one of the methods used in determining plagioclase feldspars, the zone most frequently used being that normal to the twinning plane (010), which shows equal extinction angles in the two parts of the twin.

Again, the orientation may be definitely known with respect to crystal directions, as illustrated when extinction angles are measured in cleavage fragments from a known cleavage direction. This is another method used in studying feldspars, the extinction angles of which are useful in flakes from either cleavage.

Finally, the orientation may be definitely known with respect to optical directions, as is the case when extinction angles are measured in sections normal to optic axes, bisectrices, or the optic normal. Since sections normal to optic axes are indistinguishable one from the other, and, moreover, are nearly at extinction in all positions, so that extinction positions cannot be accurately determined, these sections are rarely used for this purpose. Likewise, it is often difficult to distinguish between the acute and obtuse bisectrices (the differences will be described in the next section), but it is only necessary to know whether the bisectrix is the direction X or the direction Z, and this can always be determined readily. Therefore, the measurement of extinction angles in sections normal to bisectrices is a very useful method in the study of triclinic minerals, especially the plagioclase feldspars. It is sometimes difficult to distinguish between the optic normal and the obtuse bisectrix; whenever it can be done, extinction angles in sections normal to the former are of possible value. In the feldspars it happens that these sections do not differ as much in extinction angles as the bisectrix sections and therefore they are not as useful. But in some monoclinic minerals the measurement of such extinction angles gives better and more definite results than a search

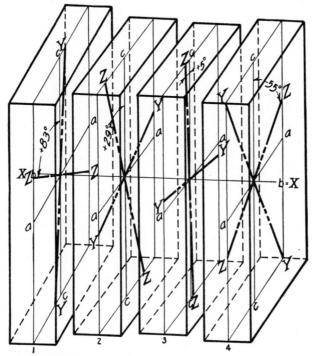

FIG. 188.—The axes, X, Y, Z in colemanite (1), vivianite (2), monazite (3), borax (4).

for the maximum extinction angle in the vertical zone, because, in those monoclinic minerals in which Y is parallel with b, the extinction angle normal to Y is not necessarily the maximum angle of the vertical zone, and also because the optic normal interference figure may be found in some minerals in which the vertical zone cannot be recognized, as in epidote. The position of the axes XYZ, in four minerals having X parallel with b, is shown in Fig. 188. The position of these axes in three minerals having Y parallel with b is shown in

Fig. 188a, and their position in four minerals having Z parallel with b is shown in Fig. 188b.

Sign of elongation.—The elongation of biaxial minerals is, in most cases, parallel with the vertical axis; epidote, wollastonite, pectolite, etc., are elongated parallel with the axis b; petalite, herderite, and some crystals of feldspar are elongated parallel with the axis a. Many biaxial minerals, including the micas, the chlorites, kaolinite, hydrar-

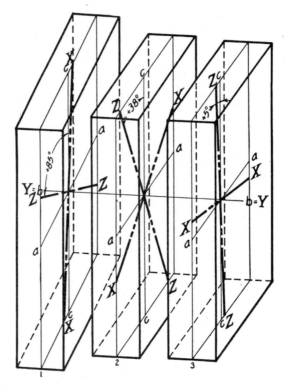

FIG. 188a.—The axes, X, Y, Z in epidote (1), diopside (2), and glaucophane (3).

gillite, talc, barite, and titanite, are elongated or flattened parallel with the base (001); a few, like some feldspar microlites, gypsum, and orpiment, are flattened parallel with the side pinacoid (010); and monazite, chrysoberyl, etc., are flattened parallel with the front pinacoid (100).

As with uniaxial minerals, the sign of elongation is determined by the relation in position of the directions of vibration and the direction of elongation (or flattening). The sign of elongation is positive in case the direction of vibration of the slow (Z) ray is nearest to, or coincides with, the axis of elongation, and it is negative in case the fast (X) ray occupies this position. If the intermediate axis, Y, is nearest to, or coincides with, the axis of elongation, the sign of elongation is plus in some sections and minus in others, and the mineral is said to have an elongation which is plus or minus $(\pm)$. Thus, if an orthorhombic mineral is elongated parallel to Y and c, and if Z is

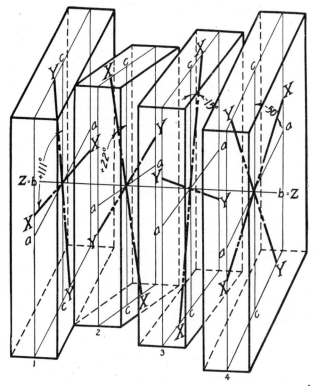

FIG. 188b.—The axes, X, Y, Z in adularia (1), brewsterite (2), arfvedsonite (3), hyalophane (4).

parallel with a, the elongation is positive in a macropinacoidal section and negative in a brachypinacoidal section, since the ray vibrating parallel to Y travels faster than the Z ray, but more slowly than the X ray.

In monoclinic and triclinic minerals in which, in general, no direction of vibration is parallel with the axis of elongation, the sign of elongation is determined by the relative velocity of that ray whose vibration direction is nearest the axis of elongation. Thus, all pyroxenes (except those varieties in which the optic plane is normal to 010) have positive elongation when the angle between Z and c is less than 45°, and negative elongation when it is greater than 45°.

In minerals which exhibit flattening (or elongation parallel to a plane), all sections except those parallel to the plane of flattening show an apparent elongation whose direction is variable, depending upon the direction in which the section is cut. In such minerals the sign of elongation is determined by the relation in position of the vibration directions (axes of the triaxial ellipsoid) and the normal to the plane of flattening. The sign of elongation is positive in case X coincides with, or is nearest to, the normal to the plane of flattening, plus or minus ($\pm$) in case Y is so situated, and negative in case Z occupies this position. Thus, all micas and many chlorites have positive elongation, since in them X is nearly normal to the basal flattening in all species.

DIRECTIONS FOR LABORATORY WORK

Interference colors.—Many sections of biaxial minerals (all sections of some biaxial minerals) produce, between crossed nicols, interference colors which are indistinguishable from those produced by uniaxial crystals; they are due to the same causes and dependent upon the same factors, namely, the birefringence of the mineral, the direction in which the section is cut, and the thickness of the section. Sections parallel to both optic axes (and therefore parallel to the optic plane) produce the highest interference colors; those normal to an optic axis produce the lowest colors. Find sections normal to an optic axis of one or more biaxial minerals (for example, augite, orthoclase, olivine) and describe the amount and kind of light transmitted by them between crossed nicols.

Some kinds of chlorite and zoisite have such strong dispersion of their vibration directions that in no position of rotation are the vibration planes for all parts of the spectrum parallel to the vibration planes of the nicols. Therefore, there is no position of complete extinction for sections of such minerals, and, near the extinction position, abnormal interference colors are observed. Find a section of chlorite, or zoisite, and describe the interference color near the position of approximate extinction.

Extinction angles.—Oriented sections may be used to advantage in the preliminary study of extinction angles.

Test the following statements and record results:

Extinction is parallel to prismatic cleavages in all sections of the vertical zone in an orthorhombic mineral, for example, hypersthene.

Extinction is symmetrical in all sections parallel to a or b and not parallel to c, in the same mineral.

Extinction is inclined in all other sections of the same mineral.

Extinction is parallel to pinacoidal cleavage in all sections parallel to any crystal axis in an orthorhombic mineral, for example, staurolite or olivine.

Extinction is inclined in all other sections of the same mineral.

Extinction is parallel to prismatic cleavage in orthopinacoidal (100) sections of a monoclinic mineral, for example, hornblende. In the same mineral it is symmetrical in other sections parallel to b, and inclined in all other sections.

Extinction is parallel to pinacoidal cleavage in all sections parallel to *b* in a monoclinic mineral, for example, orthoclase. It is inclined in all other sections of the same mineral.

Extinction is inclined to prismatic cleavage in all sections of a triclinic mineral, for example, rhodonite.

Extinction is inclined to pinacoidal cleavage in all sections of a triclinic mineral, for example, labradorite.

These facts may be used, not only to determine the crystal system and thereby gain a clue to the character of an unknown mineral, but they may be employed also to fix the orientation of sections of a known mineral. For example, find in rock slides a crystal of hornblende or augite cut parallel (or very nearly parallel) with the orthopinacoid (100).

Sign of elongation.—Determine from sections the sign of elongation of several biaxial minerals, for example, hornblende, augite, epidote. Use the same methods employed with uniaxial crystals.

CHAPTER XVIII

BIAXIAL MINERALS IN CONVERGENT POLARIZED LIGHT

Biaxial crystal plates in convergent polarized light.—Any section of a biaxial mineral placed in focus between strong lenses and crossed nicols produces an interference figure (analogous to that observed under similar conditions with a plate of a uniaxial mineral), which may be seen by inserting a Bertrand lens properly focused, or by removing the ocular. If the plate is of indefinite orientation, the interference figure may be of little service, although it commonly suffices to show at least that the crystal is biaxial. The most important plates of definite orientation are, those: first, normal to an optic axis; second, normal to a bisectrix; third, normal to the optic normal, or parallel to the optic plane.

Biaxial optic axis interference figure.—A plate normal to an optic axis of a biaxial mineral produces an interference figure (see Figs. 189–191) which is similar, in general, to that given by a basal section

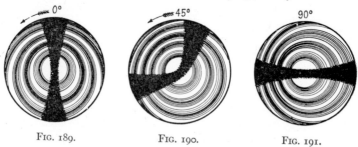

FIG. 189.   FIG. 190.   FIG. 191.

FIGS. 189–191.—Biaxial optic axis interference figure.

of a uniaxial crystal. It consists of a single isogyre, with or without color curves, which are nearly circular if the optic angle is large, and if the plate is very thick or the birefringence very strong, but are oval or nearly elliptical in shape under other conditions. With thin sections of minerals of weak birefringence, the color curves may be entirely absent, but the isogyre is never absent. The biaxial optic axis interference figure differs from the uniaxial optic axis interference

180

figure most clearly in the fact that it has only one isogyre instead of two.   It also differs in the form of the color curves, and in the fact that the single isogyre is not fixed in position, nor constantly straight, when the crystal is rotated.   The isogyre passes through the center of the interference figure in all positions; it rotates in a direction contrary to the direction of rotation of the stage.   When the plane of symmetry of the interference figure coincides with either nicol, the isogyre is straight and parallel with that nicol; in all other positions it forms a curve of hyperbolic form; at $45°$ with the nicols, the vertex of the hyperbola is the point of emergence of the optic axis and the acute bisectrix is on the convex side of the isogyre.   If the plate makes an angle of $70°-85°$ with the optic axis, instead of $90°$, the interference figure produced is similar in every way to that just described, but the central point of the figure, which is the point at which the optic axis emerges, is not in the center of the field; and on rotation of the crystal this point rotates with the stage about the center of the field of view. This interference figure is often designated briefly as the optic axis figure, without confusion with the uniaxial optic axis figure, since that is called, briefly, the uniaxial figure.

Bisectrix interference figure.—A plate normal to the acute bisectrix produces an interference figure containing two optic axis figures provided the optic angle is not too large.   It consists of two isogyres with or without color curves surrounding the optic axes.   If the birefringence is strong, as illustrated, in Figs. 192–194, the color curves

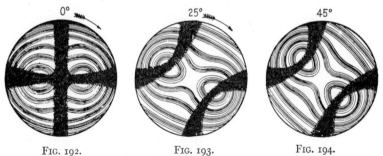

FIG. 192.   FIG. 193.   FIG. 194.

FIGS. 192–194.—Acute bisectrix interference figure.

nearest the optic axis are nearly circular, those farther away more ovate, and, after passing a pair which form a figure eight, called a lemniscate, the others are shaped like ovals more or less constricted. All these curves are called " Cassinian ovals."   The isogyres form a cross in each position in which the optic plane, including the optic axes, is parallel with the plane of vibration of either nicol; in all other positions they form hyperbolic curves passing through the optic axes; at $45°$ from the planes of the nicols the optic axes emerge at the vertices of the two hyperbolas, which have their convex sides turned toward the acute bisectrix. The isogyres are narrow where they pass through the optic axes, and broaden considerably away from these points. Each isogyre rotates about an optic axis in the direction contrary to the rotation of the stage, while the optic axes, optic plane, and color curves rotate about the center of the figure with the rotation of the crystal. If the plate makes an angle of $70°-85°$ with the acute bisectrix, instead of $90°$, the center of the interference figure is not in the center of the field of view, but rotates about the latter when the stage is turned. As in other interference figures the isogyres are the most important part of the figure, because they are always present; and they should be studied most attentively. As in the uniaxial interference figure, the distance from an optic axis to the first color curve, measured at right angles to the optic plane (or measured in any other fixed direction) depends upon (1) the birefringence of the mineral, (2) the thickness of the plate, (3) the angular aperture of the objective and of the condenser. It depends, also, upon the magnification produced, for example, by a Bertrand lens; and it varies somewhat with the mean index of refraction of the mineral. The distance between the two optic axes (the vertices of the hyperbolas at the $45°$ position) is independent of the birefringence and the thickness of the plate, and, with a given set of lenses, varies with the size of the apparent optic angle;[1] in case this angle is very large, the distance between the optic axes is greater than the diameter of the field of view, and both optic axes are outside the field; or, with sections inclined at $70°-85°$ to the acute bisectrix, one optic axis may be outside, and the other inside, the field of view. The interference figure that results if the optic angle is very large is correctly represented by cutting off the outer two-thirds of Figs. 192-194, it is very similar to the figure produced by a plate normal to the obtuse bisectrix.

A plate normal to the obtuse bisectrix produces an interference figure which consists of two isogyres, with or without color curves; the isogyres form a dark cross when the optic plane is parallel with the plane of either nicol, and swing out of the field as hyperbolic curves in opposite quadrants on rotation through a small angle from these

---

[1] The relation between the true and the apparent optic angle is explained below on p. 186.

positions, as in Figs. 195–196. On further rotation, the hyperbolic curves re-enter the field and again form a cross when the optic plane is at right angles to its first position. The isogyres revolve about the optic axes in a direction contrary to the rotation of the stage. The optic plane is always in those quadrants in which the hyperbolas leave and enter the field, both in case of the obtuse bisectric figure and also with the acute bisectrix figure of large optic angle.

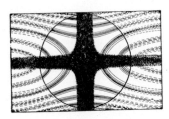
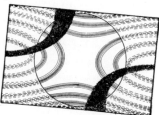

Fig. 195.   Fig. 196.

Figs. 195, 196.—Obtuse bisectrix interference figure.

Explanation of biaxial interference figures.—The explanation of biaxial interference figures is analogous to that of the uniaxial interference figure. Any color curve is the locus of points at which the emerging light has the same difference of phase. The light passing through the crystal along either optic axis, A or B, has no difference of phase, and darkness results. The light traveling so as to emerge anywhere on either curve marked 1 in Fig. 197 consists of two parts whose difference of phase, on leaving the crystal, is one wave length, and the first sensitive tint is produced. Similar statements may be made concerning the light emerging along the curves marked 2, 3, 4, 5, 6. The distance from the optic axis (marked o) to the first (or any other) color curve is greater toward the bisectrix than in the opposite direction, because the light emerging at points nearer the bisectrix has a shorter path through the crystal plate than light emerging at more distant points. If the section is strictly normal to the bisectrix, the point of emergence of the latter is exactly in the center of the field of view, and, on rotation of the stage, the color curves, as a whole, revolve about the center of the figure without changing their size or shape or relation to the optic axes. The number of color curves in an interference figure between the optic axis and the bisectrix depends upon the birefringence of the mineral and the thickness of the plate; a bisectrix interference figure may be used as an approximate method of estimating the difference of phase produced by a section, as indicated in the diagrams given in Figs. 198–201. In these diagrams D is the difference of phase (as measured in wave lengths) produced by the plate in light of normal incidence.

As in uniaxial crystals, the isogyres are the locus of all points at which the light emerges with its vibration planes parallel with the planes of the nicols. As previously stated, the directions of vibration

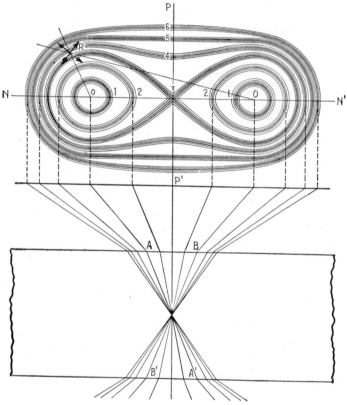

FIG. 197.—Explanation of isogyres in biaxial interference figure.

of the two rays of light emerging from the section at any point are the traces of the planes which bisect the angles between two planes each of which includes the transmitted ray and one optic axis. There-fore, the directions of vibration of the two rays emerging at the center (rays normal to the surfaces) are found by bisecting the angles between the lines connecting the center with each optic axis. The directions of vibration of the two rays emerging at any other point, R, in the interference figure (Fig. 197) are accurately constructed by the use of a stereographic projection plat, by methods which are too complicated for elementary work. If the optic angle is small, or if the point, R, is not far from the center, the directions of vibration of the two rays emerging at any point are approximately given by bisecting the angles between the lines connecting the point with each optic

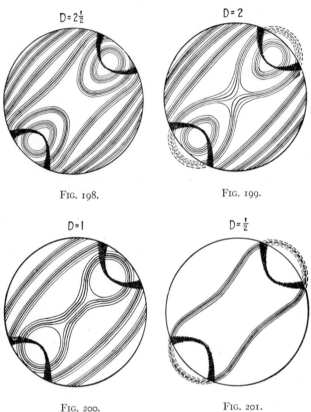

FIG. 198.   FIG. 199.

FIG. 200.   FIG. 201.

FIGS. 198–201.—Difference of phase from interference figures.

axis. By finding the directions of vibration at many points in the interference figure by this crude method, it is a simple matter to roughly locate the isogyre in any position of rotation for any interference figure, as in Fig. 202. To avoid confusion, the isogyres are not represented in Fig. 197; they would form a cross, as in Figs. 192 and 195. The same isogyres are represented in Fig. 202, after rotation of the stage to the 45° position, that is, to the position at which the optic plane makes angles of 45° with the planes of the nicols. In this drawing the directions of vibration are given for many points, as crudely obtained by bisecting the angles between the lines connecting each point with the optic axes. The isogyres include all points at which the vibration directions are parallel with the planes of the nicols. The points representing the optic axes have approximately the blended properties of both the primary and secondary optic axes; accordingly, these points are dark, not only because the light emerging at them may vibrate in any direction (and therefore may vibrate in the planes of the nicols), but also because all the light passes through at (nearly) the same velocity, and, having almost no difference of phase, the waves destroy each other.

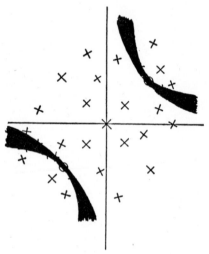

Fig. 202.—Explanation of isogyres in biaxial interference figure.

Measurement of optic angle.—As shown in Fig. 197, the distance between the optic axes in the acute bisectrix interference figure depends upon the angle between the optic axes (AA' and BB'), and also upon the amount of refraction of light traveling along these axes upon its passage into air; for such light the mineral has its mean index, N_m. The angle between the two rays of light along the optic axes, after refraction in air, is called the apparent optic angle, and is denoted by $2E$, while the true optic angle within the crystal is represented by $2V$. If the light be reversed in direction as compared with Fig. 197, then in Fig. 203, E is the angle of incidence and V is the angle of refraction of light traveling along an optic axis. Therefore

$$N_m = \frac{\sin E}{\sin V} \text{ and } \sin E = N_m \sin V.$$

The distance between the optic axes in the acute bisectrix interference figure depends only upon the lenses of the microscope and the apparent optic angle. For a given set of lenses this distance depends solely upon the apparent optic angles. After one has determined, once for all, the constant of the lenses (for a fixed position of the tube of the microscope) with a mineral of known optic angle, the measurement of this distance between the optic axes suffices to determine the apparent optic angle, from which the true or interior optic angle may be calculated, if the mean index of refraction is known. If the relative position of the lenses is changeable, as in French and Swiss microscopes, the constant of the lenses must be determined for each tube-length employed. Since a micrometer-ocular is needed to provide a scale with which to measure the distance between the optic

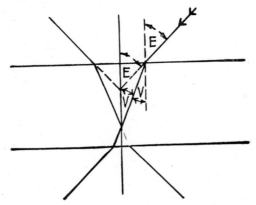

Fig. 203.—Relation between $2V$ and $2E$.

axes, the interference figure is observed as magnified by an ocular and a Bertrand lens, rather than as unmagnified. The apparent optic angle may be obtained from a measure of the distance between the optic axes, either by calculation or by graphic solution. If this distance be denoted by $2D$, it is readily seen from Figs. 197 and 203 that $\sin E$ is proportional to D. The value of the unit in the scale in which $2D$ is measured (that is, the constant of the lenses) may be determined by measuring this distance in the interference figure produced by a mineral whose apparent optic angle is known. For example if D be equal to a measured distance, a, for a mineral, aragonite, whose apparent optic angle is 30° 54′, then the constant of the lenses, M, is equal to a divided by the sine of one-half of 30° 54′; and the

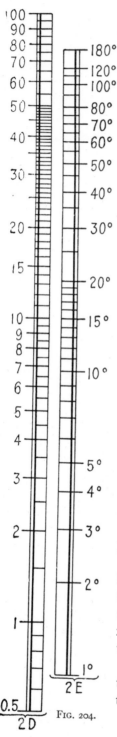

FIG. 204.

apparent optic angle of any other mineral may be obtained from the relation

$$\sin E = \frac{D}{M}.$$

A graphic solution of the same problem is furnished by Schwarzmann optic-angle scales (see Fig. 204). The constant of the lenses is determined with a mineral of known apparent optic angle, as before, and one of the two scales is moved on the other until the measured value of $2D$ corresponds to the known value of $2E$. Or, a line may be drawn between the two points, and other parallel lines between the two scales wherever desired. This being done, the scales give the value of $2E$ for the measured distance $2D$ of any other mineral.

A more accurate method of measuring the true or interior optic angle is by means of a special apparatus so constructed that the crystal can be immersed in a liquid of its own refractive index and rotated on its optic normal as an axis. By reading on a graduated circle the angle between the position when one optic axis coincides with the axis of the microscope and the position in which the other optic axis occupies this position, the true optic angle is directly measured. This method is not in common use because it requires special and expensive apparatus.

If the indices of refraction are accurately known, the true optic angle may be calculated from them; but such a calculation is not often satisfactory, because errors in the fourth decimal place in the indices lead to large errors in the calculated angle.

The true optic angle may be estimated from the amount of curvature of the isogyre in sections normal to an optic axis, by comparison with Fig. 205. The curvature depends somewhat upon the mean index of refraction, and is slightly modified by refraction at the surfaces, but the figure is very nearly correct for minerals whose mean index is 1.60, and approximately correct for all common minerals. By careful measures of the position in the field of view of two points on the isogyre in two positions of the nicols (which are rotated together, while the stage is not rotated), it is possible [1] to determine the optic angle more closely. But the method is too complicated for elementary work, and further description is unnecessary.

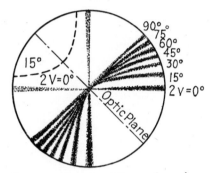

FIG. 205.—Curvature of isogyre for various values of $2V$, the index of refraction being 1.60. (After Wright.)

FIG. 206.—Color curves of optic normal interference figure at 45°.

Optic normal interference figure.—The optic normal interference figure is similar to the figure given by vertical sections of uniaxial minerals, and all the more similar the smaller the optic angle. The optic normal figure consists of isogyres with or without color curves. The isogyres are broad and poorly defined; when the vibration directions of the crystal are parallel with the planes of the nicols, the isogyres form a cross whose arms are so wide as to occupy all or most of the field. A very small rotation of the stage causes the cross to divide into two hyperbolas; the two arms of one hyperbola leave the field so quickly that they are rarely observed; they go out in the quadrants occupied by the obtuse bisectrix, and the more slowly the larger the optic angle. The two arms of the other hyperbola leave the field more slowly, but nevertheless within a rotation of a few degrees (for example, 5°–15°), and go out in the quadrants in which the acute bisectrix lies. The isogyres are seen to the best advantage by turning the stage quickly back and forth past the position of the cross.

[1] F. E. Wright: *Am. Jour. Sci.*, XXIV, 1907, p. 317; and F. Becke: *Tsch. Min. Petr. Mit.*, XIV, 1894, p. 563.

The color curves consist of two series of hyperbolic curves, having their asymptotes parallel to the optic axes; they are represented in Fig. 206. At equal distances from the center of the figure the color is lower in the directions of the acute bisectrix than in the directions normal thereto, parallel with the obtuse bisectrix. On rotation of the stage, the color curves rotate likewise about the center of the figure, their form and position remaining unchanged with reference to the traces of the bisectrices.

Uncentered biaxial interference figures.—A biaxial interference figure is centered when any one of the chief optical directions (optic axis, bisectrix, or optic normal) emerges in the center of the field of view. Uncentered figures are, therefore, so common as to be very important. Whenever the center of the figure is within the field of view, the interference figure differs so little from the centered figure that no special description is necessary. When the center of the figure is far outside the field of view the figure is frequently of little service, and figures of different orientation from the same mineral should be obtained. But, if the center of the figure is at the edge, or not far outside of the edge of the field, careful study often gives satisfactory results. In Figs. 207–231, the color curves are omitted as non-essential. In Figs. 207–216 the isogyre is straight and parallel to one nicol when it passes through the center of the field; all sections which produce an isogyre of this type are normal to a plane of symmetry of the triaxial ellipsoid. In all other uncentered interference figures, as illustrated in Figs. 217–231, when the isogyre passes through the center of the field, it is not parallel with either nicol nor is it straight in this position, though it is sensibly straight near the optic axis if the optic angle is exactly 90°. The section is normal to a line in the optic plane between an optic axis and the acute bisectrix in Figs. 207–211, and the curvature of the isogyre is in the direction contrary to the curvature of the edge of the field. If the section is normal to a line in the optic plane between an optic axis and the obtuse bisectrix, as illustrated in Figs. 212–216, the isogyre approaches parallelism with the edge of the field, on rotation of the stage. In Figs. 217–221 the section is normal to a line on the acute bisectrix side of an optic axis, but it is not normal to the optic plane; in Figs. 222–226 the section is normal to a line on the obtuse bisectrix side of an optic axis, and is not normal to the optic plane. In Figs. 227–231 the section is normal to a line in the plane of the optic normal and an optic axis. In all cases the isogyre curves so that the acute bisectrix is on the convex side.

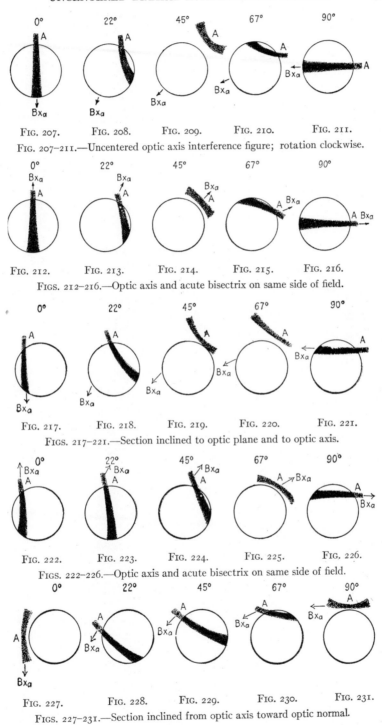

FIG. 207. FIG. 208. FIG. 209. FIG. 210. FIG. 211.

FIG. 207–211.—Uncentered optic axis interference figure; rotation clockwise.

FIG. 212. FIG. 213. FIG. 214. FIG. 215. FIG. 216.

FIGS. 212–216.—Optic axis and acute bisectrix on same side of field.

FIG. 217. FIG. 218. FIG. 219. FIG. 220. FIG. 221.

FIGS. 217–221.—Section inclined to optic plane and to optic axis.

FIG. 222. FIG. 223. FIG. 224. FIG. 225. FIG. 226.

FIGS. 222–226.—Optic axis and acute bisectrix on same side of field.

FIG. 227. FIG. 228. FIG. 229. FIG. 230. FIG. 231.

FIGS. 227–231.—Section inclined from optic axis toward optic normal.

In case a section is cut so that a bisectrix emerges at the edge of the field, as in Figs. 232–236, one or more color curves may be present and may assist the student in comprehending the figure. In the drawing it is assumed that the difference of phase produced is one-half a wave length, as in Fig. 201, so that only one color curve is visible. The relation of this curve to the isogyres and the optic plane should be carefully noted, as it is often useful in constructing unseen portions of the figure. Only one isogyre is visible in any position; the evidence that the other is present is found in the fact that the visible isogyre is rectangular. Since the biaxial isogyre is rectangular only when making the cross, the position of the other isogyre is readily inferred.

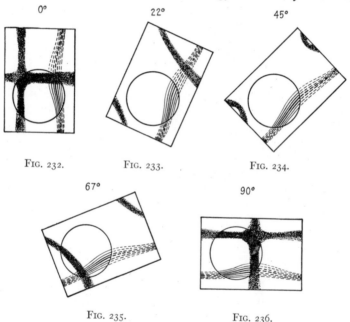

FIG. 232.   FIG. 233.   FIG. 234.

FIG. 235.   FIG. 236.

FIGS. 232–236.—Bisectrix on the edge of the field of view; rotation clockwise.

Dispersion primarily means the scattering or separation along different paths of the component colors of white light, by unequal refraction at any surface. The refracting substance produces unequal refraction of the various colors, and has unequal indices of refraction for different wave lengths of light. All substances, solid and fluid, have unequal indices for different parts of the spectrum. The same word which describes the effect upon light is used as the name of the property of the substance to which the effect is due, and substances are said to have dispersion. In biaxial crystals other properties besides refringence vary with the color of the light, notably the optic angle, and, in some cases, the position of the triaxial ellipsoid. These variations are called dispersion of the optic axes and dispersion of the ellipsoid axes. Accordingly, dispersion, in a wider sense, means the variation in value or in position of the optical constants for different colors of the spectrum.

Isometric crystals have only one type of dispersion, namely, dispersion of the index of refraction; the difference between the index in violet light and the index in red light is a measure of the dispersion. For example:

Mineral	Violet	Green	Red	Dispersion
Fluorite....................	$N = 1.437$	....	1.431	0.006
Almandite.................	$N =$	1.812	1.802	0.010+
Spinel.....................	$N =$	1.726	1.712	0.014+
Diamond...:..............	$N = 2.465$	....	2 402	0.063

Uniaxial crystals have dispersion of both indices of refraction, which is commonly unequal; the birefringence therefore varies for different colors; by variation of the birefringence through zero, the sign of the mineral may be different for the two ends of the spectrum, as illustrated by the rare mineral, torbernite (air dried to $8H_2O$), in which

$$\begin{array}{cccc} & \text{red } (650 m\mu) & \text{green } (515 m\mu) & \text{blue } (425) m\mu \\ N_o = 1.618(5) & 1.634 & 1.651 \\ N_e = 1.622 & 1.634 & 1.647 \end{array}$$

The dispersion of a few common uniaxial minerals is given below:

Mineral	(Sign)	Violet	Yellow	Red	Dispersion
Quartz	$N_o =$	1.554	1.544	1.539	0.015
	$N_e =$	1.564	1.553	1.548	0.016
	$N_e - N_o = (+)$	0.010	0.009	0.009	0.001
Calcite	$N_o =$	1.683	1.6585	1.653	0.030
	$N_e =$	1.498	1.4864	1.484	0.014
	$N_o - N_e = (-)$	0.185	0.1721	0.169	0.016
Ice	$N_o =$	1.3107 (green)	1.3090	1.2970	0.0137+
	$N_e =$	1.3163 (green)	1.3133	1.3037	0.0126+
	$N_e - N_o = (+)$	0.0056 (green)	0.0043	0.0067	0.0011±
Corundum	$N_o =$	1.7751 (blue)	1.7675	1.7643	0.0108+
	$N_e =$	1.7668 (blue)	1.7594	1.7563	0.0105+
	$N_o - N_e = (-)$	0.0083 (blue)	0.0081	0.0080	0.0003±

Orthorhombic biaxial crystals have dispersion of all three indices of refraction, the inequality of which implies dispersion of the optic axes, since the optic angle may be calculated from the indices. In general, the dispersion of the indices is not great, and the corresponding dispersion of the optic axes does not exceed a few degrees; but in brookite and goethite the optic angle changes very rapidly with the color, decreasing to zero, and then opening again in a plane at right angles to the former position as the wave length changes from that of violet to that of red. In ordinary cases, variation of the indices may lead to a larger optic angle in red than in violet light, a condition indicated briefly as $r > v$; or it may lead to the reverse condition, indicated by $r < v$. The following minerals illustrate these facts. The dispersion measured is only partial, because data for violet light are lacking:

Mineral (Sign)		Blue	Yellow	Red	Dispersion
Topaz (+)	$N_g =$	1.6279	1.6225	1.6193	0.0086
	$N_m=$	1.6213	1.6160	1.6127	0.0086
	$N_p =$	1.6187	1.6133	1.6100	0.008/
	$N_g - N_p=$	0.0092	0.0092	0.0093	0.0001
	$2V =$	64° 30'	65° 30'	66° 1'	1° 31'
					$r > v$
Natrolite (+)		Green			
	$N_g =$	1.49181	1.48866	1.48534	0.00647
	$N_m=$	1.48172	1.47897	1.47631	0.00541
	$N_p =$	1.47801	1.47543	1.47287	0.00514
	$N_g - N_p=$	0.01380	0.01323	0.01247	0.00133
	$2V =$	62° 34'	62° 15'	61° 56'	38'
					$r < v$
Brookite (+)	$N_g =$	?	2.7414	2.6444	0.0970
	$N_m=$	?	2.5856	2.5418	0.0438
	$N_p =$	2.6265	2.5832	2.5408	0.0424
	$N_g - N_p=$	?	0.1582	0.1036	0.0546
	$2V =$	?	17° 7'	23° 14'	(very great)
	$2E =$	33° 48'	0° (in yellowish-green light),		$r > y$; $v > g$

Dispersion of the optic axes is called *rhombic* dispersion, because it is the only dispersion affecting the interference figures of ortho-rhombic minerals.

In orthorhombic minerals the optic plane always includes two crystal axes, either a and b, b and c, or a and c, and the ellipsoidal

axes coincide with the crystal axes. In Fig. 237 the optic plane is
assumed to include the axes b and c, the latter being in the acute optic
angle. Fig. 238 shows the acute bisectrix interference figure resulting
from the dispersion of the optic axes, as in Fig. 237. For distinctness
in the drawings, the dispersion is represented as much greater than
that found in most minerals. The heavy curves are those visible in
violet light, and the light curves are those seen in red light. In white
light, containing all colors of the spectrum, a figure is produced in which
all are blended. The isogyre in white light occupies a position between
the isogyres seen in violet and in red light. At the point M, which is
on the convex side of the isogyre seen in white light, no violet light

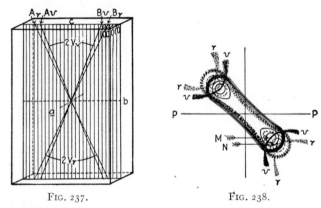

FIG. 237.   FIG. 238.

FIGS. 237–238.—Dispersion of optic axes and resultant interference figure in an orthorhombic crystal, with $\rho > v$.

can emerge, since M is a point of the isogyre in violet light; red light
emerges at this point, since it is not on the dark isogyre seen in red
light. For similar reasons violet light emerges at the point N.
Accordingly, when the isogyre in the acute bisectrix figure of an
orthorhombic mineral is bordered with red light on its convex side
within the first color curve at the 45° position, the optic angle for red
light is larger than for violet light, or $r > v$. Also, when the isogyre
is bordered with violet light on its convex side, the optic angle for
violet is larger than for red light, or $r < v$. Notice that the red color
appears on the convex side of the two isogyres, and therefore, at
points *closer* together, when the optic angle for red light is greater
than for violet.

In orthorhombic crystals the optic plane always coincides with one
of the planes of symmetry of the crystal and is at right angles to the

other two. Corresponding exactly with the symmetry of the crystal, the interference figures are symmetrical with respect to the optic plane and also with respect to the two mutually perpendicular planes normal thereto. The symmetry with respect to the optic plane and one plane normal thereto is visible in the acute bisectrix figure; the symmetry with respect to the other plane may be seen in the obtuse bisectrix and also in the optic normal interference figures.

Monoclinic biaxial crystals have dispersion not only of the indices of refraction and of the optic axes, but also of two of the ellipsoidal axes. The following minerals may serve as illustrations:

Mineral (Sign)		Violet	Yellow	Red	Dispersion
Sanidine (−)	$N_g =$	1.5356	?	1.5240	0.0116
	$N_m =$	1.5355	?	1.5239	0.0116
	$N_p =$	1.5265	?	1.5170	0.0095
	$N_g - N_p =$	0.0091	?	0.0070	0.0021
	$2V =$	11°	0°	17°	$r > y < v$
Augite (+)	$N_g =$	1.7422	1.7227	1.7169	0.0253
	$N_m =$	1.7231	1.7039	1.6990	0.0241
	$N_p =$	1.7170	1.6975	1.6928	0.0242
	$N_g - N_p =$	0.0252	0.0252	0.0241	0.0011
	$2V =$	59° 12′	61° 12′	61° 34′	2° 22′ $r > v$
	$Z \wedge c =$	−45° 39′	−44° 53′	−44° 32′	1° 7′
					$Z_v \wedge c > Z_r \wedge c$
		Green			
Titanite (+)	$N_g =$	2.0639	2.0536	2.0407	0.0232
	$N_m =$	1.9316	1.9206	1.9123	0.0193
	$N_p =$	1.9278	1.9133	1.9062	0.0216
	$N_g - N_p =$	0.1361	0.1403	0.1345	0.0016
	$2E =$	39° 53′	45° 41′	51° 3′	11° 10′
					$r > v$

The dispersion of the optic axes is not greater than a few degrees in most cases; in sanidine and in titanite it is much greater than usual. The dispersion of the ellipsoid axes is usually so slight that it has not been measured; in some brown augite and a few other minerals it results not only in modifying the interference figures, but also in giving abnormal interference colors near extinction. In monoclinic crystals one ellipsoid axis coincides exactly with the crystal axis, b, of symmetry, and cannot be dispersed. There are three types of dispersion of the ellipsoid axes in monoclinic crystals, and they are named from their effects on the acute bisectrix interference figure.

In the first type, called inclined dispersion, the acute bisectrix and the optic plane coincide with the plane of symmetry, and the optic normal, Y, is parallel with b. In the second type, called horizontal dispersion, the acute bisectrix and the optic normal are in the plane of symmetry, and the obtuse bisectrix is parallel with b. In the third type, called crossed dispersion, the acute bisectrix is parallel with b.

Inclined dispersion is represented in Figs. 239 and 240, in which the heavy lines relate to monochromatic violet light, and the light lines to red light. In white light the effects are blended, and the dark isogyre occupies a position between the isogyres of the drawing, and is

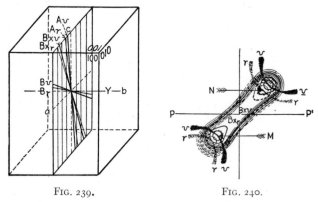

Fig. 239.   Fig. 240.

Figs. 239–240.—Inclined dispersion with $Bx_r \wedge c > Bx_v \wedge c$

bordered on the convex side (inside the first color curve) by red in one optic axis, and by violet in the other optic axis. Thus, there is a border of red light at the point M and a border of violet light at the point N. This difference in the color fringing the same side of the two isogyres is evidence of inclined dispersion, and of nothing else, provided the colors are arranged symmetrically with respect to the optic plane. Further evidence of inclined dispersion may be seen in some cases in a difference in the color curves at opposite ends of the trace of the optic plane.

In Figs. 239 and 240 inclined dispersion is represented without dispersion of the optic axes. In general, the latter is always present (though often not important) in monoclinic (and triclinic) crystals, and the interference figure of a mineral, which has inclined dispersion, is therefore not exactly like Fig. 240. For example, in brown augite from Renfrew, Canada, the acute bisectrix, Z, is dispersed $1° 7'$, with $Z_r \wedge c < Z_v \wedge c$, and the optic axes are dispersed $2° 22'$ with

$r > v$; the result is that one optic axis shows no perceptible dispersion, (4′), and the other is dispersed $2°$ 18′, as shown in Fig. 241.

All interference figures showing inclined dispersion, with or without dispersion of the optic axes, are symmetrical with respect to the optic plane, which is the plane of symmetry of the crystal. Any monoclinic crystal which exhibits inclined dispersion in the acute bisectrix interference figure has the same type of dispersion in the obtuse bisectrix figure.

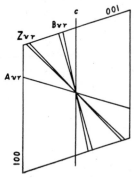

FIG. 241.—Dispersion in augite from Renfrew, Canada.

If the acute bisectrix is in the plane of symmetry to which the optic plane is at right angles, **horizontal dispersion** results, as illustrated in Figs. 242 and 243. The optic plane for red light may make a larger (as in the figures) or a smaller angle with the vertical axis than the optic plane for violet light. The amount of the dispersion is usually small, and it is exaggerated in the figures, for distinctness. For simplicity, rhombic dispersion is not shown in the figures, although it is present in monoclinic crystals. The heavy lines show the optic elements and interference figure curves in violet light, and the lighter

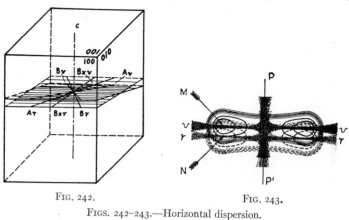

FIG. 242.   FIG. 243.

FIGS. 242–243.—Horizontal dispersion.

lines show them as seen in red light. In white light, with these effects blended, the isogyre marking the optic plane is between those represented and is bordered within the first color curve by red above as at M, and violet (or blue) below as at N. The color curves may also differ on the two sides of the optic plane. In all cases the figure is symmetrical with respect to a plane normal to the optic plane and to that plane only; the same plane is the plane of symmetry of the crystal. A monoclinic crystal exhibiting horizontal dispersion in the acute bisectrix figure shows crossed dispersion in the obtuse bisectrix.

If the acute bisectrix coincides with the axis of symmetry (b), **crossed dispersion** results, as illustrated in Figs. 244 and 245. The optic plane for red light may make a smaller angle (as in the figures) or a larger angle with the vertical axis than the optic plane for violet light. The amount of the dispersion is usually small, and it is exaggerated in the figures, for distinctness. For simplicity, rhombic dispersion is not shown in the figures, although it is present in crystals giving crossed dispersion. The heavy lines show the optic elements and interference figure curves in violet light, and the lighter lines

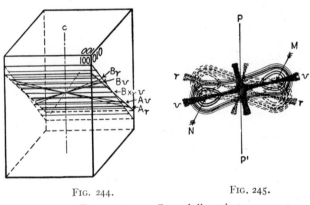

FIG. 244.   FIG. 245.

FIGS. 244–245.—Crossed dispersion.

exhibit them as seen in red light. In white light, with these effects blended, the isogyre marking the optic plane is between those represented and is bordered, within the first color curve, by red above in one optic axis, as at M, and below in the other optic axis, as at N, blue being on the other side in each case. The color curves may show corresponding differences above and below the optic axes. The figure is not symmetrical with reference to any plane, but its center is a center of symmetry; the same point is the pole of the axis of symmetry of the crystal. A monoclinic crystal showing crossed dispersion in the acute bisectrix figure exhibits horizontal dispersion in the obtuse bisectrix figure.

Triclinic biaxial crystals have dispersion, not only of the indices of refraction and of the optic axes, but also of all the ellipsoid axes. The axes of the triaxial ellipsoid for any given color are at right angles to each other, as in other biaxial crystals, and, in general, the dispersion is not great in amount, but the position of the axes for red light may vary in any direction whatever from the position in violet light. It is possible and customary approximately to describe the resulting dispersion as consisting of two or more of the types of dispersion already described. The characteristic feature of the interference figures given by triclinic minerals is that they have no symmetry of any kind, although all dispersion may be so weak that the lack of symmetry is not apparent in some cases.

In summary, the different kinds of dispersion exhibited only by biaxial crystals, and their relations to the crystal systems and symmetry, are as follows:

DISPERSION OF BIAXIAL INTERFERENCE FIGURES

Dispersion	Interference Figures are Symmetrical to	Crystal System
Rhombic, Figs. 237–238	Optic plane and the plane normal thereto	Orthorhombic
(Axial and) Inclined, Figs. 239–241 Horizontal, Figs. 242–243 Crossed, Figs. 244–245	Optic plane Plane normal to optic plane Center (= the bisectrix)	Monoclinic
Combinations	No point nor plane	Triclinic

Distinctions between uniaxial and biaxial interference figures.— In case the interference figures are centered, it is a very simple matter to distinguish the uniaxial optic axis figure from any biaxial figure (except an acute bisectrix of an extremely small optic angle); but it is usually impossible to distinguish with certainty between the interference figure from vertical sections of uniaxial minerals and the optic normal figure of biaxial crystals. It is best to eliminate such figures, when determining whether a certain mineral is uniaxial or biaxial, by avoiding those sections of the given mineral which give the highest interference colors. In ordinary thin sections uncentered interference figures are, of course, much commoner than centered figures; uncentered biaxial interference figures from sections normal to the optic plane, or to the plane XY or YZ, are not easily distinguished from uncentered uniaxial figures, although the curvature of the isogyre is greater in the former, unless the point of emergence of the optic axis is far outside of the field. But all other uncentered biaxial interference figures differ distinctly from uniaxial figures in that the isogyre is curved when it passes through the center of the field (unless the optic angle ($2V$) is 90°, a condition which is rare in common minerals), and the isogyre is not parallel with either nicol when it passes through the same point. (If the optic angle is very small, the lack of parallelism and the curvature are much reduced.)

Distinctions between various biaxial interference figures.—Biaxial optic axis interference figures are very easily distinguished from all others, since they have one isogyre which turns about the point of emergence of the optic axis in a direction contrary to the direction of rotation of the stage. If the point of emergence of the optic axis is in the center of the field, this is a point of no motion for the isogyre. All other centered interference figures (biaxial or uniaxial) have two isogyres.

Acute bisectrix figures are also easily distinguished from all others in case the points of emergence of the optic axes are within the field of view, a condition which obtains for those minerals whose apparent optic angle is less than 120°, assuming that the bisectrix figure is exactly centered, and that the high-power objective (Nachet 7, Fuess 7, Leitz 7, Bausch & Lomb 4 mm.) is in use. Also, any uncentered figure, in which a bisectrix (that is, the center of the black cross made by the isogyres when they meet) and one optic axis are inside of the field of view, is an uncentered acute bisectrix figure. But many common minerals, notably most of the feldspars, have apparent optic angles greater than 120°, and in such cases special tests are necessary to distinguish between acute and obtuse bisectrix figures. With centered interference figures, if the angle between the position of the black cross and the position at which the isogyres are tangent to the edge of the field be called the angle of rotation, acute bisectrix figures always have a greater angle of rotation than obtuse bisectrix figures from the same mineral; when this angle is greater than 35°, in minerals having the refringence of feldspars, the section is normal to the acute bisectrix. If the center of the figure is more than two-thirds of the radius of the field away from its center, no satisfactory measure of the angle of rotation can be made; in case the eccentricity is less, the angle of rotation is approximately equal to the average of the four angles from the position of the cross to tangency in the four quadrants. Furthermore, assuming that the thickness of the section is uniform (a condition very nearly reached in all good sections, except for occasional thinning very near the margins),

crystals or grains cut normal to the acute bisectrix give a lower interference color than crystals or grains of the same mineral cut normal
to the obtuse bisectrix (or the optic normal).   The larger the optic
angle the more closely alike are the acute and obtuse bisectrix figures,
and the interference colors produced by sections giving such figures;
at the limiting value, $2V = 90°$, which is rarely found in minerals,
there is no difference between the acute and obtuse bisectrices.   Also,
the smaller the optic angle, the more an acute bisectrix figure approaches a uniaxial figure, which is the limiting case of the former.

Obtuse bisectrix figures are distinguished from acute bisectrix
figures by the methods just described; they are distinguished from
optic normal figures by similar means.   Thus, an angle of rotation
less than 10° is characteristic of the optic normal, and an angle less
than 15°, given by a feldspar or any mineral of similar refringence,
implies a section normal to an obtuse bisectrix or an optic normal.
If the angle of rotation is between 10° and 35°, the safe method of
distinguishing between the various biaxial figures consists in finding
crystals or grains of a given mineral, which give each type of biaxial
interference figure (except the optic axis), and comparing them.   In
a given mineral the angle of rotation is always greatest in the acute
bisectrix figure, less in the obtuse bisectrix figure, and smallest in the
optic normal figure.   Furthermore, the interference color of a single
mineral, in crystals or grains of uniform thickness, is highest in sections normal to an optic normal, somewhat lower in crystals cut
normal to an obtuse bisectrix, still lower in those cut normal to an
acute bisectrix, and lowest in sections giving an optic axis interference
figure.

The birefringence of a mineral is measured by the difference
between its maximum and minimum indices of refraction; and the
only section through which light travels in such a direction that, for
the two rays produced, the crystal has these indices is the section parallel to the optic plane, which gives the optic normal interference figure.
The birefringence of all other sections is less than the birefringence
of the mineral; the birefringence in any given case may be called
a partial birefringence of the mineral, or the birefringence of a given
section.   The birefringence of a section giving a bisectrix is related
in a simple way to the birefringence of the mineral and the optic
angle; indeed if:

$2V_a$ = the acute optic angle;
$2V_o$ = the obtuse optic angle;

B_m = the birefringence of the mineral;
B_a = the birefringence of the acute bisectrix section;
B_o = the birefringence of the obtuse bisectrix section.

Then: [1]

$$\sin^2 V_a = \frac{B_a}{B_m} = K \quad \text{and} \quad \sin^2 V_o = \frac{B_o}{B_m} = K'.$$

A graphic solution of these equations is given in Fig. 246, a diagram which may be used to deduce the optic angle if any two bire-

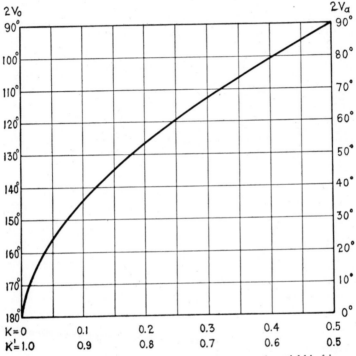

FIG. 246.—Relation between optic angle, birefringence, and partial birefringence:
$$K \text{ and } K' = \frac{\text{partial birefringence}}{\text{birefringence}}.$$

fringences (B_m, B_a, B_o) are known; or the birefringence of the mineral, if the optic angle and either partial birefringence are known; or either partial birefringence, if the optic angle and the birefringence of the mineral are known. In ordinary work, results obtained are only approximations, because the usual measurements of the birefringence and of the optic angle are not very accurate.

[1] Compare the equations on pages 169, 170.

Uses of biaxial interference figures.—Biaxial interference figures are useful in even more ways than uniaxial figures. The more important uses to which they may be put relate to (1) dispersion; (2) pleochroism and absorption; (3) system of crystallization; (4) crystallographic orientation of section and of optic plane; (5) birefringence of the mineral and of bisectrix sections; (6) size of optic angle; (7) sign of the mineral.

1. Dispersion.—In thin sections the type of dispersion is indeterminable in many cases, because the dispersion is weak in most minerals, and a much thicker section is required to make the effects visible. If the kind of dispersion can be determined, it is of aid in identifying the mineral, and also may lead to a knowledge of the system of crystallization and of the orientation of the section. If a bisectrix figure is symmetrical with respect to the optic plane and the plane normal thereto, the only dispersion is that of the optic axes, which may be $r > v$ or $r < v$, according as the convex side of the isogyre is bordered by red or by blue. If the bisectrix figure is symmetrical with respect to the optic plane, or to the plane normal thereto, or to the center of the figure, the dispersion is inclined, or horizontal, or crossed, and the dispersion of the optic axes, also present, may be either $r > v$ or $r < v$. If the bisectrix figure is without any symmetry, the dispersion is conveniently described as a combination of the preceding types.

2. Pleochroism and absorption.—Biaxial minerals may have three different colors, of three different intensities, along three rectangular axes, which coincide with the ellipsoid axes in orthorhombic crystals and nearly coincide with them in all biaxial minerals. Accordingly, it is customary to describe the pleochroism and absorption of each ellipsoid axis. A section normal to a bisectrix or an optic normal is sufficient to give the colors and intensities for the two ellipsoid axes in the plane of the section. The color and intensity for a given ellipsoid axis are seen, without the upper nicol, by placing that axis in the plane of vibration of the lower nicol, so that the light passes through the mineral vibrating in the direction of that axis. From a section normal to a different bisectrix or to the optic normal, the color and intensity of two ellipsoid axes are obtained, and one of these two is the one not obtained from the first section. Thus, the complete pleochroism and absorption formulas are obtained from two sections of suitable orientation.

3. System of crystallization.—Any kind of a biaxial interference

figure serves at once to prove that the mineral producing it is orthorhombic, or monoclinic, or triclinic in crystallization.   In case the
dispersion can be made out, it suffices to fix exactly the system of
crystallization, since dispersion only of the optic axes implies the
orthorhombic system, while inclined, horizontal, or crossed dispersion belongs to monoclinic crystals, and combinations of dispersion
of several types are characteristic of the triclinic system.

4. **Crystallographic orientation of section and of optic plane.**—
Without a knowledge of the dispersion, a biaxial interference figure
gives no information in regard to the crystallographic orientation of
a section producing it, unless the system of crystallization of the mineral is known.   If a mineral is known from its dispersion or crystal
form, or from some other source, to be orthorhombic, it follows that
any section which gives a centered bisectrix or optic normal figure
must be parallel to one of the pinacoids, either 100, 010, or 001.   If a
mineral is known, from its dispersion or by other means, to be monoclinic, any section giving a bisectrix or optic normal figure is, in general,
not parallel with either 100 or 001, but either parallel or normal to
010.   If a crystal is triclinic, a section producing a centered interference figure may have any relation whatever to the crystal faces,
depending only upon the mineral itself.   The following table summar-
izes the relations between dispersion and orientation:

RELATIONS BETWEEN DISPERSION AND ORIENTATION

Dispersion of Bisectrix	Plane of Section is	Optic Plane is
Rhombic............................	Parallel to a pinacoid	Parallel to a pinacoid
Inclined............................	Normal to 010	Parallel to 010
Horizontal......	Normal to 010	Normal to 010
Crossed............................	Parallel to 010	Normal to 010
Combination........................	Unknown	Unknown

5. **Birefringence.**—In general, the birefringence of any mineral
is most readily estimated by finding the highest interference color
which it gives, learning the thickness of the section, and using these
data to deduce the difference in the indices from Fig. 131 or the colored table of birefringences of Michel Lévy.   If the thickness of the
section is known, a bisectrix figure may also be used to estimate the
birefringence, by employing the fact that the retardation is equal
to the number of red (or more accurately, sensitive tint) color curves
between the optic axis and the center of the figure, as illustrated in

Figs. 198–201.   The birefringence of a bisectrix figure may be used to distinguish between it and the other bisectrix or the optic normal figure, as previously explained.   It may also be used, in connection with the optic angle, to deduce the birefringence of other sections, by means of the relation given in Fig. 246.

6. Size of optic angle.—An acute bisectrix figure may be used to determine the size of the apparent optic angle, if the two optic axes are in the field of view, by measuring from one to the other, and calculating the angle or using the graphic solution of Fig. 204.   An optic axis figure may be used to estimate the true optic angle by comparison with Fig. 205.

7. Sign of the mineral.—The most important use to which biaxial interference figures are put is probably the determination of the optical character, or sign, of the mineral.

Biaxial minerals are positive in case Z, the direction of vibration of the slowest ray (for which the crystal has the greatest index) is the acute bisectrix; and negative in case X, the direction of vibration of the fastest ray (for which the index is the least) bisects the acute optic angle.   The sign may be determined from any one of the biaxial interference figures, that is, from either bisectrix, from the optic normal, or from either optic axis; and no interference figure in which no one of these directions emerges within (or at least very near) the field of view should be used for this purpose.

Determination of sign from optic axis figure.—The simplest methods of determining the sign of biaxial minerals are those involving the use of optic axis interference figures.   In every section normal to an optic axis, the acute bisectrix is on the convex side of the isogyre in the 45° position, at which position the isogyre has its maximum curvature.   In the same position the optic plane is normal to the tangent to the isogyre at its vertex, and Y is normal to the optic plane.   In case the optic angle is very nearly equal to 90°, the direction of curvature is indeterminable (as may be seen in Fig. 205), and the sign cannot be learned from the optic axis interference figure.   Fortunately, minerals whose optic angle is very near 90° are not common; when the sign is indeterminable from an optic axis figure (assuming that the figure is well centered), it is difficult or impossible to determine it by any microscopic methods.   If the optic axis figure is not well centered, it may be impossible to distinguish the direction of curvature and to learn the sign from it, although a bisectrix or a well-centered optic axis might give it promptly.

In order to understand the determination of the optic sign of a mineral from an optic axis interference figure it is important to recall the fact that light traveling through a crystal in all directions within the plane of the optic axes produces two wave fronts, as shown in Fig. 246a and described more fully in connection with Fig. 178 (page 162). The light traveling along any one path in this plane (not an optic axis) consists of two rays which differ in velocity; one ray vibrates normal to the optic plane (therefore parallel with Y) and the other vibrates in the optic plane and at right angles to the wave-

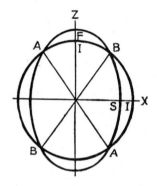

FIG. 246a.—Wave fronts in the plane of the optic axes.

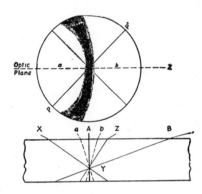

FIG. 247.—Sign from the optic axis figure.

normal of the ray. The velocity of each ray is determined by the vibration direction and not by its direction of propagation. Light traveling along X consists of two rays, one vibrating parallel with Y and one vibrating parallel with Z; by definition the latter is the slow ray. Light traveling along Z consists of two rays, one vibrating parallel with Y and one vibrating parallel with X; by definition the latter is the fast ray. It is evident from Fig. 246a that any light traveling along any path between the optic axis and Z consists of two rays of which the ray vibrating parallel with Y is the slow one, while that vibrating nearly parallel with X is the fast one. Similarly, light traveling along any path between A and X consists of two rays of which the ray vibrating parallel with Y is the fast one and that vibrating nearly parallel with Z is the slow one. Therefore the ray vibrating parallel with Y is the slow ray for light emerging at a point b (Fig. 247) between A and Z and is the fast ray for light emerging at a point a between A and X. Accordingly, if any one of the auxiliary plates (mica plate, sensitive tint plate, or quartz wedge) is superposed over this interference figure with the direction of vibration of its slow ray parallel with the optic plane, the retardation of the slow rays on the concave side is increased, while the difference of phase due to the speed of the fast rays on the convex side is decreased. The interference color at any point on the concave side is raised, and at any point on the convex side it is lowered. More specifically, if the mica plate is used, a dark spot is produced at some point on the convex side where the lowering of the interference color amounts to compensation; if a sensitive tint plate is used, a yellow color appears instead of a dark spot; if a quartz wedge is used the colors move toward the acute bisectrix. If the acute bisectrix is the direction of vibration of the fast ray, that is, the ellipsoid axis X, all these effects are reversed. In the first case the mineral is positive; in the second case it is negative.

If a mica plate is superposed over an optic axis interference figure in its $45°$ position with the Z axis of the plate parallel with the optic plane of the mineral, the latter is positive if a dark spot appears on the convex side of the isogyre, and negative if it appears on the concave side.

If a sensitive tint plate is used in the same way, the mineral is positive if the isogyre is bordered by yellow on the convex side, and negative if the yellow color appears on the concave side.

If a quartz wedge is used in the same way, the mineral is positive if the colors move toward the acute bisectrix on insertion of the wedge thin edge forward, and the negative if they move toward the obtuse bisectrix.

Determination of sign from the acute bisectrix figure.—The determination of the sign from a bisectrix interference figure is a process consisting of two parts; it is necessary, first, to find out whether the figure is that of the acute or that of the obtuse bisectrix, and second, to learn whether X or Z is normal to the section. The first step is accomplished by using the distinctions between acute and obtuse bisectrices already described. If the figure is the acute bisectrix, the sign is positive if Z is normal to the section, and negative if X is normal thereto.

If the optic angle is not very large, so that one or both optic axes are inside the field of view, the sign may be determined by the same methods applied to uniaxial figures from basal sections, by turning the stage to the position of the dark cross and inserting one of the plates. The dark spots produced by a mica plate do not appear along the line bisecting the quadrants, and the line connecting them is not parallel (or normal) to the direction of vibration of the plate. But they appear in opposite quadrants near the optic axes, as in Figs. 248–249, and a line connecting them makes an approximate plus or minus sign with the arrow of the plate (as with uniaxial minerals); or a substitute line connecting the central points of the given quadrants may be used to make the sign. If the sensitive tint plate is used, yellow spots appear near each optic axis within the first color curve, in place of the dark spots. With the quartz wedge the colors move out from the center and from the optic axes in those quadrants in which the dark spots are formed with the mica plate, and move in toward these points in the other quadrants. The first pair of quadrants may be used to give the sign. But the movement of the color curves may be seen to better advantage in the 45° position, as in Fig. 250. If the wedge is inserted thin edge forward, with the axis of vibration of the slow ray parallel with the optic plane, the mineral is positive if the colors move from the optic axes to the bisectrix and thence outward at right angles to the optic plane, as indicated by the arrows in the figure. If this motion is reversed the mineral is nega-

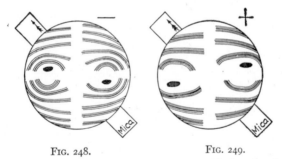

FIG. 248.   FIG. 249.

FIGS. 248, 249.—Sign from acute bisectrix figure with the mica plate.

tive. Notice that the shafts of the arrows near their heads make a plus sign with the arrow of the plate.

If the optic angle is large and the optic axes are outside of the field of view, other methods are commonly employed. When the stage is rotated to the 45° position, the trace of the optic plane is in those quadrants in which the isogyres left the field, and Y is at right angles to the optic plane. If color curves are present, the sign may be determined with the quartz wedge by the method just described. Otherwise, after Y has been located from the interference figure, the ocular may be replaced, or the Bertrand lens removed so that the mineral may be seen; if the interference color of the mineral rises upon the introduction of a mica or sensitive tint plate with its axis Z

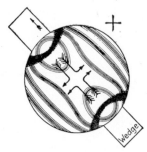

parallel with Y of the mineral, the direction of vibration in the plane of the section at right angles to Y must be X, since the ray vibrating parallel to Y travels more slowly than that vibrating parallel to X, but more rapidly than that vibrating to Z; therefore X is the obtuse bisectrix, Z is the acute bisectrix and the mineral is positive. If the interference color falls when the plate is introduced in this way, the mineral is negative.

FIG. 250.—Sign from acute bisectrix figure with the quartz wedge.

Determination of sign from obtuse bisectrix or optic normal figure. —It is necessary, first of all, to distinguish between these figures and the acute bisectrix, but it is not necessary to distinguish the obtuse bisectrix figure from the optic normal figure, so far as its use in determining the sign is concerned. The methods just described for acute bisectrix figures from minerals of large optic angle apply equally well to obtuse bisectrix and optic normal figures, if the statement of results is reversed. With the obtuse bisectrix figure the trace of the optic plane is in those quadrants in which the isogyres leave and enter the field, and therefore the acute bisectrix is in these quadrants; with the optic normal figure the acute bisectrix is in the same quadrants. If the slow ray vibrates in the direction of the acute bisectrix, the mineral is positive; otherwise it is negative.

DIRECTIONS FOR LABORATORY WORK

Biaxial interference figures.—Observe biaxial interference figures in thick plates with a conoscope; also with a microscope; use oriented sections and thick cleavage pieces of muscovite. Note especially the movements of the dark isogyres as the stage is rotated. The distance from the point of emergence of an optic axis to the first color curve depends upon the same factors as the distance from the center of the black cross to the first colored ring in uniaxial interference figures. Prove this by suitable experiments. Make drawings of several biaxial interference figures at the position of extinction and at the 45° position. Use oriented plates and sections and indicate the position of the vibration planes of the nicols in your drawings.

Study the differences between interference figures in sections (1) normal to an optic axis, (2) normal to the acute bisectrix (muscovite lamella), (3) normal to the obtuse bisectrix, (4) normal to the optic normal. Notice that the interference color varies in these different sections even when the mineral and the thickness remain constant.

Why? How can these interference figures be distinguished one from another? Note especially methods of distinguishing between the acute and the obtuse bisectrix. Use the difference in interference colors to find interference figures of definite orientation in thin sections. Make drawings showing, for each mineral, each of the four oriented interference figures (optic axis, optic normal, and two bisectrices). Draw the complete interference figure (the unseen portion in dotted lines), and indicate the position of the field of view and the planes of the nicols.

Study biaxial interference figures of indefinite orientation. Such figures are not as simple as homologous uniaxial figures, but they are even more important. Make several drawings illustrating cases in which the approximate position of the whole interference figure can be determined from such " partial " figures.

Measurement of optic angle.—The optic angle cannot be measured by ordinary microscopic methods, except in cases in which the apparent angle is so small that both optic axes are in the field of view.

Measure the distance $2D$, in such a figure, and calculate $2E$, after establishing the constant of your microscope with a section of a mineral, like aragonite, having a small known optic angle. Also use Schwarzmann's double scale to obtain $2E$. Use oriented sections and muscovite cleavages.

Study the dispersion of the optic axes in orthorhombic crystals with the conoscope and the microscope. Use oriented sections and plates. Notice that the dispersion is usually too weak to be important in thin sections. But brookite, goethite, etc., show strong dispersion even in thin sections.

Study the dispersion of the bisectrices in monoclinic crystals, with the conoscope and the microscope. Use oriented sections and plates and compare your results with the drawings. Notice the relation of the symmetry of the interference figure to that of the crystal.

Distinctions between biaxial and uniaxial interference figures.—There is no difficulty in distinguishing biaxial from uniaxial interference figures when both are of definite orientation, except in the case of the optic normal and the uniaxial figure from a vertical section. In general, the last-named figures should not be used for this purpose. They are readily eliminated, since they are produced by anhedra or crystals giving the highest interference colors. With interference figures of indefinite orientation, the distinction can often (but not always) be made. For this purpose remember that the black lines of the uniaxial figure remain straight or very nearly so, except in the case already eliminated, while the isogyres of biaxial figures usually show very marked curvature. Also, it often happens that the biaxial isogyre is neither straight nor parallel with a nicol when it passes through the center of the field; in the same position the uniaxial isogyre is always straight and parallel with one nicol. Use thin sections of granite or of a related rock.

Relative velocities of transmitted rays.—The relative velocities of transmitted rays can be determined in exactly the same ways as with uniaxial minerals. But with biaxial minerals, instead of two characteristic velocities, there are three, corresponding to the three axes of the ellipsoid. When the interference figure shows that the section is perpendicular to any one of these axes, light will travel through the section with the velocities characteristic of the other two axes. Any interference figure of definite orientation will give the location of the optic plane, normal to which is the axis Y. Consequently, any section normal to X, Y, or Z can be used to determine the position of the other two axes (since X is the axis of vibration of the fastest ray and Z of the slowest). For this purpose use oriented sections first, and then use sections of hornblende in diorite.

Pleochroism and absorption formulas are determined in biaxial minerals in much the same way as in uniaxial crystals, but each formula relates to three ellipsoid axes instead of two. Determine the pleochroism and the absorption formula of hornblende in sections of diorite.

Optic orientation.—In studying the optic orientation of a mineral it is necessary to know something about the crystallographic characters. These may be either crystal form, cleavages, or twinning planes. The following illustrations will make this clear.

Staurolite is orthorhombic, and the crystals are usually short prisms with the base and brachypinacoid. It has distinct cleavage parallel to the brachypinacoid and less distinct cleavage parallel to the prism faces. Examine oriented sections which are cut parallel to the base, and show the four prism faces and the brachypinacoid faces. How can you distinguish which faces are brachypinacoidal? Where is the best cleavage? To what face is extinction parallel? Now get the interference figure. How is the plane of the optic axes related to the brachypinacoid? The axis a is parallel to the brachypinacoid and b is normal to it. How is the optic plane related to a and b? To which crystal axis is Y parallel? By determining the relative velocities of the transmitted rays, find out whether Z or X is in the plane of the section with Y. Since Y is parallel to a, either Z or X must be parallel to b, and the other must be parallel to c. Now write the formula, showing the optic orientation of staurolite. ($Z \parallel$?. $Y \parallel$?. $X \parallel$?). Then study slides of different orientation, namely, those which are cut parallel to oɪo. The elongation, with poor prismatic cleavage, locates c; a is normal to c. Notice that extinction is parallel to the cleavage. Find the optic plane and determine the optic orientation from this section also. Make diagrams of a section of staurolite cut (1) parallel to ooɪ, (2) parallel to oɪo, (3) parallel to ɪoo, and indicate in each, as far as possible, the position of the cleavage, the crystallographic axes, the ellipsoid axes, the optic axes, the optic plane, and the optic angle.

Orthoclase is monoclinic, and simple crystals are usually short prisms with the clinopinacoid, base, and frequently an orthodome and unit pyramid. It has perfect cleavage parallel to the base, and very good cleavage parallel to the clinopinacoid. Examine slides which are cut parallel to the base. Find the direction of the clinopinacoid. The interference figure is that of the optic normal, and the hyperbolas locate the acute bisectrix. Notice extinction parallel with the cleavage. By determining the relative velocities of the transmitted rays, find out whether Z or X is the acute bisectrix. Since the section is practically normal to Y, what axis is parallel to b? Now draw a diagram of a clinopinacoidal section ($\beta = 116°$), showing the crystal outline, the cleavages, the crystallographic axes, the axes of the triaxial ellipsoid, and the optic plane. Then study slides which are cut parallel to the clinopinacoid. To what face is the cleavage parallel? Is the extinction parallel with the cleavage? Determine whether X or Z is in the section with Y. The other must be normal to the section. The interference figure is the obtuse bisectrix, as is indicated by the rapid movement of the hyperbolas on rotation. What is the sign of orthoclase? Assuming that the optic angle ($2V$) is 70°, make a drawing showing the relation of the optic axes and ellipsoid axes to the crystallographic axes and crystal faces.

Thus far, the optic orientation has been determined only from oriented sections. By using interference figures, the optic orientation may be determined from ordinary rock sections when the crystallographic directions are in any way recognizable. For example, careful study of a rock slide, which is a random section containing numerous crystals of olivine or augite, often reveals the acute bisectrix and also the obtuse bisectrix. Detailed study of these crystals will give the optic orientation.

Determine the direction of each axis of the ellipsoid with respect to the crystallographic axes in augite or olivine, in sections of gabbro or some related coarsely crystalline rock.

Determination of sign.—Biaxial minerals are positive if Z is the acute bisectrix, and negative if X is the acute bisectrix. Consequently, the determination of the sign requires two steps: (1) finding the location of the acute bisectrix, (2) determining whether X or Z occupies this location. With optic axis figures, the first step is accomplished by noting that the acute bisectrix is on the convex side of the isogyre. Before using bisectrix figures, review the distinctions between acute and obtuse bisectrices and note that if both optic axes are in the field or only a short distance outside the field of view, the section is normal to the acute bisectrix; the same is true if one optic axis and the bisectrix are inside the field of view.

Determine the sign from sections normal to an optic axis. Use oriented sections, if possible, and also crystals or grains in rock sections (the crystals of correct orientation may be found by selecting those of the given mineral which give the lowest interference color—usually almost dark and showing little change on rotation). Use the dark spot produced by a mica plate, the yellow spot produced by a sensitive tint plate, and the direction of movement of the colors produced by a quartz wedge.

Determine the optic sign from sections normal to the acute bisectrix in minerals of small optic angle. Do this directly from the interference figure, by observing the quadrants in which the dark spots are produced by a mica plate or the yellow color by the sensitive tint plate. Do this also by finding the position of Y, inserting the ocular, and determining whether X or Z is in the plane of the section with Y. Use oriented sections first, and then use sections of muscovite or hornblende in rock slides.

Determine the optic sign from sections normal to an acute bisectrix in minerals of large optic angle. Trial will show that the first method of the preceding paragraph is usually inapplicable, but the second method is satisfactory. Determine the optic sign of augite from sections normal to the acute bisectrix in slides of gabbro.

Determine the optic sign from sections normal to an obtuse bisectrix. The methods used with an acute bisectrix in minerals of large optic angle are also applicable to obtuse bisectrices in any mineral. It is only necessary to remember that, if Z or X is proved to be in the obtuse bisectrix, then the other one will occupy the acute bisectrix and determine the sign. Determine the optic sign of olivine from crystals cut normal to an obtuse bisectrix in slides of olivine gabbro.

Determine the optic sign from sections normal to the optic normal, by the use of the sensitive tint plate or mica plate. Use oriented sections and sections of hornblende in slides of diorite.

CHAPTER XIX

BIAXIAL MINERALS

MOST of the important rock-forming minerals have two optic axes; therefore, the microscopic characters of biaxial minerals are extremely important. They may be tabulated, as a guide in study, as follows:

A. Chief Microscopic Characters of Biaxial Minerals.

I. With ordinary light or with plane polarized light through lower nicol.
1. Estimate the index of refraction from the relief.
2. Observe the color or colors.
3. Study the cleavage.
4. Determine the crystal system. This may be done sometimes by the aid of crystal outline or cleavage forms, but frequently it is necessary to use crossed nicols and extinction angles or dispersion.
5. Study inclusions.
6. Study alterations. Inclusions and alterations are often studied to advantage between crossed nicols.

II. With parallel or with convergent light between crossed nicols.
7. Determine the birefringence by means of the highest interference color.
8. Determine the optic sign.
9. Estimate the optic angle.
10. Study the dispersion.
11. Determine the optic orientation. This is only possible with recognizable crystal form or cleavages.
12. Determine extinction angles.
13. Determine the direction and sign of elongation.
14. Study the twinning.
15. Determine the absorption formula.
16. Determine the pleochroism formula.
17. Study the textural relations to adjacent minerals.
18. Study the associated minerals.
19. Study the petrologic or geologic mode of occurrence.
20. Note the diagnostics.

B. Orthorhombic Minerals

In addition to the orthorhombic minerals selected for study, others of importance include two which are common alteration products, namely, serpentine and talc; one that is produced by

214

mineralizing gases, namely, topaz; and three that are characteristic of metamorphic rocks, namely, andalusite, sillimanite, and cordierite.

The following descriptions give a few of the more prominent characters as a guide in preliminary study. Refer to descriptive textbooks, in all cases, for more complete descriptions.

Enstatite, $MgSiO_3$.—Colorless with rather high relief (1.66) and weak birefringence (0.009). Distinct prismatic cleavage making an angle of about 93°. Parallel extinction. Positive with large optic angle.

Hypersthene, $(Mg,Fe)SiO_3$.—Distinct prismatic cleavage at an angle of about 93°. Weakly pleochroic in green and brown tints. Refringence high (1.70); birefringence moderate (0.013). Negative.

Learn the distinctions between orthorhombic and monoclinic pyroxenes, which are as follows:

1. Extinction in vertical zone: parallel in orthorhombic; inclined in monoclinic, except in sections cut parallel to 100.
2. Interference figures in cross and orthopinacoidal sections: bisectrix in orthorhombic; usually optic axis in monoclinic.
3. Parting usually parallel to optic plane in orthorhombic; usually perpendicular to same plane in monoclinic.
4. Schiller structure: especially marked in orthorhombic.
5. Dispersion: only axial dispersion in orthorhombic; axial and inclined dispersion in monoclinic.
6. Pleochroism: greater in orthorhombic than in monoclinic of the same colors.
7. Crystal outline.

Chrysolite, $(Mg,Fe)_2SiO_4$.—Refringence high (1.679); birefringence strong (0.036). Colorless. When altered it becomes yellowish, greenish, and sometimes reddish. Shagreen surface. Alters readily.

Zoisite, $HCa_2Al_3Si_3O_{13}$.—Refringence high (1.703); birefringence weak (0.005). No other common orthorhombic mineral has such weak birefringence with so high an index of refraction. Commonly an alteration product of plagioclase and then frequently in short prisms. Colorless to reddish or yellowish, and when colored, strongly pleochroic. One variety is blue between crossed nicols on account of strong dispersion.

C. Monoclinic Minerals

Besides the monoclinic minerals listed below, certain others are worthy of mention; kaolinite is a common alteration product; chondrodite and clinohumite are found in limestone metamorphosed by igneous contact; three others, namely, tremolite, glaucophane and chloritoid are found chiefly in metamorphic rocks; gypsum occurs chiefly in sedimentary rocks, especially those formed by excessive evaporation; and allanite, acmite, arfvedsonite, and riebeckite are rare constituents of igneous rocks.

The following descriptions are merely preliminary; refer to a descriptive textbook in all cases:

Augite.—Silicate of Ca, Mg, Fe, and Al, with a little Na, etc. Index of refraction high (1.715). Positive. Birefringence rather strong (0.022). Maximum extinction angle in vertical zone 38° to 54°. Colorless, pinkish or greenish. Distinct prismatic cleavages at an angle of about 93°. Augite is the common monoclinic pyroxene. When a parting parallel to 100 is developed, the mineral is sometimes called diallage. Usually not pleochroic. Alters to hornblende.

Diopside, $Ca(Mg,Fe)(SiO_3)_2$.—Closely related to augite. As Fe replaces Mg, diopside grades through salite into hedenbergite, $CaFe(SiO_3)_2$. Diopside is colorless and has stronger birefringence than augite; often it has also less dispersion and a smaller extinction angle. Positive.

Hornblende.—Chemical composition similar to that of augite. Color green to brown; absorption and pleochroism marked. Refringence moderate (1.642); birefringence rather strong (0.023), increasing with iron content to extreme. Distinct prismatic cleavages at an angle of about 124°. When studying this mineral, learn the distinctions between amphiboles and pyroxenes, which are as follows:

AMPHIBOLES	PYROXENES
Prismatic cleavage angle about 124°.	Prismatic cleavage angle about 93°.
Crystals usually long prismatic to fibrous.	Crystals usually short prismatic to granular.
Color and pleochroism marked in common species.	Color and pleochroism weak or absent in common species.
Maximum extinction angle in vertical zone 0°–25° (except arfvedsonite, etc., which have marked pleochroism in blue, green, and yellow tints).	Maximum extinction angle in vertical zone 0°–95°. Excluding orthorhombic species, it is 26°–60°, except in acmite which has negative elongation.
Most species are negative.	Most species are positive.
Alter to chlorite, biotite, etc. (Change to pyroxene only through refusion.)	Alter to amphibole, chlorite, etc.

Biotite.—Silicate of Mg, Fe, Al, K, etc. Refringence moderate; birefringence very strong (0.033 to 0.060). Basal cleavage perfect. Optic angle usually near 0°. Acute bisectrix (negative) practically perpendicular to cleavage. Color yellowish to brown or green. Absorption very marked, ray vibrating parallel to the cleavage much absorbed.

Muscovite, $H_2KAl_3(SiO_4)_3$.—Index of refraction medium (1.592). Birefringence strong (0.037). Colorless. Cleavage as in biotite, and negative acute bisectrix perpendicular to cleavage.

Chlorite.—Hydrous silicate of Mg, Fe, and Al. Index of refraction low (1.58). Birefringence weak (0.001 to 0.011). Color greenish. Usually shows a little absorption, ray vibrating parallel to cleavage being the more absorbed. Sometimes " ultra " blue under crossed nicols on account of strong dispersion.

Epidote, $HCa_2(Al,Fe)_3Si_3O_{13}$.—Index of refraction very high (1.750). Birefringence usually strong (0.037) and variable. Colorless to yellowish or greenish, usually yellowish. Pleochroic, if distinctly colored.

Titanite, $CaTiSiO_5$.—Index of refraction very high (1.905). Birefringence extreme (0.121). Colorless, yellowish, grayish, or reddish, usually the last. Sometimes pleochroic.

Orthoclase, $KAlSi_3O_8$.—Review your study of the optic orientation of orthoclase. Refringence low (1.526); birefringence weak (0.007). Simple twinning common. Negative. Optic angle usually large. Distinct rectangular cleavages (001 and 010).

D. Triclinic Minerals.

Besides the triclinic minerals selected for study, there are two uncommon ore minerals, namely, chalcanthite and rhodonite; two rare constituents of igneous rocks, namely, ænigmatite and babingtonite; one constituent of metamorphic schists, namely, cyanite; and one fumarolic product, namely, axinite, which are important.

For additional descriptions of the following minerals refer to descriptive textbooks.

The important minerals of the feldspar group are orthoclase, microcline, and the plagioclase series. Orthoclase is monoclinic; review your study of it. It is never polysynthetically twinned, but often shows simple twinning. Draw a simple and twinned crystal of orthoclase. Learn how to distinguish orthoclase from quartz and plagioclase in thin section.

Microcline, $KAlSi_3O_8$.—Like orthoclase, but almost always shows the " grating structure " due to multiple twinning on two planes nearly at right angles. Draw a section showing this structure.

Plagioclase series, $NaAlSi_3O_8$ to $CaAl_2Si_2O_8$.—Colorless. Refringence low (1.535 to 1.585); birefringence weak (0.008±). Optic angle very large; optic sign + or −. Distinct nearly rectangular cleavages (oo1 and o1o). Polysynthetic twinning very frequent. Draw two adjacent twinning lamellæ of plagioclase, showing equal extinction angles, and indicate in each lamella the position of the cleavage and the vibration directions for light.

It should be noticed that orthoclase, microcline, and plagioclase can be roughly separated by means of the twinning, since orthoclase never shows multiple twinning, while microcline almost always shows the grating structure, and plagioclase is very frequently polysynthetically twinned. But such a separation is only approximate, and in careful work it must be verified or corrected by other means. This is all the more important since, even in twinned crystals of microcline, sections parallel to o1o show only one direction of twinning, and even in twinned plagioclase similar sections show no twinning (of the ordinary type). The other characters of special importance as diagnostics include: (1) extinction angles in sections normal to a bisectrix, an optic axis or an optic normal, (2) extinction angles in sections of recognizable zones, especially the zone normal to o1o, (3) extinction angles in cleavage flakes, (4) index of refraction as compared with that of Canada balsam or quartz by means of the method of normal or of oblique illumination.

The feldspars are so abundant and important that their correct determination is indispensable; the simple distinction between orthoclase, microcline, and plagioclase is not sufficient; the exact species of plagioclase must be determined. For this purpose two types of optical methods are especially useful; one is based on variations in the indices of refraction and their comparison with substances of known index, such as Canada balsam and quartz; the other is based on extinction angles in definite zones or in sections of known orientation. The most important data for these methods are assembled in graphic form in Fig. 251, which is only slightly modified from the diagram prepared by F. E. Wright.[1]

The curves showing extinction angles in combined albite-Carlsbad twinning permit the determination of the composition of the plagioclase from a single crystal or anhedron which is cut in the zone normal to o1o, if both these types of twinning are present. Such crystals may be recognized by the fact that at the 45° position the albite twinning disappears and the crystal appears as a simple Carlsbad twin, and at the o° position both the albite and Carlsbad twinning dis-

[1] *Am. Jour. Sci.*, XXXVI, 1913.

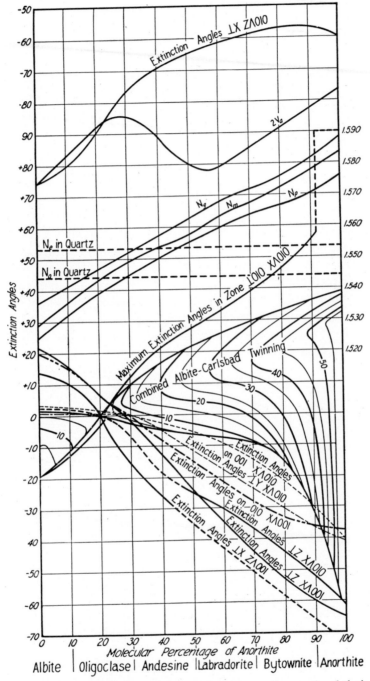

FIG. 251.—Diagrammatic summary of the more important optic properties of plagioclase. Optic angle curve modified from Nikitin: *Tsch. Min. Pet. Mit.* XLIV, 1933, p. 117. Maximum equal extinction angle curve (in zone normal to 010) as corrected by S. Tsuboi: Proc. Imp. Acad. Tokyo, XI, 1935, p. 423.

appear, except for fine black lines due to overlapping of the albite lamellæ. Such sections will give symmetrical extinction angles in the albite lamellæ in each part of the Carlsbad twin. In the diagram, the horizontal lines express the symmetrical extinction angles of that part of the Carlsbad twin which gives the smaller equal extinction angles, while the full line curves express the symmetrical extinction angles of the other part of the Carlsbad twin. The vertical lines give the percentage of anorthite.

In using these curves there is no possibility of confusion except in cases in which both pairs of symmetrical extinction angles are 16° or less; and in such cases, if the two parts of the Carlsbad twin show practically no difference in birefringence at the 45° position, the plagioclase is more acid than oligoclase (Ab_5An_1); and if a distinct difference (0.003 or more) appears, the plagioclase is more basic than oligoclase. Sections inclined as much as 10° from the zone normal to 010 may be used with approximate accuracy, by adopting the average of the unsymmetrical extinctions as equivalent to the symmetrical extinction angle that would be obtained if the orientation were correct.

CHAPTER XX

SPECIAL METHODS OF STUDY

There are certain methods of microscopic study of minerals which are becoming steadily more important as their technique becomes simplified and more widely known. Probably the most important of these are the methods of the universal stage and the index-variation methods with immersion liquids. Both these methods can be studied to the best advantage only after acquiring a thorough knowledge of the petrographic microscope and the optical principles controlling the effects of all types of crystals upon polarized light.

The universal stage of Fedoroff is a device which is intended to replace, or be used upon, the ordinary stage of a petrographic microscope; its chief feature is the provision for inclining or rotating the stage, not only about the axis of the microscope (as in the ordinary stage), but also about other axes which are horizontal or make variable angles with the axis of the microscope. Another essential feature of the universal stage is the presence of glass hemispheres, one above and one below the stage bearing the thin section. With these two features provided, it is possible to observe the effects of a thin section of a mineral upon light passing through it not only normal to its surfaces, but also at any angle [1] to those surfaces in any direction from the normal. Furthermore, the universal stage is equipped with scales so that the angular rotation about any of its axes may be read off directly.

The universal stage has certain inherent limitations which have delayed its wide usage. These are particularly:

1. As at present constructed (see Fig. 252), the universal stage requires a considerable working distance between the objective and

---

[1] Theoretically the limit of this angle is 90°, but this requires that the mineral, the immersion liquids, the glass slide, the cover glass, and the glass hemispheres all have exactly the same index of refraction; practically, the ordinary limit of this angle is about 60° or 70°.

the condenser, which is greater than is available on older petrographic microscopes. However, modern microscopes have sufficient working distance and some of them are specially provided with threaded screw-holes to enable the universal stage to be attached easily to the ordinary stage of the microscope.

2. The presence of the large glass hemispheres makes it impossible to use objectives of high magnification with the universal stage. It is therefore not possible to observe interference figures of large angular

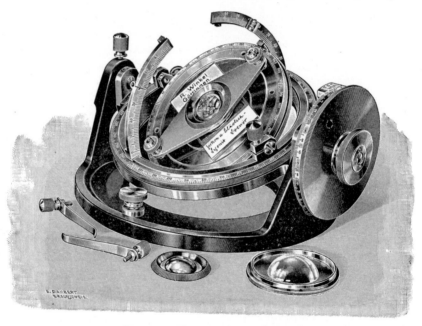

FIG. 252.—The Fedoroff universal stage.

aperture while using it. However, universal stage methods give better extinction with objectives of very small angular aperture, usually accomplished with an adjustable diaphragm in the objective. Such objectives are made with satisfactory magnification up to 20× while retaining a working distance to accommodate the standard hemispheres of universal stages. Moreover, a special objective used with a very small hemisphere (see Fig. 89 on page 69) and a high power ocular permits magnifications of 500 diameters, and observation of interference figures with about five sevenths of the ordinary angular aperture.

3. To obtain good results with the universal stage it is necessary

to use parallel light; therefore the plane mirror should be employed and the condenser should be removed. Indeed, for highly accurate results, it is worth while to have special objectives of very small aperture, which so reduce the amount of light transmitted that a powerful light-source is also desirable, such as direct sunlight or a "Lilliput" arc light.

Uniaxial minerals are in general so simple in optic orientation and identification that the universal stage is not needed in their study.

The object of the universal stage is to determine the complete optic orientation of any transparent biaxial mineral in a rock thin section with sufficient accuracy for the determination of the mineral. The determination of the complete optic orientation naturally includes learning the exact position, not only of the axes X, Y, and Z, but also of the optic axes, A and B. It therefore includes the measurement of the true optic angle, the determination of the optic sign, and the determination of the position of the axes, X, Y, and Z, not only with respect to A and B, but also with respect to the normal to the section and with respect to any crystallographic directions or planes which may be observed.

The theory of the universal stage is very simple. Fig. 253 represents a vertical section through a thin section of a mineral (M) on the object glass (P) and beneath the cover-glass (C). Glass hemispheres (H) are placed above and below the thin section and air is

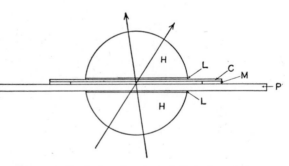

FIG. 253.—Vertical section through the universal stage.

excluded by means of a suitable oil or other liquid (L) between the hemispheres and the section. Then it is obvious that if the mineral to be studied is placed in the center of the hemispheres, light may travel in any direction through it without suffering refraction at the surfaces which are in contact with air, since these surfaces are normal to the path of the light no matter what its direction may be, as illustrated by the arrows. Now, if the mineral, the object-glass, the cover-glass, the hemispheres and the immersion liquids (including balsam or other liquid next to the mineral) all have exactly the same index of refraction, light will pass through the mineral in any direction without suffering refraction at any surface. This is an ideal condition rarely attained; but, since all the surfaces between the hemispheres are parallel, any refraction at these surfaces will only offset the path of the light slightly without changing its direction. Therefore it is possible to measure the angle between the optic axes of any mineral, provided the directions of the optic axes can be found and recognized. In ordinary petrographic work without the universal stage such directions are commonly recognized by obtaining interference figures; when using the universal stage it is impossible to obtain interference figures of large angular aperture [1] and therefore a different method is used to recognize the directions of the optic axes. The optic axes are directions of no double refraction; therefore, these directions may be recognized by the fact that when the light travels along one of them the section remains dark in all positions of rotation about the axis of the microscope. In order to make this method of recognizing the optic axial directions at all accurate, it is evident that parallel light must be employed; otherwise, only part of the light would be traveling in the given direction. Therefore objectives of low power should be used, preferably of very small aperture, and iris diaphragms are also useful to further reduce the angular aperture. For very accurate work it is desirable to reduce the aperture so much that ordinary daylight is not sufficiently intense as a source of light, and direct sunlight or some arc light, such as a "Lilliput," is needed.

However, the direction of the light through the glass hemispheres is not exactly the same as the direction of the light through the mineral, unless the index of refraction of the mineral is exactly the same as that of the glass, and such a condition is almost never realized. In general, with the universal stage, every direction which is measured, such as the position of an optic axis, A or B, or a triaxial ellipsoid axis, X, Y or Z, is the direction which the light (traveling in the mineral along the given axis) takes in the glass hemispheres. To find its direction in the mineral it is necessary to correct the measured angle between the given direction and the normal to the surface of the thin section by means of the relation between the index of the mineral and that of the glass hemispheres. This correction is easily understood by referring to Fig. 203 on page 187 which is used to explain a similar correc-

---

[1] The special objective made by Bausch and Lomb described on page 222 gives a numerical aperture of 0.50, as compared with a numerical aperture of 0.65 found in ordinary objectives, and a numerical aperture of 0.20 found in objectives usually employed with the universal stage.

tion to change the angle E to V. In using the universal stage the mathematical relation is:

$$\frac{N \text{ (of mineral)}}{N \text{ (of glass)}} = \frac{\text{sine of observed angle}}{\text{sine of angle of mineral}}$$

It would be very difficult to find the optic axes in a random section directly; they are found by making use of one more fact, namely: any section at extinction which is cut parallel with X (or Y or Z) can be rotated on X (or Y or Z) without disturbing the extinction. Expressed in other words, if the normal to the section lies in any one of the planes XY, YZ, or XZ (that is, in any one of the planes of symmetry of the triaxial ellipsoid or optic symmetry planes of the mineral), the section may be rotated on a horizontal [1] axis normal to that plane without disturbing the extinction. This is the fact which is used in finding the optic symmetry planes of the mineral, that is, the planes XY, YZ, and XZ. It is evident that with the universal stage it is quite unnecessary to hunt for a section which is parallel with X, Y or Z; or, in other words, one whose normal lies in one of the planes XY, YZ, or XZ; on the contrary, any section can be turned or tilted on one or both of the horizontal axes until it is equivalent to such a section, that is, until an axis X, Y or Z lies in the horizontal plane. Then it may be turned on a vertical axis until this X, Y or Z axis coincides with the N–S cross-hair; in this position the crystal can be turned on the E–W horizontal axis [2] without disturbing the extinction. When this has been accomplished one of the planes, XY, YZ, or XZ is in vertical position, including the axis of the microscope and the N–S cross-hair. The coordinates of this optic symmetry plane (on the scales for the N–S horizontal axis and for the inner stage vertical axis) are read and recorded. The next step is to find the position of a second optic symmetry plane in the same crystal. This may be done in an entirely similar manner; when its coordinates have been obtained the coordinates of the line of intersection of the two planes (which must be one of the optic symmetry axes, X, Y or Z) may be obtained graphically by the aid of a stereographic plat such as shown in Fig. 254, or by direct calculation by means of the following equations: [3]

---

[1] In using the universal stage the microscope may be assumed to be always upright with the stage horizontal.

[2] The nomenclature of the universal stage used here is fully described on page 240.

[3] M. Berek: N. Jahrb. Min. Beil. Bd., XLVIII, 1923, p. 50.

$$\tan (\alpha'_{I\text{-}S} - \alpha'''_{I\text{-}S}) = \frac{1}{\sin (\alpha'_{I\text{-}S} - \alpha''_{I\text{-}S})} \frac{\tan \alpha''_{N\text{-}S}}{\tan \alpha'_{N\text{-}S}} - \cot (\alpha'_{I\text{-}S} - \alpha''_{I\text{-}S})$$

$$\tan \alpha'''_{N\text{-}S} = \frac{\tan \alpha'_{N\text{-}S}}{\cos (\alpha'_{I\text{-}S} - \alpha'''_{I\text{-}S})},$$

if $\alpha'_{I\text{-}S}$ and $\alpha'_{N\text{-}S}$ are the coordinates of the first optic symmetry plane on the inner stage axis and the $N\text{-}S$ horizontal axis, $\alpha''_{I\text{-}S}$ and

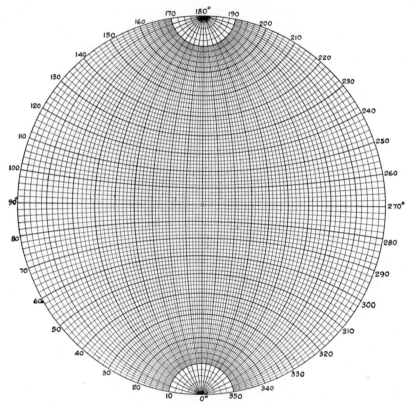

Fig. 254.—Stereographic plat of Wulff (*Zeit. Kryst.*, xxxi, p. 1).

$\alpha''_{N\text{-}S}$ are the coordinates of the second optic symmetry plane on the inner stage axis and the $N\text{-}S$ horizontal axis, and $\alpha'''_{I\text{-}S}$ and $\alpha'''_{N\text{-}S}$ are the required coordinates on the same axes for the optic symmetry axis (X, Y or Z). Now this optic symmetry axis should be placed parallel with the axis of the microscope and the vibration directions of the fast and slow rays should be determined by means of a mica or gypsum plate after rotating the section on the axis of the microscope to 45° from extinction. Then, if the optic symmetry axis which has been found is X or Z, it will be possible to turn the section in this 45° position on the E–W horizontal axis from the position with X or Z in the axis of the microscope to a position with an optic axis (A or B) in the axis of the microscope, and this position can easily be recognized, since it will be a position of extinction and one at which extinction will continue throughout rotation on the axis of the microscope. The angle between X or Z and A or B is one-half the optic angle, either acute or obtuse, and $2V_a$ or $2V_o$ is twice this angle. Knowing whether X or Z is in this acute or obtuse angle, the sign of

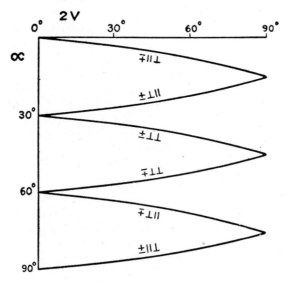

Fig. 255.—Determination of the optic angle and optic orientation from the extinction angle, α. (After Berek.)

the mineral is known. In some cases it is possible to measure directly the entire optic angle ($2V_a$ or even $2V_o$) by turning from one optic axis to the other. Finally, if the optic symmetry axis, which has been found, is Y, it is necessary to turn to X or Z before measuring the optic angle directly; of course, some crystals are oriented with X or Z (and also A and B) so nearly in the plane of the section that no direct measurement of the optic angle is possible. Berek[1] has shown that the optic angle can be obtained from such crystals by measuring certain extinction angles and using a graph shown in Fig. 255. In fact, Berek's method can be applied to any section of any biaxial mineral after finding any one of the three axes X, Y or Z. It is only neces-

[1] M. Berek: *N. Jahrb. Min. Beil. Bd.*, XLVIII, 1923, p. 34.

sary to turn the crystal to the 45° position, then rotate it about a horizontal axis coinciding with one of the vibration planes of the nicols through an angle of 54.7°, and finally turn it back to extinction by reversing the direction of turn about the vertical axis used in turning to the 45° position. From the last angle of rotation (α) the diagram (Fig. 255) gives the true optic angle and optic sign, as well as the position of the acute and obtuse bisectrices with respect to the X, Y or Z axis which was placed in the axis of the microscope. (See page 243.)

The universal stage has been much improved recently by the addition of another horizontal axis as suggested by Emmons. (See

FIG. 256.—Bausch and Lomb model of the improved universal stage.

Fig. 256.) The importance of this improvement lies in the fact that it permits rotation of the stage upon two horizontal axes (N–S and E–W) *after* the crystal has been inclined to any desired position, thus greatly reducing the time required to place an ellipsoid axis, X, Y, or Z, in the axis of the microscope.

Index-variation methods with immersion liquids are designed primarily to accomplish the accurate measurement of the index (or indices) of refraction of any solid substance. They have several very important advantages over ordinary immersion methods of estimating the index of refraction, namely:

1. Immersion methods give only a comparison of indices, while the index-variation methods give a direct measure of the index of refraction.

2. In order to learn the value of the index of refraction of a solid by the immersion method it must be immersed successively in several different liquids, while the value can be learned with the index-variation methods by immersion in one liquid. When a large amount of a pure mineral is available, this is not an important difference, but in the frequent case of a sample containing several minerals it is quite important, since it is difficult, if not impossible, to transfer a particle (invisible without the microscope) from one liquid to another, and, even if the transfer is accomplished, it is very likely to introduce some of the first liquid into the second, thus changing its index. Index-variation methods are far superior to any other method in the study of soils and other powdered crystalline aggregates, whether natural or artificial.

3. Immersion methods give the value of the index of refraction with an accuracy of about ±.003 under favorable conditions, while the index-variation methods reach an accuracy of at least ±.001 under similarly favorable conditions. This increase in accuracy is extremely important because it permits correspondingly accurate calculations of the birefringence, the optic sign and the optic angle, and thus makes possible the precise determination of the mineral in many cases left doubtful by immersion methods.

4. Immersion methods give information regarding the index of refraction in daylight or sodium light; they are not sufficiently accurate to give data regarding the dispersion; on the other hand, the double variation method measures the index of refraction in sodium light and simultaneously measures the index for other wave-lengths, and therefore measures the dispersion, thus furnishing an additional means of determining the mineral.

5. Immersion methods give information regarding the index of refraction for one vibration direction in the mineral; they are often not sufficiently accurate to determine whether the index is the same or slightly different for different vibration directions; on the other hand, the index-variation methods measure the index directly and therefore permit the recognition of differences in the index in different directions even when these are less than .001.

There are two types of index-variation methods which deserve attention; one kind uses only one means of varying the refractive index and may be called the single variation method; the other kind uses two means of varying the refractive index and may be called the double variation method.

The single variation method (also called the dispersion method), as proposed by Merwin [1] and applied by Eskola [2] and Tsuboi,[3] depends upon variation in wave-length (or color) to vary the index of the liquid. This method is far superior in accuracy to the ordinary immersion methods, but requires equipment which is nearly as expensive as that required for the double variation method and is not as convenient as the latter. It requires the use of special equipment consisting of a dark room, a monochromator and a refractometer. The technique of measuring indices of refraction by this method is the same as that involved in using the double variation method with the single exception that all measures are made at room temperature and there-

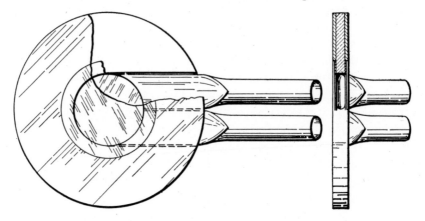

FIG. 257.—Emmons' temperature cell for dispersion methods.

fore many more liquids are required than are needed for the double variation method.

The single variation method of Emmons [4] depends upon variations of temperature to vary the index of the liquid. This method is as accurate as Merwin's method, if carried out with a dark room, sodium light, a refractometer and a device for controlling and varying the temperature. Even without the refractometer accurate results can be obtained if suitable liquids of known index and known thermal variation of index are available.

The single variation method of Emmons requires the use of a special cell shown in Fig. 257 designed so as to make it possible to vary

[1] *Jour. Am. Chem. Soc.*, XLIV, 1922, p. 1970.

[2] *Am. Jour. Sci.*, IV, 1922, p. 331.

[3] *Jour. Geol. Soc. Tokyo*, XXXII, 1925, No. 377; *Mineral. Mag.*, XX, 1925, p. 108.

[4] *Amer. Mineral.*, XIII, 1928.

the temperature of the immersion liquid through a suitable range, such as 10° to 50° C. The cell is used on the stage of an ordinary petrographic microscope; water of variable temperature passes through it between parallel glass windows; the upper glass window is thin to reduce thermal insulation; on its upper surface the mineral grain or powder is mounted in an immersion liquid and protected by a cover glass in the usual way. The temperature is measured by means of two ordinary thermometers, one giving the temperature of the water before it enters the cell and the other giving its temperature after it leaves the cell (or, after it leaves the refractometer, if one is used). In practice it is safe to assume that the immersion liquid has the same temperature as the water when the readings of the two thermometers differ by no more than one degree.

The theory of the single variation method of measuring index of refraction is very simple, depending merely on the two facts that the index of refraction of liquids decreases as the temperature rises, while that of solids, though decreasing slightly, is so nearly constant that the temperature range employed causes changes, in general, only in the fourth or fifth decimal place. Therefore, by using a suitable liquid and varying its temperature the index of the liquid can be made to equal exactly that of the mineral. When this is accomplished the "Becke line" disappears and the particle becomes nearly invisible. Then the index of the same liquid can be read on a refractometer which is connected with the same water circulation and is therefore at the same temperature. If no refractometer is available it is necessary to assume that the index of the liquid is exactly the same as it was when measured at some previous time, perhaps before its purchase. In order to make this as probable as possible it is important to use only liquids which are pure compounds rather than solutions or mixtures because then there is no variation in index with varying concentration during evaporation. It is also important to use liquids of high thermal variation of index, and to have a series of liquids representing all indices of refraction from about 1.40 to the highest available (about 1.74), with moderate overlaps. The set of liquids recommended by Emmons is given in the following table, which also includes preliminary data as to their index of refraction and thermal index-variation. The purity of these liquids is extremely important, as small amounts of impurities destroy their value for index work.

Single Variation Liquids	N_D at 25° C.	dN/dT
1. Methylene iodide...............................	1.737	.00068
2. Methylene iodide+iodobenzene....................	1.715	.00065
3. α-Iodonaphthalene.............................	1.699	.00047
4. α-Iodonaphthalene+α-bromnaphthalene............	1.675	.00047
5. Orthobromiodobenzene..........................	1.661	.00048
6. Phenylisothiocyanate...........................	1.647	.00056
7. s-Tetrabromoethane............................	1.634	.00053
8. Iodobenzene..................................	1.616	.00057
9. Bromoform *.................................	1.594	.00060
10. Aniline.......................................	1.583	.00052
11. Orthotoluidine................................	1.569	.00051
12. Nitrobenzene..................................	1.549	.00048
13. Ethylene bromide..............................	1.535	.00056
14. Propylene bromide.............................	1.516	.00054
15. Pentachlorethane..............................	1.501	.00048
16. Methyl furoate................................	1.485	.00045
17. Methyl thiocyanate............................	1.466	.00054
18. Isoamylsulphide...............................	1.451	.00045
19. Ethyl dichloroacetate..........................	1.434	.00047
20. Ethyl monochloroacetate........................	1.419	.00047

* Bromoform will be replaced by a liquid of less volatility when possible, because when used hot it is necessary to replenish the supply often.

The double variation method [1] makes use of two methods to vary the index of the liquid, namely, change of temperature and change of wave-length (color) of the light employed. The index of refraction of liquids increases as the wave-length of the light decreases, and this variation (known as dispersion) is greater (in general) for liquids than it is for solids. Also, as already noted, the index of refraction of liquids decreases as the temperature increases, and this thermal index-variation is considerable in many liquids and negligible (affecting only the fourth or fifth decimal place) in crystals. Therefore, by using both these methods of varying the index of the liquid, it is possible, not only to reduce the number of liquids which must be employed, but also to make the index of the liquid exactly equal to that of the solid at several different wave-lengths (and temperatures) and thus determine the standard index in sodium light and also in all other kinds of light in many cases with a single immersion liquid; knowing the index throughout the spectrum the dispersion is easily derived. Theoretically this method can be used with pure liquids of known thermal and chromatic index-variation and no additional apparatus except the special cell

[1] R. C. Emmons: *Amer. Mineral.*, XI, 1926, p. 115, and XIII, 1928.

described in connection with the single variation method and a burner to give "monochromatic" red light with lithium, yellow light with sodium, and green light with thallium salts in a dark room. However, it is much better to use a monochromator and a refractometer, so as to be able to measure the index of refraction of the same liquid in which the mineral is immersed, employing the same temperature and the same wave-length of light as that used while observing microscopically that the index of the liquid is equal to that of the solid. A convenient assembly of the apparatus desirable for this method is illustrated i.

FIG. 258.—Bausch and Lomb set-up of the double variation apparatus.

Fig. 258, which shows the artificial source of light at the left, the monochromator in the rear, the microscope (which may be equipped with a universal stage) at the right, and the refractometer in the foreground.

For the double variation method of measuring index of refraction, liquids should be pure compounds having high chromatic and high thermal index-variation, and they should be selected so as to include the greatest possible range in index of refraction (from 1.40 upwards) with no interruptions and with considerable overlaps. It is one of the advantages of this method that it requires only 13 liquids to cover the same range as the set of 60 liquids used for ordinary immersion work with daylight. The liquids recommended by Emmons follow (see below), with data regarding their index in sodium light, their dispersion and their thermal index-variation. These data are summarized in convenient form in Fig. 259 on page 235.

It should be noted that the double variation method can be used to measure indices of refraction both above and below the range covered by the set recommended by Emmons. For the measurement of indices higher than 1.71 the ordinary Abbe refractometer does not suffice; the Spencer Lens Company supplies a special Abbe refractometer whose range is from 1.45 to 1.84; for such measurements above 1.71 convenient liquids can be prepared by dissolving sulphur with or without iodoform and iodides in methylene iodide. Methylene iodide saturated with sulphur [1] at 25° C. has $N = 1.78 \pm C$, $1.790 \pm D$, $1.806 \pm E$, and $dN/dT = .00065$. Methylene iodide saturated with sulphur and also with iodoform and arsenic iodide at 25° C. has $N = 1.835 \, D$ at 50° C.

The exact measurement of the index or indices of refraction of a mineral grain leads to a very wide knowledge of its optic properties. For such work it is possible to use an ordinary microscope without nicols,[2] though a petrographic microscope is more convenient. With a

Double Variation Liquids	N_C at 50° C.	N_D at 25° C.	N_D at 50° C.	N_F at 50° C.	dN/dT
1. Methylene iodide.........	1.711	1.737	1.721	1.747	.00068
2. α-Iodonaphthalene........	1.678	1.699	1.687	1.714	.00047
3. α-Iodonaphthalene+					
α-bromnaphthalene.....	1.654	1.675	1.663	1.687	.00047
3a. Orthobromoiodobenzene...	1.640	1.660	1.647	1.665	.00052
4. Phenylisothiocyanate......	1.624	1.647	1.633	1.659	.00056
4a. s-Tetrabromoethane.......	1.611	1.634	1.619	1.635	.00057
5. Iodobenzene.............	1.596	1.616	1.602	1.620	.00057
6. Bromoform.............	1.574	1.594	1.579	1.592	.00060
7. Orthotoluidine...........	1.550	1.569	1.557	1.572	.00051
8. Orthonitrotoluene........	1.525	1.544	1.531	1.548	.00049
8a. Ethylene bromide........	1.519	1.536	1.522	1.535	.00054
9. Propylene bromide.......	1.499	1.516	1.502	1.511	.00054
9a. Pentachlorethane........	1.483	1.502	1.489	1.499	.00048
10. Methyl furoate..........	1.469	1.485	1.473	1.485	.00045
11. Methyl thiocyanate.......	1.449	1.466	1.452	1.459	.00054
12. Trimethylene chloride.....	1.431	1.446	1.434	1.439	.00049
13. Ethyl monochloroacetate...	1.405	1.419	1.407	1.412	.00047

[1] As measured by W. L. C. Greer at the University of Wisconsin, 1931.

[2] If a microscope without nicols is employed, the light should be polarized by repeated reflection from mirrors; then a grain, which has the same index throughout rotation of the stage, and even when rolled over, is isotropic; otherwise, it is anisotropic, etc.

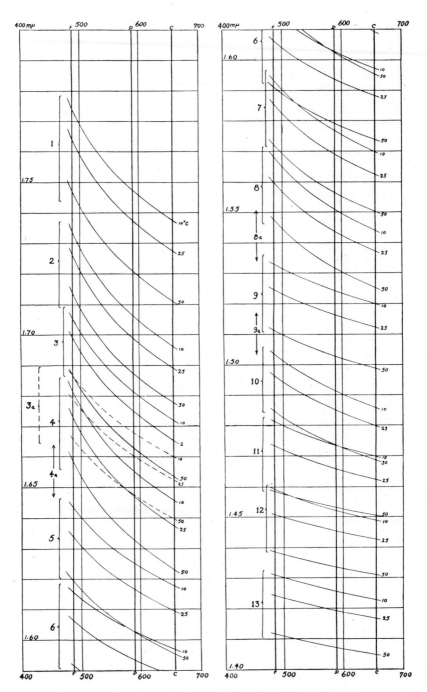

FIG. 259.—Curves of refractive indices of double variation liquids.

petrographic microscope, grains which are dark between crossed nicols in all positions of rotation of the stage, and even after being rolled over about 90°, are isotropic and have only one index of refraction. Their isotropic character can be demonstrated also by observing that they remain almost invisible during rotation when immersed in a liquid having the same index of refraction. Grains, which are dark between crossed nicols, not because they are isotropic, but because they have an optic axis in the axis of the microscope, do not remain dark when rolled over on a horizontal axis. When studying anisotropic minerals by the index-variation method of measuring indices, it is convenient to choose first those grains which show the lowest interference colors; no matter what their crystal system such grains will give invariably the standard index of refraction (N, N_o or N_m) of the mineral, because they are grains of an isotropic mineral, or anisotropic grains having an optic axis nearly or exactly in the axis of the microscope. If the interference color is *very* low, the optic axis is exactly in the axis of the microscope and the grain will have the same index of refraction in all positions of rotation; if the interference color is not so low extinction positions can be observed. The index of refraction should be measured at two extinction positions, 90° apart. Next, it is desirable to turn the grain 90° on a horizontal axis coinciding with one of the extinction directions; this can usually be done only approximately by rolling the grain over about 90°; then measure the index of refraction again at both positions of extinction; finally the grain should be rolled over about 90° on a horizontal axis as nearly as possible at right angles to the one first used. Then measure the index of refraction again at both positions of extinction. Turning a grain over in this way is often difficult; if several grains of the same mineral are available they may be used instead of trying to turn one of them. In this case it is well to include one grain showing the lowest interference color and another showing the highest interference color.

After obtaining such a series of measures from one grain in several positions, or from several grains of the same mineral in different crystallographic positions, it is easy to draw very valuable conclusions. Thus, if one index in each measured pair (representing the two extinction positions of one grain) has a constant value the mineral is uniaxial and the constant value is the index, N_o, since the index for the ordinary ray is constant in any uniaxial mineral, no matter what the orientation may be. Next, if the other index is higher than N_o, the mineral is positive, and, if it is lower, the mineral is negative. The index for the extraordinary ray, N_e, is variable, depending on the orientation. The maximum difference between N_o and N_e is the birefringence of the mineral. Again, if there is no constant value, both indices varying, the mineral is biaxial. In this case the index measured on the grain with the lowest interference color is N_m and the indices obtained from the grain with the highest interference color are N_g and N_p, assuming that the lowest and highest possible colors have been found. If such is not the case, and only grains in random position have been used, the highest value found from any grain will be very near N_g, the lowest value will be very near N_p, and N_m can be found by arranging the measured indices as follows:

Mineral	Extinction Position With Higher Index	Extinction Position With Lower Index
First grain or position		
Second grain or position		
Third grain or position		
Fourth, etc.		

Then, since every grain of a biaxial mineral, no matter what its orientation may be, always has one index of refraction which is equal to or greater than N_m and another index of refraction which is equal to or less than N_m, the value of N_m can not be higher than the lowest value in the first column of indices in the table and can not be lower than the highest value in the second column of indices in the table. After measuring several grains this will give N_m accurately. Now, if N_g-N_m is very nearly equal to N_m-N_p the optic angle is near $90°$ and the optic sign is uncertain. If N_g-N_m is less than N_m-N_p the sign of the mineral is negative and the optic angle can be deduced from the diagram of Fig. 246 on page 203. If N_g-N_m is greater than N_m-N_p the sign of the mineral is positive and the optic angle can be obtained in the same way. Of course N_g-N_p is the measure of the birefringence.

The improved universal stage is very useful in connection with the double variation method, because it permits rotation of any grain on any axis to exactly the correct position to measure critical indices of refraction, such as N_g, N_m, and N_p. In ordinary immersion mounts, mineral grains will not stay in one position after the stage is tilted. This difficulty may be obviated in large measure by crushing a tiny grain (after mounting it between cover glasses on the universal stage) by means of tightening the screws holding the mount in place. Many of the broken fragments thus produced are held by the cover glass so that they do not turn. Experience shows that tiny grains may be broken in this way with very little danger of breaking the cover glass.

Microscope refractometer method.—Lindley [1] has devised an apparatus (Fig. 260) for measuring the index of refraction of a small mineral fragment under the microscope by refractometer methods.

Fig. 260.—Lindley microscope refractometer.

It consists of three parts to be attached to an ordinary polarizing microscope, namely, a special objective, an autocollimating Ramsden ocular, and a refractometer stage.

The special feature of the apparatus is the stage which resembles the Fedoroff universal stage in some respects, but has only three axes of rotation (in addition to the rotation of the stage of the microscope on which it is mounted). The stage platform of the Lindley apparatus may be rotated on an east-west axis; and the amount of this rotation may be read to the nearest minute on the large graduated arc (with vernier). Inset on the stage platform is a circle with a disc of glass which may be rotated on an axis normal to the platform. On the edge of this circle and at an angle of about 10° with its surface is mounted

[1] K. H. Scheumann: *Tsch. Min. Pet. Mit.* (*Zeit. Krist.* Abt. B), XLI, 1931, p. 58. See also D. J. Fisher: *Am. Mineral.*, XVI, 1931, p. 550.

a pin which may be rotated on its axis; the pin terminates near the center of the top of the glass disc and near the center of the field of view of the objective.

To use the apparatus a grain must be mounted on the end of the pin, using some adhesive not soluble in the immersion liquids; therefore the grain or fragment can not be of the extremely small size that can be studied by the double variation method, but ordinarily must be at least about o.5 mm. in diameter. It may be oriented optically by the use of interference figures, easily obtained.

The objective, which corresponds to a No. 3 in power, ends in a projecting lens which is intended for immersion in the liquid to be used. The objective has part of its lens system mounted on a slider, so that by removing this part the microscope becomes a telescope.

When the mineral grain mounted on the pin is immersed in a suitable liquid held by capillarity between the glass disc and the immersion lens, the index of the liquid is made equal to that of the mineral (in a given direction) by changing the light from a monochromator, or by changing the temperature, or by adding a suitable amount of another miscible liquid. Then one of the two lower prisms of the stage is inserted, the sliding lens is removed from the objective, and the stage is tilted until the border between the bright and dark fields cuts the cross-hair intersection. From the angle reading on the large graduated arc the value of the index of refraction of the liquid (and therefore of the mineral) may be read from a simple graph ($n = y \sin \alpha$). The apparatus may be used for indices from 1.32 to 2.05, and even higher with suitable liquids, when these are obtained.

DIRECTIONS FOR LABORATORY WORK

Light for the universal stage.—In order to obtain good results with the universal stage in daylight, the plane mirror should be employed; the condenser should be removed; the objective of lowest available magnification should be used; for better results it is desirable to use an objective of very low magnifying power (for example, one with a focal distance of 35 mm.); further, the microscope should have one or even two substage diaphragms, a diaphragm above the Bertrand lens and an ocular containing a diaphragm. When such equipment is used daylight is not sufficiently intense and it is better to use direct sunlight or a "Lilliput" arc light or at least a strong incandescent light.

Preparation for use of universal stage.—The universal stage is capable of such high precision that it is worth while to test the microscope in all particulars before using it. That is, the accurate crossing of the nicols may be checked by removing all lenses and looking through the instrument directly at the sun; the correct placing of the cross-hairs parallel with the vibration planes of the nicols may be verified by reading the extinction angle on a vertical section of a uniaxial or orthorhombic mineral, and the accurate centering of the objective with respect to the axis of the microscope may be accomplished.

Moreover, the objective used must be sufficiently free from polarization effects; to test this Berek [1] recommends turning the objective between crossed nicols after removing the ocular; if its upper surface shows alternate light and dark it is not satisfactory, but may still be used if the light and dark effect can be eliminated by nearly closing its diaphragm. Those glass hemispheres whose index of refraction is nearest the estimated or known mean index of the mineral should be used, but any difference which is less than 0.1 is not serious.

Nomenclature of the universal stage.—The universal stage has four possible means of rotation not counting the rotation of the whole apparatus on the stage of the microscope. These will be designated briefly by describing their position or the position of the axis about which rotation is accomplished, as follows: (1) Rotation of the section about a vertical axis by means of turning the ordinary stage of the microscope may be called rotation on the microscope stage (or M–S) axis, or axis 1. (2) Rotation of the section by tilting it on the horizontal axis which runs from right to left or from east to west may be called rotation on the east–west (or E–W) axis, or axis 2. (3) Rotation of the section (about an axis which is vertical when the universal stage is horizontal) by means of turning the outer metal ring may be called rotation on the outer stage (or O–S) axis, or axis 3. (4) Rotation of the section by tilting it on the horizontal axis which runs from north to south when the outer stage scale is set at 90° or 270° may be called rotation on the north–south (or N–S) axis, or axis 4. (5) Rotation of the section (about an axis which is vertical when the universal stage is horizontal) by means of turning the innermost metal ring with respect to the next outer ring may be called rotation about the inner stage (or I–S) axis, or axis 5. Then the axes of uneven number are all vertical; those of even number are horizontal; and rotation on any axis turns all the axes whose numbers are larger. Furthermore, angles of rotation on these axes may be indicated briefly by the following symbols:

$$\alpha_{M-S}, \quad \alpha_{E-W}, \quad \alpha_{O-S}, \quad \alpha_{N-S}, \quad \alpha_{I-S}.$$

Directions for adjusting the universal stage.[2]—Remove the ring in the stage of the microscope which enlarges the aperture in the stage. Put the microscope in the vertical position and fasten the universal stage loosely in place on the stage of the microscope with its drum to the right. Adjust the universal stage so that the scales for the E–W and N–S horizontal axes read 0° and fasten these by means of their set-screws. The microscope is then focused on a thin section on the stage of the universal apparatus after removing the analyzer; centering can be accomplished by slight movement of the universal stage on the stage of the microscope, which the loose-fitting screws permit; the required amount of movement can be learned by rotating the section about the outer stage axis. In the correct position the set-screws should be tightened. Extreme precision of centering is unnecessary. Turn the section on the outer stage axis until its scale reads 270° and tighten the set-screw. Next raise the tube of the microscope so as to focus on dust particles on the outer surface of the upper glass hemisphere; loosen the set-screws of the horizontal axes and turn the section about the E–W axis; turn the whole apparatus about the microscope stage axis until dust particles on the hemisphere move exactly parallel with the N–S cross-hair. By a slight inclination of the hemisphere on the E–W axis, if needed, it is easy to put a dust particle exactly on the N–S cross-hair so as to accomplish this adjustment accurately. Then tighten the set-screws of the horizontal axes and of the microscope stage axis. The scale reading of the microscope stage axis is its zero position. The E–W and N–S axes are exactly parallel with the vibration planes of the nicols. When using an artificial source of light of large surface it is desirable to close the

---

[1] *N. Jahrb. Min., Beil. Bd.* XLVIII, 1923, p. 34.

[2] These directions for adjusting and using the universal stage are adapted from Berek: *N. Jahrb. Min., Beil. Bd.* XLVIII, 1923, p. 34.

diaphragm of the low-power objective and insert the swing-out condenser with its lower diaphragm also closed. When using an artificial source of light of small surface it is usually sufficient to insert the swing-out condenser without using its diaphragm, though the diaphragm of the objective should be closed in all cases in order to exclude reflections from the upper glass hemisphere. The iris diaphragm in the ocular is needed only to prevent adjoining crystals or anhedra from interfering with accurate observations upon the crystal under observation.

Procedure in the use of the universal stage.—All five axes used in universal stage work are now at their respective zero points (which should be recorded). Now turn the section of any crystal or anhedron about the inner stage axis to extinction; the screw-knobs of the upper glass hemisphere are convenient handles for this rotation. Then loosen the set-screw holding the E–W axis and ascertain whether the section remains at extinction when it is turned on this axis. Then, after turning back on the E–W axis to the original position of extinction, make a similar test by rotating the stage on the N–S horizontal axis after loosening its set-screw. These tests may lead to any one of three results, namely:

1. The section may remain at extinction during rotation on each horizontal axis. This is a rare case since it means that the section is exactly normal to X, Y or Z; in other words, X, Y or Z is in the axis of the microscope.

2. The section may remain at extinction during rotation on one horizontal axis, but not during rotation on the other. This condition is also improbable; it means that the mineral section includes X, Y or Z (but not two of these axes) and is therefore normal to an optic symmetry plane; (XY, YZ or XZ); in other words, the rotation axis, which does not disturb extinction, is normal to an optic symmetry plane of the mineral. Now, if this rotation axis is not the N–S horizontal axis, turn the section on the inner stage axis through 90° so that it becomes the N–S axis. Then incline the stage notably on the E–W axis and restore extinction by rotating the stage on the N–S axis. The reading of the scale of the N–S axis at extinction (that is, α_{N-S}) gives the coordinate of the optic symmetry axis, X, Y or Z, which is the intersection line of the two optic symmetry planes which are thus located. Accordingly it is only necessary to turn the E–W axis back to its zero position and turn the N–S axis to the reading α_{N-S} to orient the section exactly normal to an optic symmetry axis, X, Y or Z; in other words, X, Y or Z is then in the axis of the microscope.

3. The section may not remain at extinction during rotation about either horizontal axis. This is the ordinary case, in which the plane of the section has no simple relation to any of the axes, X, Y or Z. It is necessary to find two of the optic symmetry planes (XY, YZ and XZ), whose intersection will give the direction of an optic symmetry axis (X, Y or Z) which is required.

Finding the first optic symmetry plane. That extinction direction which shows less illumination on rotation should be made parallel with the N–S cross-hair by rotation of the section about the inner stage axis. Then incline the stage a little on the N–S axis and restore the extinction by rotation of the section about the inner stage axis. Now, if the section remains more nearly than before at extinction on rotation about the E–W axis, the section is more nearly in the correct position, and the process of inclining it a little on the N–S axis and restoring extinction by rotation on the inner stage axis should be repeated until the correct position is reached. On the other hand, if the section departs from extinction more than before on rotation about the E–W axis, the section is less nearly in the correct position and inclination on the N–S axis in the opposite direction is necessary. In this way, using the N–S and inner stage axis successively and then testing the condition with respect to extinction on rotation on the E–W axis, it is possible to find the position in which rotation on the E–W axis does not disturb the extinction. In this position an optic plane of symmetry (XY, YX, or XZ) is normal to the E–W axis. The coordinates of this plane should be read on the scales of the inner stage axis and the N–S axis; they may be designated α'_{I-S} and α'_{N-S}. If α'_{N-S} is larger than $35.3°$, the optic symmetry plane which has been found is not that of the one which is most nearly normal to the plane of the section.

Finding the second optic symmetry plane.—After finding the first optic symmetry plane and recording its coordinates, the section should be turned back to the horizontal position by restoring the horizontal axes to their zero positions; then the trace of the first optic symmetry plane must coincide with the N–S cross-hair and this plane must be tilted to the right (or east) above, if α'_{N-S} was read on the auxiliary arc to the left. Now

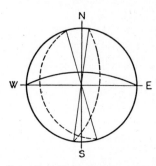

rotate the section exactly $90°$ on the inner stage axis in a direction such that the first optic symmetry plane will be tilted to the north above after rotation; that is, the rotation should be anticlockwise if α'_{N-S} was read on the auxiliary arc to the right and clockwise in the contrary case. The trace of the first symmetry plane will then coincide with the E–W cross-hair and this plane will be tilted to the north above, as shown in the full line curve in Fig. 261. In this position the mutual line of intersection of the two other optic symmetry planes (which are normal to each other and to the first optic symmetry plane) is inclined downward to the north, and neither one of the two lines of inter-

FIG. 261.—Stereographic projection of the optic symmetry planes. (After Berek.)

section of these planes with the first optic symmetry plane is horizontal. One of the two other optic symmetry planes is tilted to the right (or east) above and its line of intersection with a horizontal plane runs from the northeast quadrant to the southwest quadrant. Call this plane RP. The other optic symmetry plane is tilted to the left (or west) above and its line of intersection with a horizontal plane runs from the northwest quadrant to the southeast quadrant; call this plane LP. Possible positions for these two optic symmetry planes are shown by the dash-line curves in Fig. 261. Now a study of the relations of these optic symmetry planes to the horizontal plane (see the figure) will show that to place plane RP normal to the E–W axis it is necessary to turn the section anticlockwise on the inner stage axis and tilt it on the N–S axis so that the left side goes down; also, to place plane LP normal to the E–W axis it is necessary to turn the section clockwise on the inner stage axis and tilt it on the N–S axis so that the right side goes down. Also, the smaller the angle α'_{N-S}, the smaller the rotation on the inner stage axis that will be necessary to find the second optic symmetry plane; so, if α'_{N-S} is small, it is desirable to incline the stage a little on the N–S axis, and rotate it very cautiously on the inner stage axis in searching for the second symmetry plane. Only one other optic symmetry plane is needed and that one should be found which is more nearly normal to the plane of the section. Therefore, if no optic symmetry plane is found by inclining the stage on the N–S axis in one direction up to $45°$, the opposite direction should be used. With these facts and relations in mind the search for the second optic symmetry plane may be carried out in a manner entirely similar to the search for the first optic symmetry plane. When found, the coordinates of the second optic symmetry plane should be read and recorded; they may be designated α''_{I-S} and α''_{N-S}.

Placing the optic symmetry axis (X, Y or Z) in the axis of the microscope.—The intersection line of the two optic symmetry planes which have been found is one of the optic symmetry axes, X, Y, or Z. By proper rotation of the section on the inner stage axis and the N–S axis it is possible to place this optic symmetry axis exactly in the axis of the microscope. Let the necessary rotations be designated α'''_{I-S} and α'''_{N-S}. These angles can be obtained graphically by plotting the coordinates of the first and second optic symmetry planes on a stereographic net, such as shown in Fig. 254, or by direct mathematical calculation from the same coordinates; a slide rule suffices to obtain the required coordinates quickly by means of the equations given on page 226.

To increase the accuracy of the determination of the coordinates α'''_{I-S} and α'''_{N-S} it is desirable to measure the coordinates of the two optic symmetry planes several times and use the average values, thus obtained, to derive the coordinates of the optic symmetry axis, X, Y or Z.

Determination of the other optic symmetry elements.—After placing an optic symmetry axis (X, Y or Z) exactly in the axis of the microscope, the vibration directions of the fast and slow rays should be determined by means of a mica or gypsum plate after

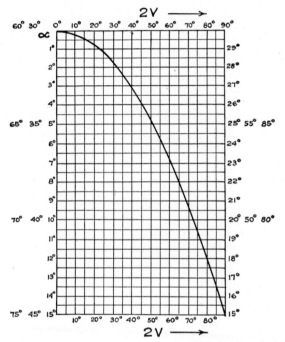

FIG. 262.—Determination of optic angle from the extinction angle α. (After Berek.)

rotation of precisely $+45°$ on the outer stage axis. Let us assume that the slow ray in this position vibrates in the $NW-SE$ direction. Then turn the section on the $E-W$ axis exactly $54.7°$ in that direction which decreases the angle between the normal to the section and the axis of the microscope. Finally, turn the section anticlockwise on the microscope stage axis to exactly restore extinction; this last angle of rotation (α) may be used in connection with Fig. 255 to learn the true optic angle, the optic sign, and the position of the acute and obtuse bisectrices with respect to the X, Y or Z axis which was placed in the axis of the microscope. In fact, the upper part of the double sign on each curve ($\pm$ or $\mp$) gives the sign of the mineral, if the vibration plane of the slow ray was in the direction assumed, and the lower part of the same double sign gives the sign of the mineral in the contrary case. Also, if the angle is between $30°$ and $60°$, the axis Y is in the axis of the microscope. Finally, the position of the acute bisectrix with respect to the axis of the microscope is given by the second sign (‖ or ⊥) along each curve, and the position of the obtuse bisectrix with respect to the axis of the microscope is given by the third sign (‖ or ⊥) along each curve. For the more accurate reading of $2V$ from this diagram it is convenient to use an enlarged drawing, as in Fig. 262.

Single variation method.—With equipment for the single variation method, first make a preliminary examination of the unknown material in powder form by the ordinary immersion method in daylight in order to learn the approximate refractive index, so as to be able to choose the proper immersion liquid for dispersion work. This step is quite unnecessary if the purpose in mind is to identify all the minerals of an aggregate like a sample of soil; in that case a sample of the aggregate should be studied in each one of the liquids of the single variation set, beginning with the one of the lowest index, until a liquid is reached which has a higher index than any mineral in the aggregate. In case the aggregate contains one or more minerals having indices higher than $1.75\pm$, these minerals must be studied by other methods, such as immersion in piperine and iodides or in sulphur-selenium melts. When a grain is found not widely different in index from the index of the liquid at one of its extinction positions, the temperature of the liquid is raised or lowered as may be necessary to make the index of the liquid exactly equal to that of the mineral. Of course, the temperature must be raised by circulating warm water through the cell, if the index of the liquid is higher than that of the mineral; otherwise, the temperature must be lowered. When the index of the liquid exactly matches that of the mineral grain, the "Becke line" disappears and the grain becomes nearly invisible. Such a result can not be obtained with white light because of the difference in dispersion between the liquid and the solid. Monochromatic light is needed; it is easily obtained by vaporizing NaCl in a Bunsen burner flame in a dark room. Then the index of the same liquid should be read on a refractometer using the same water circulation and therefore at the same temperature. If no refractometer is available, the index of the liquid for the temperature in question must be taken from tables, such as given on page 232. Next the grain should be rotated 90° to its second extinction position and the temperature changed again until the index of the liquid again matches that of the solid, if that is possible. If that is not possible, it should be noted that the second index of the mineral is higher than the highest index attainable with the given liquid or lower than the lowest attainable. The next step is to roll the grain over to another position, unless other grains are available which are known to be the same mineral. Then the index of refraction in both positions of extinction should be measured in the same way on the grain in the new position or on another grain of the same mineral. Finally, the grain should be rolled over to a third position approximately 90° from both the preceding ones and the two indices of refraction measured once more. If several grains of the same mineral are available, it is usually sufficient to read the one index of refraction of a grain showing minimum birefringence and both indices of refraction of a grain showing maximum birefringence. The first index measured will be very near N_o or N_m and the two others will be very near N_o and N_e or N_g and N_p. After completing the task with a given immersion liquid, another sample of the aggregate should be studied in another immersion liquid in the same way. The data thus assembled should permit the identification of most, if not all, of the minerals in the aggregate by the use of tables for the determination of minerals by means of their optic properties.

Double variation method.—With equipment for the double variation method a smaller number of liquids suffices to cover the same range of refractive indices ($1.40-1.75\pm$). With this method one thermometer should read the temperature of the circulating water before it enters the special cell and the other after it leaves the refractometer. The same immersion liquid is put on the refractometer that is used to mount the sample. A monochromator is an important part of the equipment for this method; if necessary, monochromatic light from lithium, sodium and thallium salts can be used as a substitute.

The ordinary refractometer reads directly in sodium light; a correction curve must be obtained or made in order to convert readings at other wave-lengths to their true values. Before using this method the same preliminary examination should be made as for the single variation method. Then the powdered sample should be mounted in a suitable immersion liquid on the thin upper glass of the temperature cell and protected with a cover glass. When the index of the liquid has been brought to equality with that of a mineral grain at an extinction position the index of the same liquid should be read at the given temperature and with the same light on the refractometer. If this is accomplished first at a temperature of about 50° C. and with a wave-length in green, a lower tempera- ture, such as 35° C. should be used next. At this temperature the index of the liquid will be higher than before while that of the mineral will be practically unchanged. By grad- ually increasing the wave-length of the light, the index of the liquid will again become

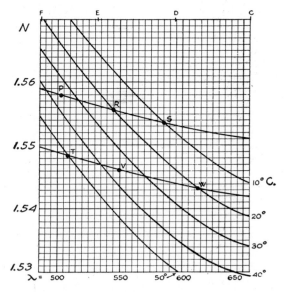

FIG. 263.—Determination of refractive indices and dispersion of quartz by the double variation method.

equal to that of the mineral, perhaps in yellow. This result is due to the fact that increase of wave-length lowers the index of the liquid faster than it does the index of the mineral. By repeating this process for a third temperature and a third wave-length, perhaps in red, three points can be found which will locate a curve representing the index of refraction of the mineral for all wave-lengths. From such a curve, illustrated in Fig. 263, two optic properties of the mineral may be read easily and accurately, namely, the index of refrac- tion for sodium light (used because sodium light is obtained so easily and because this index is approximately equal to the mean value for white light) and the dispersion, or difference in index of refraction of the mineral for different wave-lengths. The standard difference used in expressing the dispersion is that between the index for thallium light and for lithium light, or, preferably, that for the F line in blue and the C line in red; this may be expressed briefly as N_F-N_C.

As a test of the double variation method, powder a fragment of quartz and immerse it in liquid number 8 (orthonitrotoluene) on the upper surface of Emmons' temperature cell. Find a grain showing maximum interference colors. Using a monochromator and a refractometer in a dark room with the cell and refractometer at 10° C., the higher index of the grain will equal that of the liquid at wave-length 587 and the refractometer reading will give as the index: 1.5537, thus locating the point S, on Fig. 263; the wave-length can not be increased sufficiently (within the range $F–C$) to make the index of the liquid equal to that of the grain in the other extinction position. Then, at 20° C., the points R and W can be located in the same way; at 35° C., the points P and V can be located; finally, at 50° C. the point T can be located. Next, trying a grain showing the lowest interference color, the single index of refraction will be found for various temperatures exactly along the line TVW. Therefore the mineral is uniaxial and positive. It is easy to read from the diagram that $N_o = 1.542$ C, 1.544 D, 1.550 F, $N_e = 1.551$ C, 1.553 D, 1.559 F; therefore $N_e–N_o = .009$ D, and $N_F–N_C = .008$. These are the correct data for quartz.

The use of the improved universal stage.—The improved universal stage may be used in the study of thin sections with a great saving in the time required to place an optical symmetry axis, X, Y or Z, in the axis of the microscope. However, it was designed primarily for use with the double variation method of measuring indices of refraction.

The six axes of rotation of the improved stage, enumerated from the center outward, as described by Emmons,[1] are as follows: First, a *vertical inner stage axis*. (See Fig. 264

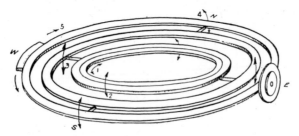

I. Inner stage vertical axis rotation. 3. N.S. horizontal axis rotation.
2. Inner stage E.W. horizontal axis rotation.
4. Outer stage E.W. horizontal axis rotation.
5 Outer stage vertical axis rotation.

FIG. 264.

and also Fig. 256 on page 228.) This is used to turn the fragment or grain to extinction. Second, an *inner east–west horizontal axis* which is used to tilt the grain (after extinction is reached) in order to bring the first optic symmetry plane into a position parallel with the $E–W$ nicol. Third, a *north–south horizontal axis*, which is used to bring one of the critical vibration directions, which lie in the first optic symmetry plane, into a position parallel with the axis of the microscope. It is also used to search the first optic symmetry plane for optic axes. Fourth, an *outer east–west horizontal axis*, which is used to search the second optic symmetry plane for optic axes and also to measure the optic angle in either the first or second optic symmetry plane. Fifth, a *vertical outer stage axis*, which is used to rotate the first optic symmetry plane into a north–south position in case it should be found to be the optic axial plane, in order to use the vernier scale for the measurement of the optic axial angle. Sixth, the *microscope stage vertical axis* (or, better still, the axis of simultaneous rotation of both nicols, found on some microscopes), which is used to rotate the stage (or nicols) to the 45° position just before making the actual measurement

[1] *Am. Mineral.*, XIV, 1929, p. 441.

of the optic axial angle, since this position gives the sharpest extinction when an optic axis is brought into the axis of the microscope. The order in which these axes are described is essentially the order in which they are used.

In order to measure the true indices of refraction, N_g, N_m, and N_p, of a biaxial grain or crystal fragment mounted on the universal stage, it is necessary to turn the grain to such a position that one of its axes, X, Y or Z, coincides with the axis of the microscope. The process of turning the crystal to this position may be described in four steps, involving three rotations.

1. Rotate the grain on the vertical inner stage axis to a position of extinction.

2. Test the grain to see whether its birefringence is less when rotated on the N–S axis or when rotated on the E–W axis. If the birefringence is greater on rotation on the N–S axis turn the grain 90° on the vertical inner stage axis, so that when all horizontal axes are at 0° the steepest optic symmetry plane may strike about E–W and dip either north or south. The steeper the dip the less the birefringence of the grain when rotated on the N–S axis. Also, the steepest optic symmetry plane can not strike exactly E–W at extinction without being in a vertical position; and, when it is in a vertical position, rotation on the N–S axis will not disturb the extinction. These facts may be used to make the steepest optic symmetry plane vertical, as follows:

3. Rotate the grain a few degrees on the inner E–W axis in either direction and restore extinction by a small rotation on the inner stage vertical axis. If the rotation on the E–W axis was in the right direction, rotation of the grain in its new position on the N–S axis will produce weaker birefringence than before. If the birefringence produced is greater than before, the rotation on the inner E–W axis was in the wrong direction. By repeating this process several times, gradually reducing the amount of rotation on the E–W axis, a position can finally be reached at which rotation on the N–S axis does not disturb the extinction. In this position the optic symmetry plane is necessarily vertical and strikes E–W.

With the old style universal stage it is necessary to repeat these three steps in order to find another optic symmetry plane, and then, by plotting coordinates or by calculations, it is necessary to find the line of intersection of the two optic symmetry planes, and turn the grain to that position. With the improved universal stage the procedure is much simpler, because there are two " horizontal " axes (the N–S and the outer E–W) which are still actually horizontal. These should now be used as follows:

4. Rotate the grain moderately (say 15°) on the outer stage E–W horizontal axis, which destroys extinction. Then rotate the grain on the N–S horizontal axis in either direction until extinction is restored. Finally, reverse the rotation on the outer stage E–W axis and return it to the zero position. The grain is then oriented so that one of the axes X, Y or Z, is in the axis of the microscope and the other two are normal to that axis. Therefore, those two indices of refraction which correspond with the two axes (X, Y or Y, Z or X, Z) which are normal to the axis of the microscope can be accurately measured. If it is possible to restore extinction, after rotation on the outer stage E–W horizontal axis, by rotating the grain on the N–S horizontal axis in the direction not previously used, then by restoring the zero reading on the outer stage E–W axis another one of the axes X, Y, Z can be made to coincide with the vertical axis of the microscope and all three indices of refraction (N_g, N_m and N_p) can be measured accurately, two in the first position and another pair in the second position. In the contrary case, one of the three indices of refraction must be obtained by extrapolation from indices measured in known positions. The position which gives X, Y or Z in the axis of the microscope should be recorded for each rotation axis.

Having turned the grain or fragment so that one of the axes, X, Y, Z, is in the axis of the microscope, it is not difficult to determine which of these axes is so placed. For this purpose rotate the nicols to the 45° position—if the microscope is not provided with means for simultaneous rotation of the nicols, rotate the stage of the microscope 45°—then rotate the grain carefully both ways on the outer stage E–W horizontal axis and also on the N–S horizontal axis; if an extinction position is found in any of these rotations, that is because an optic axis has come into the axis of the microscope; this optic axis, together with the axis X or Z originally in the axis of the microscope, determines the position of the optic plane, to which Y is normal. By returning to the position with X or Z in the axis of the microscope, it is easy to determine, by superposing a mica or sensitive tint plate, whether the ray vibrating parallel to Y is faster or slower than the ray vibrating in the optic plane; if it is faster, then Z is horizontal and X is in the axis of the microscope. Finally, if no extinction position can be found when the grain is rotated both ways on the outer stage E–W axis and also on the N–S horizontal axis, the axis Y is in the axis of the microscope, and X and Z are normal thereto, unless the optic angle is small and the obtuse bisectrix is in the axis of the microscope. In order to distinguish between these two possibilities it is necessary either to measure the three indices of refraction or to use Berek's method of determining the optic angle and the optic orientations from an extinction angle as described on pages 227 and 241.

The angle between the axis X or Z and either optic axis, measured by turning the grain from the position with X or Z in the axis of the microscope to the position with an optic axis in the axis of the microscope, may be corrected[1] from the observed value to the true value in the crystal and is then equal to one-half the optic axial angle—it may be one-half of the acute optic angle ($2V_a$) or one-half of the obtuse optic angle ($2V_o$).

GRAPHIC METHODS FOR THE IMPROVED UNIVERSAL STAGE[2]
By R. C. EMMONS

The rotations of the universal stage are complicated to follow in making necessary corrections for directions of light transmission. They are considerably simplified, however, if traced out on a stereographic projection such as the Wulff net (Fig. 254) or the more convenient Fedoroff net shown in Plate III.[3] This plate is a stereographic projection on which are marked four sets of rotations about the center in 10° intervals. When the horizontal axes of the universal stage read 0°, then the perpendicular to the inner stage is located at the center of the projection. If, now, to find X, Y or Z, the inner E–W axis is rotated 30° S, then the new position of the perpendicular is found by tracing downward on the central vertical line to the intersection of this line with the 30° great arc. Assume that the stage is rotated (as the next step to find X, Y or Z) on the N–S axis 30° W, then the movement of the perpendicular may be traced westward parallel to one of the small arcs to the intersection with the 30° N–S great arc.[4] This makes X, Y or Z parallel to the axis of the microscope. To find the angular distance of the perpendicular to the inner stage from the axis X, Y or Z measure on the concentric 10° circles radially from the center interpolating for the final figure. It is slightly over 41°.

Typically, the optic axis is located next. Suppose, for instance, that a rotation of 40° N on the outer E–W axis makes an optic axis parallel to the axis of the microscope. (This is a normal rotation for the purpose.) Measure 40° N parallel to small arcs counting on the E–W great arcs. This point is 29° from the center. The optic angle, $2V$, is then twice 40°, if the hemisphere and crystal agree in refractive index; but they

---

[1] The method of correcting this reading is given on pages 224, 225.

[2] Part of a complete description of the improved universal stage by Professor Emmons prepared for publication elsewhere.

[3] Plates I–IV are in the pocket on the inside of the back cover.

[4] These readings on the horizontal axes are taken directly from the instrument after X, Y or Z is oriented. They are found on the Wright arcs.

never do. A correction is necessary to learn the true direction of the path of light within the crystal; it is based on the relationship between the index of the hemisphere and the index of the crystal, and the angle made by the perpendicular to the inner stage with the axis of the microscope. It is expressed as a modification of this angle. In order to correct the reading of the angle V, therefore, two angles must be corrected, $41°$ and $29°$, and the angle V is then read between the corrected points on the diagram (Plate III). If the index of the hemisphere is 1.516 and the index of the crystal is 1.600, the readings $41°$ and $29°$ correct to $39°$ and $27.5°$ by the method shown in Fig. 265 as applied to Plate I.[1] A correction is diagrammatically represented in Fig. 266. The corrected points $39°$ and $27.5°$ are plotted on the radials through the original points $41°$ and $29°$. The angular distance between these corrected points is now measured, counting on the E–W great arcs. This distance is the true angle V.[2] In actual practice the indices of the crystal are learned first and *the correct indices for the specific directions of transmission are used,*

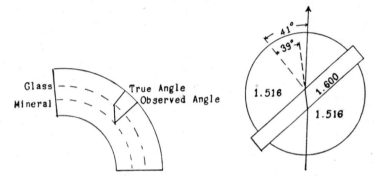

FIG. 265.—Key to Plate I.   FIG. 266.—Explanation of Plate I.

unless the crystal is one of weak birefringence, in which case an average index is satisfactory.

A calculation, the aim of which is to determine one index by extrapolation from another, may be carried out with the aid of Plate II.[1] If a uniaxial crystal is oriented with the optic axis parallel to the axis of the microscope, and it is not possible to rotate far enough to make the optic axis perpendicular to the axis of the microscope (which is the position needed to obtain N_e), then rotate as far as convenient, correct the observed angle of rotation on Plates I and III (see last paragraph) and measure the two refractive indices in this position. One is N_o and the other is N_e'. To find N_e use Plate II. Locate the index difference (between N_o and N_e') on the ordinate or abscissa according to whether N_e' is less than or greater than N_o. Follow horizontally (or vertically) to the inclined line which indicates the number of degrees of rotation (corrected), then on the other coordinate is the figure to subtract (or add) to N_e' to give N_e.

If the crystal is biaxial, then, on a bisectrix or optic normal grain, measure two indices. Here, as with uniaxial crystals, it is usually not possible to rotate a full 90° to the third critical position. The same plate (II) facilitates the extrapolation. Rotate as far as

[1] Plates I–IV are in the pocket on the inside of the back cover.

[2] The line joining the corrected points is seldom exactly parallel to one of the small arcs. This introduces an error in measuring the angle between them, but this error is regarded as negligible.

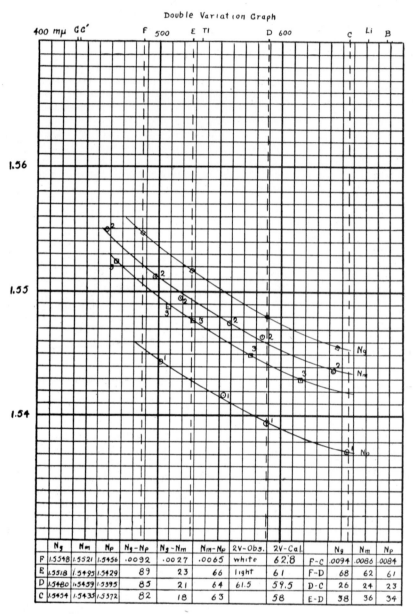

FIG. 267.—Dispersion curves for cordierite.

DATA SHEET No. 6

Mineral	*Cordierite*	Locality	*Bodenmais*

Inner *E–W* Axis....	$o.5°\ N$	Hemisphere	1.649
N–S Axis..........	$5.2°\ W$		
Optic Axes 1.......	$54.3°\ N$		
2......	$53.5°\ S$	Liquid	8
2*V*-Direct........	$61.5°$		
2*V*-Calculated.....	$58–62.8\ (C–F)$		
Extinction Angle...		Apparatus	III

Ray	T. 1.	T. 2.	λ	Ref.	Cor.	Index	Rot. °	From	Rot.° Cor.
1	26° C.	26° C.	654	1.5438	−.0068	1.5370			
2	25.5	25.5	559	1.5434	+.0040	1.5474			
3	25.2	25.2	576	1.5432	+.0017	1.5449	45° N	1	48.6°
3	33.8	33.8	528	1.5387	+.0089	1.5476	"	1	"
1	"	"	589	1.5394	——	1.5394			
2	"	"	519	1.5389	+.0106	1.5495			
2	38.9	38.6	497	1.5360	+.0151	1.5511			
1	"	"	553	1.5368	+.0049	1.5417			
3	38.5	38.3	509	1.5361	+.0126	1.5487	"	1	"
3	50	49.5	465	1.5293	+.0231	1.5524	"	1	"
1	"	"	501	1.5300	+.0122	1.5422			
2	"	"	458	1.5300	+.0250	1.5550			
2	21	21	585	1.5460	+.0005	1.5465			
3	"	"	616	1.5460	−.0030	1.5430	"	1	"
2	14.5	14.8	642	1.5491	−.0057	1.5434			

convenient toward the third critical index, and measure the new index. Care must be taken in making this rotation to note which ray is being transmitted and to rotate on a horizontal axis that is perpendicular to the plane of vibration of the lower nicol. The index difference and the corrected rotation are then used on Plate II as was done for uniaxial crystals, and the correct third index is obtained.

From the three refractive indices thus determined, the optic angle may be calculated from Wright's diagram (Plate IV).[1] Maximum birefringence is found on the abscissa, and N_g-N_m or N_m-N_p is found on the ordinate. At the intersection of these, the inclined lines indicate V or its complement.

Rotation corrections are best traced out in the order in which they are made. An example will serve the purpose. (See Fig. 267 and the copy of the data sheet for the same figure given on page 251.) At the top of the data sheet are recorded the rotation readings for critical positions of the crystal. The first two readings place the crystal in such a way that X, Y or Z is parallel to the axis of the microscope. The third and fourth readings place the two optic axes in a position parallel to the axes of the microscope. These rotations must be followed out first on Plate III, which traces the movements of the perpendicular to the inner stage on the various rotations. It happens that in this example the first two rotations are small; usually they are larger than this. First, follow a *straight* line north 0.5° from the center on Plate III. Then, from this point follow a small arc west 5.2°, counting on the great arcs which run from north to south. Now count the angular distance from the center along a radial line, counting the degrees on the concentric circles. This value, 5.2°, is more than either of the rotations used to make it up, but it is essentially the same as the one when the other is approximately 0°. It is the observed or apparent angle between the original direction of the light path through the crystal and the present direction; that is, it is the apparent angle between the perpendicular to the inner stage and one of the principal directions. It must be corrected for the difference in index between the crystal for this direction and that of the hemisphere (Fig. 266). The index of the crystal for white light (about 550 mμ) (ray No. 1) is approximately 1.542. Turn to Plate I. Find the reading 5.2° on the circumference, trace radially to the index of the mineral, 1.542, follow a vertical line to 1.649 (the index of the hemisphere) and follow thence a radial to the circumference. This gives the corrected value as 5.6°. Spot this point on Plate III.

The optic axis or, if possible, both optic axes are to be located next. From the uncorrected position of the principal direction, already located, follow a small arc north 54.3° (see data sheet) counting the degrees on the great arcs extending from the west to east poles. Measure the angular distance radially as before. It must be greater than 54.3°, but in this case only slightly greater (about 54.4°). Correct it on Plate I, using the value of the index for the mean ray in white light (1.548), which gives a corrected value of 59.7°. Spot this point on Plate III. Similarly, measure south 53.5° and correct this on Plate I (58.7°) and spot it on Plate III. The distance between the two corrected points spotted on Plate III, counting on the east-west great arcs, is $2V$. Or, if the second optic axis could not be found, as is commonly the case for wide angles, then the distance to the position of X, Y or Z is V. In this example, $2V$ is 118.5° about the obtuse bisectrix, and $2V$ about the acute bisectrix is 61.5° for white light.

Rotation readings for ray No. 3 may be corrected next. As an example choose the first rotation reading, on the data sheet. The corrected index for the new position at 45° N from ray 1 is 1.5449. This figure, 45°, corrected on Plates III and I, as above, becomes 48.6°. The difference in index between this value, 1.5449, and the value (1.5402) on the curve for ray No. 1 at the same wave-length (576 mμ) is 0.0047. That is, the rotation of 45° (or crystallographically 48.6°) from ray 1 has caused an *increase* in the index of 0.0047, and this is approximately one-half the increase necessary to reach the true value

[1] Plates I–IV are in the pocket on the inside of the back cover.

for ray No. 3. On Plate II find this value (0.0047) on the abscissa. (If this were an index decrease then this value should be found on the ordinate.) Follow a vertical line to its intersection with the inclined line for 48.6°. Then, on the ordinate is the additive correction +.0038, which is the remaining difference in index for the balance of the rotation from 48.6° to 90°. This value added to 1.5449 gives a point on ray 3 (N_g), 1.5487. So also for other points. Or, as an alternative procedure, if all rotation readings are made at the same angle of rotation (45°) then draw the dispersion curve through these points and use index values for the Fraunhofer lines as is done in the example (Fig. 266).

It remains to calculate the optic angle from the indices, as a check. Find N_g-N_p and N_g-N_m (or N_m-N_p) for the wave-lengths desired. On Plate III, trace these values to their intersection and follow the inclined line to the right-hand side. This gives the value for V (or its complement).

The optic sign may be read from the dispersion curves. If the curve for N_m is closer to that for N_p than to that for N_g then the crystal is positive, and in the opposite case it is negative.

EXPLANATION OF PLATES
(In pocket inside of back cover)

PLATE I.—Relation between true and observed angles on the universal stage when the crystal and hemisphere differ in refringence (sin $i = n$ sin r). (After Fedoroff.) This is used to correct angular readings between the normal to the inner stage (or the section) and the direction of observation. The correction is based, first, on the index of the mineral, and, second, on the index of the glass hemisphere that is being used. All angles to be used on Plate II must first be corrected on this graph or its equivalent. The procedure is shown in the key,—the observed angle as read on the scales is traced from the circumference to that circle which indicates the index of the mineral, thence along a vertical line (up or down) to that circle which indicates the index of the glass hemisphere, and thence radially to the circumference on which the true angle within the mineral is read.

PLATE II.—Variation in the refractive index with change in angular position in a symmetry plane of the triaxial ellipsoid. $(\epsilon_1 = \epsilon\omega/\sqrt{\omega^2 \sin^2 \phi + \epsilon^2 \cos^2 \phi}.)$ (The small triangle is intended only for substances of strong birefringence, and only for such substances is it necessary to make the indicated corrections for the position of the substance on the refractive scale).

The use of the diagram may be outlined as follows:

Assume that a crystal has been oriented with X, Y, or Z parallel to the axis of the microscope (which can always be done) and that two indices have been determined in this position by the double variation method. Assume, further, that it is impossible to rotate on a horizontal axis through 90° to either of the other two principal positions, which is a common difficulty. Then rotate, with the grain at extinction as far as is conveniently possible on that horizontal axis which permits the greater rotation (up to 90°), and rotate the lower nicol (or the stage), if necessary, to make its plane of vibration perpendicular to the axis of rotation. Note the amount of rotation of the horizontal axis and correct it according to Plate I. Measure the refractive index in the new position and find the difference in index between this value and that of the principal index already measured for the ray which vibrates in the same plane. This difference is found on the ordinate or abscissa as follows: If the rotation has caused a change from a greater to a smaller index, use the ordinate scale; if the rotation has caused a change from a smaller to a greater index, use the abscissa scale. Follow this value horizontally (or vertically) to the intersection with the proper degree of rotation line. Then follow the inclined line to its extremity where is indicated the total difference in index for a full 90° rotation. By simple addition or subtraction the third principal index may then be obtained.

For substances of stronger birefringence the smaller triangle is used similarly with this difference—if the index is not that for which the diagram was constructed, then a small correction must be applied. First determine the total difference in index as outlined for a 90° rotation. Select the proper small plat, follow the proper total "index-difference" curve to its intersection with the "degree of rotation" line (vertical) at which the reading was made. The correction is at the left.

PLATE III.—Universal stage protractor. The diagram is a substitute for the Nikitin hemisphere. It gives the angular distance of the perpendicular to the inner stage from the axis of the microscope. This angle is corrected for refractive index on Plate I. After making the corrections and locating the modified positions on this plate, then such angles as V or $2V$, and angles to be used on Plate II, may be read. This plate is a stereographic projection of angular rotations in divisions of 10 degrees.

PLATE IV.—Relation between optic angle and differences in principal refractive indices in a biaxial crystal. $(\sin^2 V = N_m - N_p/N_g - N_p.)$ (After F. E. Wright.) If the three principal refractive indices of a crystal are known, the optic angle can be obtained quickly by means of this graph. The total birefringence $(N_g - N_p)$ is found on the abscissa, and the partial birefringence $(N_g - N_m$ or $N_m - N_p)$ is found on the ordinate. The inclined lines indicate V.

INDEX

255